'No one is invulnerable against love'
– *Guillaume le Clerc, Scotland, 13th century*

Illustration from *Codex Manesse*
Germany, 14th century

MEDIEVAL
LEGENDS
of
LOVE & LUST

Rosalind Kerven

First published in the UK by Talking Stone 2021

Text copyright © Rosalind Kerven 2021

Talking Stone
Swindonburn Cottage West, Sharperton
Morpeth, Northumberland, NE65 7AP

Cover main image: Detail from 'Duke and Ladies in a Garden'
from *Collected Works of Christine de Pisan*, 1410–1411
Small motifs from 'St Denis', Master of Sir John Fastolf, c.1440

Chapter head images from *Page d'un livre de prière*,
Maître de Catherine de Clèves, c.1438

To the best of the publisher's knowledge,
all illustrations in this book are
out of copyright and in the public domain

ISBN: 9780953745494

CONTENTS

12th CENTURY

13th CENTURY

14th CENTURY

15th CENTURY

MEDIEVAL PEOPLE
AND THEIR BOOKS

This is a collection of romantic stories written in western Europe between the early 12th and late 15th centuries – the High to Late Middle Ages. They are based on translations of the primary texts, carefully retold to preserve the plots, characters and spirit of the originals, whilst making them accessible to the modern reader.

During the long period when they were composed, western Europe was a complex, highly structured region, subject to regular periods of flux. It was largely rural, with the vast majority of people living off the land. Yet urbanisation was steadily increasing, with small towns providing a focus for scholarship and trade. There were numerous castles all over the continent, built mainly for military purposes, since warfare was endemic.

The social hierarchy was clearly defined. At the bottom were serfs tied to their lords' estates. Above them were free peasants, craftworkers and vassals, with both men and women labouring on farms, processing food, producing utility goods, providing services and running businesses. At the top was the nobility, with ultimate power in the hands of kings; though their influence was rivalled by the Church.

In the earlier years, trade and industry flourished, stimulating the growth of wealth. But later, adverse climate change and a series of famines and plagues decimated

Europe's population, and the continent was troubled by social unrest and conflict.

Culture was dominated by Christianity, with the exception of Spain and Portugal, where large areas were predominantly Muslim. The Bible defined distinct roles for men and women, although these were often resisted in real life, and especially in romantic stories. Males were considered superior, with authority over 'imperfect' females; throughout her life, a woman was expected to defer and submit first to her family patriarch, and then to her husband. The Church portrayed women as either virginal and 'perfect', reflecting the Virgin Mary; or as intrinsically dangerous and evil, like Eve who was cursed in the Bible to submit to her husband, and to suffer pain in childbirth. Female sexuality was regarded as menacing, particularly where it affected the integrity and honour of the wider family. Sexual activity was supposedly for reproduction only – an idea strongly refuted by the popular love stories!

Political power was officially vested in the male nobility. Yet women sometimes inherited their fathers' realms, ruled as regents on behalf of their husbands and sons, or played an active political role as wives of kings. Although laws gave women little status, some managed to conduct their own legal and business affairs. An upper class woman received a share of her family's inheritance in the form of a dowry – the property or money she brought to her husband when they married. Nuns played a significant role in medieval society, with abbesses often wielding considerable power.

The bulk of surviving medieval literature was religious in nature, with writers assuming their readers were familiar with the Bible. Other books told of real or imaginary warrior heroes, often transcribing oral legends and folktales that had been in wide circulation across the continent for centuries, particularly those of the Arthurian cycle. They made much use of the stylised social codes of chivalry, which promoted courage, honour, courtesy, justice and assistance to vulnerable people. References to characters and events from classical Greece and Rome were also common. Some plots referred to the ongoing conflict in the Crusades between Christians and their Muslim opponents, the Saracens.

For most of the Middle Ages, books were produced by scribes, commissioned either from a monastery or privately in a town. They were handwritten on parchment – the prepared skins of cows, goats or sheep. The finest parchments were made from animal foetuses; the next best quality was calfskin and lambskin. Pens were bird quills, or fashioned from cane, reeds or metal. Illuminations were added at the end; some surviving manuscripts were beautifully decorated and illustrated. The covers were made of wood, sometimes covered with leather. Wealthy people had their books ornamented with gold and jewels. Some books contained a variety of different texts in a single volume.

It took many months to inscribe a single book. Copies were made by painstakingly reproducing the original. At the end of the period, the invention of the European printing press by Johann Gutenberg, in Germany in the 1450s, made it possible to produce multiple copies of a book within a relatively short time. This new technology spread rapidly, and Thomas Malory's *Le Morte d'Arthur* (see p.400) was first published as a print edition.

Outside the nobility and the Church, the majority of medieval people were illiterate. Nevertheless, they enjoyed books by listening to them read aloud. Such readings often took place as court events, with professional storytellers, musicians and poets giving lively performances that included acting and musical interludes.

RETELLING
MEDIEVAL STORIES

What is the 'correct' way to retell a medieval story for modern readers? This is a complicated question, since there was no universal style in which they were originally written. Even romantic stories varied widely; generally speaking there were three main types.

Firstly, chivalric legends had as their heroes quintessential knights errant, who combined fortitude with extreme passions. The ladies in these stories were more varied, ranging from strong, proactive women to helpless maidens imprisoned in towers. Then there were tales reflecting real-life people: inn-keeping couples, scholars, merchants, nuns and so on. Finally, there were highly creative stories composed by outstanding literary authors, in which the central plot was embroidered with fantasy and philosophical musings.

All the sources used for this book were translations from the originals – even those written in English, which has evolved almost beyond recognition since the Middle Ages. Many of these originals took the form of verse narratives involving complex rhythmic and rhyming structures. Some translations attempt to replicate this, but a good many have been converted to prose.

Some sources were short and simple, detailing the bare bones of the plot with little characterisation and few descriptions; others filled several volumes, with richly developed sub-plots and characters. Some were stand-alone stories; others formed part of multi-tale collections. Some were new compositions by named authors; others were straightforward transcriptions of vintage oral legends and folk tales, or a mix of both. Sometimes the same story was written down by different authors in different countries, so it was a matter of choosing which version to use.

The longer sources were written in a leisurely style, with remarkably detailed and vivid descriptions of the characters' appearances and clothes, treasures, locations, battles and ensuing wounds. Physical appearance was presented as intrinsic to the characters, with virtuous women and men depicted as very beautiful, whilst evil characters were hideous and deformed. Dreams played a significant role, and in fact sometimes formed the main framework for entire stories. Allegorical characters were widely used, with the personification of 'Love' as a deity (either male or female) appearing in a number of tales. Some stories diverted into extended passages discussing theology or the classics, before returning to the plot. One frustrating convention was that the names of the key characters were often not revealed until well into the story – or in some short tales, not until the very end.

Even in the Middle Ages there was no universal agreement about the most authentic way to retell an old story. In the 12th century, the author Wace wrote in his book *Roman de Brut*:

The minstrel has sung his ballad, the storyteller told over his story so frequently, little by little he has decked and painted, till by reason of his embellishment the truth stands hid in the trappings of a tale.

Some medieval authors were very inventive. For example, in *Decameron* (p.226), Bocaccio composed a frame-story of aristocratic narrators within which he reworked a hundred different folk tales; whilst the two separate authors of *The Romance of the Rose* (p.171) cleverly developed a fantasy in the form of an extended dream. Writing in the 12th century, Marie de France (p.63) specifically gave permission for all retellers to be innovative:

> Whoever has good material for a story is grieved if the tale is not well told... Anyone who intends to present a new story must approach the problem in a new way and speak so persuasively that the tale brings pleasure to people.

It is in this spirit that the stories in this volume are brought back to life for the modern reader. They are all authentic in their plots and characters. Where appropriate, idiosyncrasies of style and expression in the source texts have been reproduced. However, they have been disentangled from the lengthy, tedious details that make the originals so difficult to read. These retellings aim to delight and entertain 21st century readers, as much as they did readers of their day in the earliest versions many hundreds of years ago.

WHAT IS LOVE?

Andreas Capellanus: *De Amore (About Love)*,
France, 12th century

Love is a kind of inner suffering derived from observing the beauty of the opposite sex, and thinking excessively about it. This causes both parties to be obsessed with longing for the embraces of the other.

Before the love becomes equally balanced on both sides there is the most terrible torment. The lover lives in fear of never winning his desire, and that he is wasting his efforts.

If he is a poor man, he fears that the woman may scorn his poverty. If he is ugly, he fears she may despise him for that, and give her love to a more handsome man. If he is rich, he fears she will consider him an ungenerous miser.

Even if both parties are in love, each still lives in fear of losing the other, by causing offence in some way – which is worse even than never winning any love at all.

A true lover would rather be deprived of all his money and of everything that the human mind can imagine as indispensable to life, than to be without love.

Oh what a wonderful thing love is!

Illustration from *Corpus Pelagianum*,
Spain, 1142

12th
CENTURY

A time of fluid borders, openness, expanding knowledge and liberal attitudes. Despite the Crusades, there was general tolerance of different races and religions.

Wandering scholars, poets and storytellers, some attached to aristocratic courts, contributed to the development of both oral and written literature in vernacular languages.

Early in the century, people were gripped by the real life love scandal of Abelard and Heloise. This was later eclipsed by the publication of many romantic fantasies based on ancient legends, particularly the works of Chrétien de Troyes and Marie de France.

ABELARD & HELOISE

The Letters of Abelard and Heloise,
France, written c.1132 – 1138

In the second decade of the 12th century, the chattering classes of Paris were rocked by a scandalous liaison. It involved one of the most celebrated and controversial theologians of the age, and the innocent yet brilliant young niece of the clergyman with whom he lodged. Was it true love between the pair, or a case of gratuitous lust, exploitation and and rape? All was finally revealed in the late 13th century, with the discovery of a lost set of extraordinarily intimate letters that the pair had exchanged.

Some scholars have questioned whether this correspondence is authentic. There are no original manuscripts of any of the letters. The oldest versions date from c.1280 when, it is claimed, the originals were brought to Paris and copied. This was over one hundred and forty years after the couple supposedly wrote to each other between 1133 and 1138.

The oldest known texts of the letters are associated with Jean de Meun, one of the authors of The Romance of the Rose (p. 170), who translated them from Latin into French, then published them in Paris. There has been speculation that, if they are in fact forgeries, this very creative author may have been responsible. That idea has been dismissed by other academics. It has also been suggested that Abelard was the author of all the letters, rather than just those written in his name. Though a brilliant and charismatic scholar, he was described by two of his contemporaries as a seducer, and was famed for his outrageous views. At a later point in his career, these views had him condemned for heresy; his books were burned by the Pope himself, who issued orders to arrest Abelard on sight. Heloise, on the other hand, became a highly respected abbess. She had been renowned from a young age for her learning, intellect, musical skills and creative writing in both prose and verse; and some have suggested that her explicit revelations in the letters seem unlikely for a pious woman within the medieval Christian context.

Rigorous study has now fairly conclusively proven that all the letter texts are genuine.

There are eight letters in all, each long enough to have filled many pages. The most informative letter, known as *Historia Calamitatum,* ('The Story of his Misfortunes') is written by Abelard and addressed to a friend. It gives an account of his colourful life to date (c.1132), opening with the admission that he has a volatile temperament, alongside his talent for learning. He states he was born in the town of le Pallet near Nantes, the eldest son of a knight who valued scholarship. Much of this section is taken up with the development of his career as an academic, specialising in dialectic and philosophy. He says that his debating skills quickly won him enemies – a problem which plagued his whole life. He opened two successful schools near Paris, at one point falling ill from overwork and returning home for several years. Both his parents eventually entered religious orders. After surviving various academic controversies and plots, Abelard boasts that he won both fame and support from his growing band of admirers; then admits that this caused him to become inflated with pride, leading to his weakness and downfall. The next section of this letter gives the full, sensational details of his illicit affair with Heloise, ending in his calamitous punishment. The final part continues at some length about his often dangerously controversial career as a 'philosopher of God', in which he narrowly escapes being arrested as a heretic. It ends with his role in installing Heloise –'now my sister in Christ' – in the convent of le Paraclete. It claims that Abelard himself is now virtually destitute.

Of the remaining seven letters, four are from Abelard to Heloise, and the remainder from her to him. The final three letters are mainly theological in content. The source book also includes some correspondence between Heloise and Peter the Venerable, abbot of Cluny; an absolution for Abelard, and two hymns attributed to him.

Independent documents verify that Abelard was a brilliant – and very controversial – theologian and philosopher; and that Heloise was a scholar of some eminence from an early age, even before she met Abelard. Eventually, she became the esteemed abbess of le Paraclet, which she governed for 35 years. It is assumed that Heloise kept the letters there, though it is a mystery how she obtained *Historia Calamitatum*. It is not known how the correspondence eventually came to light in the late 13th century.

In the following account of their affair, all the letters quoted are reworded from the originals in translation. However, the story of their discovery and subsequent re-concealment is the present author's creative speculation, following a traditional narrative style.

In the year of Our Lord 1179, at the Convent of Le Paraclet in northern France, Melisende was elected to be the new abbess. She celebrated by arranging for the entire premises to be thoroughly cleansed. Whilst the younger nuns scoured the kitchen, lavatorium, garderobe and infirmary, the more elderly sisters were set to renovate the library, where the shelves of precious books were almost overwhelmed by piles of old letters and bills.

That afternoon, during nones prayers, Abbess Melisende's concentration was distracted by two of these elders constantly turning their heads to exchange glances, as if in a state of consternation. Later, when the sisters had returned to their chores and the abbess was in her office working on the ledger, there came a timid knocking at her door and the same two elderly sisters walked in. One was clutching a thick roll of yellowing papers bound with a scarlet ribbon.

'Reverend mother,' said she, 'we have made a most disturbing discovery. As we were dusting the back of the library shelves, a loose panel came away in our hands. In the wall behind it, was a small cavity – in which we found hidden these extraordinary letters.'

'To call them extraordinary is an understatement,' interjected her companion. 'Their revelations are shocking, scandalous and abominable.'

'Please calm down,' said the abbess. 'Who are these letters from, and to whom are they addressed? What kind of matters do they concern?'

The two nuns grimaced. 'You ordered us to peruse every paper in the library carefully before either filing or destroying it,' said the one holding the letters. 'But may God forgive us for reading the impious filth in these.' She thrust them onto the desk with a shudder. 'The few pages we looked at are shameful. We considered burning them on the spot. However, the correspondents are both so significant to this abbey's history, that we felt we must defer to your authority on the matter.'

'But who are the correspondents?' the abbess asked.

'Some were written by the man who founded this abbey himself, Peter Abelard,' said the second sister. 'And…'

'In that case, you certainly must not burn them,' exclaimed the abbess. 'Not only was Abelard our gracious founding father, but he was also an eminent scholar and a devout churchman. These are valuable documents.'

'We do not think you will say that when you know what they contain,' said the first nun. 'In these letters, he openly confessed serious transgressions against the Almighty's commandments. And the other letters were written by the original Mother Superior of Le Paraclet, Abbess Heloise. How we all revered her and wept at her passing fifteen years ago! Now we two bitterly regret this, since her own writings reveal sins equal to Abelard's – or even worse.'

The two nuns stood with eyes cast down, violently trembling. Abbess Melisende was deeply disturbed. 'Thank you for drawing this to my attention,' she said gently. 'Now return to your work, sisters, and leave this matter with me. Be assured that you have committed no offence by obeying my instructions. I issued them in total ignorance of the disquiet they would cause.'

She waited until they had closed the door behind them, then reached out to the bundle and carefully untied the scarlet ribbon. The papers dropped out onto her desk in a disordered heap. She picked out a clutch at random. It comprised several parchments, neatly sewn together with silver thread, and written in Latin in an elegant feminine hand. She began to read:

> To her lord, or rather father; to her husband or rather brother; from his handmaid, or rather daughter; from his wife or rather sister; to Abelard – Heloise writes this...

Abbess Melisende's heart jumped uncomfortably at this intimate salutation. Her mouth felt dry, as she read on:

> Not long ago, my beloved, by chance a letter which you had sent to a friend was passed into my keeping. Since the writer is so dear to me, you can imagine my eagerness to read it. I was astonished to find my name mentioned a hundred times or more within its pages, each time followed by some heavy calamity, thus forming a detailed and melancholy account of our shared misfortunes. I must admit my sorrow when I read the bitter regrets and self-pity you expressed. These seemed so far removed from the brilliant and adoring man to whom I once fully submitted my heart, soul and body.

For my part, the only regret is that you have not written to me for so long since we were parted in the most terrible circumstances; you have not once attempted to comfort my own long grief. And this despite our being bound by the ties of the marriage sacrament, not to mention my often expressed boundless love! I beg you now to write to me at once, whether it be of good or ill, and to sign yourself as a husband to a wife.

You are sole possessor both of my body and my will, the one to whom I gave myself for the gratification of your own pleasures and desires. You taught me that the freedom of love is superior to the chains of marriage. I never put pressure on you to marry me, but would willingly have consented to remain your concubine, your whore...

Concubine! Whore! Abbess Melisende stopped reading for a moment and rubbed her eyes. Initially, she had doubted the immoderate claims of her two nuns. But here was proof, before her very eyes. She thought back to the kindly, venerable dame who had presided over the nunnery when she had first arrived as a novice, and for so many years afterwards. It was hard to believe that these words could really have been written by her. Yet there was her name, and that of her celebrated correspondent, clearly inscribed at the top. She wondered if the letter was dated; and saw in small letters above the salutation:

The 1st day of April in the year of Our Lord 1134

She recalled that Abbess Heloise had died at the age of 63 in the year 1163; so she had been 34 years of age when she had written this letter. Even so, the events referred to must surely have taken place long before that time. She turned the page and skimmed down the next parchment, then the next. Now the writer abandoned her emotional entreaties for philosophical discourse. A brief reading of these paragraphs confirmed the insightful, considering mind that Abbess Melisende clearly remembered from her dealings with Heloise. Then another colourful passage suddenly caught her eye:

> What king or philosopher could match your fame?
> You were gifted with every possible charm of mind
> and body. Every lady and girl sighed for you from
> afar and was on fire in your presence! Noblewomen,
> even queens, envied my happiness and my bed. You
> won all their hearts with your compositions and
> singing, though for you it was nothing but an
> amusing game. All those songs you once crooned! It
> was an open secret that their lyrics and sweet tunes
> referred to our own romance. Thus I too, against my
> will, became constantly gossiped about and envied…

Was this really a description of the celebrated Peter Abelard? The abbess thought back to what she had heard of him. She recalled hearing that, long ago, he had indeed been a popular balladeer – a talent in great contrast to his renown as a formidable and controversial theologian. She had also heard it suggested that Abbess Heloise had briefly been married to him. But not happily, it seemed; for the next lines were deeply disturbing, suggesting that he had begun their relationship by raping her, then tried to placate her with empty talk of love:

> Now I believe what the gossipmongers have always
> implied: that nothing bound you to me except pure

lust. Is it because you are no longer able to use me in this way, that you no longer show me any love or affection? Have you lost all feeling for me? Why have you not written to me for so many years? When you desired me for sinful pleasures, your letters came thick and fast. Later, when you ordered me to turn my back on the world that I loved so much and take up the veil, I dutifully obeyed. Yet my only reward is your complete neglect.

There followed several pages of ardent complaints and pleadings, before it ended:

I beg you, do not forget me! Remember what you owe me. Love me as your mistress, cherish me as your child, your sister, your wife! For my part, I strive to stop loving you, but cannot succeed. I shake with despair, and blot my paper with tears. Farewell, my only love.

Abbess Melisende put the letter down and wiped her eyes. She was shocked indeed, but could not feel the outrage for Heloise that the elderly sisters had expressed. From the tone of this letter, she had been an innocent young victim who had suffered a tragic outcome for acquiescing to this illustrious master's lechery and sense of entitlement. 'The oldest story in the world,' she sighed as she reached out for another of Heloise's letters.

Here was more anguish, combined with a brazenness that made the abbess gasp:

I can't forget our shared love pleasures, which I still dream of constantly, even during Mass. I do not

23

repent my sins, but yearn for what I can no longer
enjoy.

She put down the letter hastily and took up another in a
different hand, which opened with a salutation from
Abelard. Ashamed of her own salaciousness, she skimmed
through it quickly, seeking further clues to the nature of the
liaison that Heloise had written about so openly. But this
letter was mainly a theological treatise, peppered with
admonitions to Heloise to live a life befitting her new status
as a nun. 'Poor woman,' the abbess thought, 'her adoration
of him was so easily discarded. But then, 'twas ever thus.'
She picked up another letter in his writing. This was full of
tedious statements that combined schoolmasterish
instruction with self-justification; but then she sat up with a
start:

After you moved to the convent, I came secretly to
visit you. Surely you recall my savage desires that
night when I took my pleasure of you in the corner of
the refectory – heedless of the fact that we were in a
building dedicated to the Holy Virgin! When you
tried to resist me, I did not hesitate to force myself on
you, using threats and even violence until you had no
choice but to submit. I beg you not to elevate my
attitude to you by calling it 'love'. It was unbridled
lust, and it brought us both down to the very depths
of sin. We deserve every punishment that God can
devise for us. On my part, He has afflicted me with
daily, relentless torment.

Hurried footsteps were pattering outside: the sisters were
on the way to vespers, early evening prayers. Hastily Abbess
Melisende gathered the letters together and hid them under

her desk. No wonder the nuns who discovered them had been so shocked. She wondered how much they had read; and whether either of those two elders knew enough of the world to make sense of the revelations. She swallowed, composed her features and went out to lead the service.

Later, eating supper at the head of the table, she looked around the refectory with new eyes. Where did he do it to her? How was it that no one disturbed them? Afterwards, how did she manage to keep her humiliation secret from the other sisters? She could not get it out of her mind.

In the darkest hours of the night, she returned to her office, took out the letters out and read on. The dates on them showed that the correspondence had continued for several years, but most of the later letters mainly contained discussion about theology, alongside practical concerns about running the convent that Abelard had founded and Heloise had risen to govern. 'I should be glad,' thought Abbess Melisende, 'that good sense took over as they matured, and the follies of youth were left far behind. Maybe former sinners turn out to be the most devout people in the end?' She knew that Abelard and Heloise had ended their short marriage to dedicate their lives to God – which was not exceptional amongst highly religious people.

There was still one parchment left to look at, written in Abelard's hand. It was longer than the others, addressed not to Heloise, but to a man who must have been a friend, for the opening lines expressed Abelard's wish to comfort the recipient's distress by confessing his own misfortunes.

The first pages were an interesting account of Abelard's early life and achievements, confirming that he had been exceptionally brilliant, with intellectual powers and accomplishments far beyond the run of normal men. But halfway through, it began to explicitly discuss the subject of the other letters:

...By now I had become so renowned as a scholar that I succumbed to pride and all the other sins that accompany it. I forsook the chastity I had carefully nurtured until then, and yielded to the carnal pleasures of which I had often heard other men boast. The first and only object of my lust was not a whore or a married gentlewoman, but an upright young girl in Paris who was only fifteen years of age when our liaison began.

Her name was Heloise, and she was the niece of a respected canon called Fulbert, who had raised her as his own daughter. He showered her with the love that her lost father should have given her, and spared nothing to educate her. Her looks were not remarkable, but her intellect certainly was – such a rare gift in a woman! By the time I met her, she had already won much acclaim both for her scholarship, and for her abilities in composing music and poetry.

Once I had chosen her, I began to taste the unbridled fires of desire. Thus I wasted no time in courting her, with the excuse that we were both scholars. I made full use of my renown in the world of learning, alongside my good looks and carefully nurtured charm.

When we had become well acquainted, I approached Heloise's uncle and offered to further her education, in return for lodging in his house. Fulbert accepted this suggestion with alacrity, for he was keen to advance his niece; and who could be a more illustrious tutor than me? He urged me to devote all my free time to Heloise's lessons, by night as well as day if I were willing. Moreover, he stated that if she succumbed to idleness, I had his explicit permission to punish her in whatever I considered the most appropriate way. I was astonished – and excited – by her guardian's naivety in entrusting such an innocent to an older stranger's care. But of course, until then I was as much famed for my continence as for my scholarship. This meant that Fulbert had no reason to fear I might prove untrustworthy.

So now I lived in the same house as Heloise, and we legitimately spent long hours alone together. I soon replaced my academic lessons with instruction in the art of love! Behind closed doors, though open books still lay before us, we abandoned all pretence of scholarship and instead practised new skills: kissing, caressing and every kind of lovemaking. At first she resisted me. However, since her uncle had explicitly given me permission to punish her, I easily bent her to my will with threats and blows. These were not needed for long, for I soon awoke desires in her that more than matched my own. Neither of us was ever satiated.

However, the endless sleepless nights of intimacy left me constantly weary, causing me to neglect my outside work. So I gave up research, writing and lecturing, and instead took up a less demanding and more worldly pursuit: writing and performing love songs. I was as successful in this as I had been in my scholarship, and many of my compositions became widely popular.

Naturally, the change in my public persona did not go unnoticed, and sordid rumours began to spread that Heloise was the subject of my songs. At first, Fulbert refused to believe this; but after several months I was caught in flagrante delicto with my young mistress.

Her uncle was outraged and absolute in his condemnation. He kicked me out and refused to let us have any more contact; but this only increased our mutual ardour. We managed from time to time to contrive secret meetings, and on such occasions our passion and abandonment were even stronger than before.

Soon after our discovery, Heloise wrote me a joyful letter, announcing she was carrying our child, and asking what to do. Fortunately, her uncle Fulbert was absent at that time, so I arranged for her to be taken to the house of my sister in the countryside of Brittany. There she gave birth to a healthy baby boy, whom she christened Astralabe.

When Canon Fulbert returned home and discovered I had made Heloise pregnant, and that her child was with my family, he went out of his mind with remorse for causing the downfall of his beloved niece. His first instinct was to attack and kill me; but he refrained for fear that my relations might harm Heloise in retaliation.

Nevertheless, I knew he would be seeking some method of revenge, so I was constantly on my guard. In the end, I decided the safest course was to openly confess my guilt to him. I tried to excuse myself as an innocent victim of love's power which, since the beginning of time, has often caused women to ruin even the most honourable men. I promised to make amends by marrying her, requesting that this should be done in secret so that my reputation was not damaged on account of our illegitimate child. He agreed to this formally, though with little enthusiasm.

So I hastened to Brittany to bring Heloise back for our wedding. I assumed she would be delighted to become a respectable married woman, and at the same time legitimise our son. However, to my consternation, she was strongly opposed to it.

Firstly, she argued that this would not appease her uncle, who would continue to feel betrayed, exploited and humiliated by my duplicitous behaviour. 'Once we are married,' she said, 'he is bound to reveal the secret affair which led to it. This will bring much shame on you, and cut short your acclaimed career, which is still far from reaching its zenith. Nature created you to benefit all mankind, and it would be pitiful if your talents were wasted because of me.'

Moreover, and to my astonishment, she declared that she absolutely rejected the concept of marriage. To substantiate this viewpoint, so atypical of women, she referred to ancient texts that she had studied long before I had begun to instruct her. She quoted philosophers who had warned against the insufferable irritations, distractions and anxieties with which marriage burdened men, with its endless stream of infants, muddle and squalor.

'Don't forget,' she chided me, 'that St Paul said, "Marriage brings pain and grief", and that is why monks practise celibacy. If you are determined to bring me back to Paris, I wish to be known as your "friend" rather than your "wife", for that will cause you less harm. I trust you will remain faithful to me, not through the constriction of marriage, but because you freely wish to continue giving me your love.'

I refused to be persuaded by her pleadings. At last she capitulated, as she always did. 'But as a result, we shall both be destroyed,' she insisted. 'And this will cause suffering even greater than our love.'

Shortly afterwards, she followed me home, leaving our son in my sister's care. In the dead of night, a secret marriage ceremony was conducted in the presence of Fulbert and a select few friends. Afterwards, we continued to live separately, arranging only rare and furtive meetings, in an attempt to keep our married state from the public eye and thus avoid scandal.

Despite our best efforts, Fulbert's staff discovered what they considered to be my exploitation of his niece. They were greatly affronted, and spread malicious rumours about us. Heloise courageously denied these. However, her uncle was now in a perpetual state of agitation and constantly rebuked her for bringing trouble into his previously tranquil life.

For Heloise's own safety, I therefore took her from Fulbert's house to the convent of Argenteuil, where she had been raised as a young orphan before her uncle adopted her. I ordered her to wear the habit of a novice, but not the veil. Unfortunately, this only stoked the anger of Fulbert and his supporters, who accused me of hiding her away in a religious house for my own convenience.

Their retribution was not long in coming. One night as I slept incautiously in my lodgings, a gang of them bribed one of my own servants to admit them to my room. There they brutally cut off the parts of my body with which I had committed my crimes.

By the following morning, news of the horrific attack on me had spread right around the city. People came crowding to my house to commiserate, including my clerks and students. However, I found their sympathy worse even than the pain of my wound; for in this single strike, my whole reputation had been blotted out. I avoided them all, for if I were to show my face in public now, I would only be insulted and derided. Moreover, now I had become a eunuch, the law officially defined me as an abomination.

I had but one choice left: to follow the fate I had inflicted upon Heloise and enter a religious house. Thus it was that I become a monk at the abbey of St Denis – not with a sense of vocation, but in shame and confusion. On hearing of my fate, Heloise ignored protests that she was too young for such penance, and took up the veil to become a full nun...

Abbess Melisende put the letter down, then fell to her knees in fervent prayer. At last she was startled by the early morning bell summoning the sisters to lauds prayers. As light footsteps tripped past, she staggered to her feet, gathered the letters neatly together and rolled them up, carefully re-tying the scarlet ribbon around them.

She decided to copy Abbess Heloise's trick and hide them. There was a loose flagstone in the floor by the rear wall of her office. She bent over it, carefully levered it open, laid the letters inside, replaced the stone and stamped it back into place.

And there the letters of Abelard and Heloise stayed undiscovered, for the next hundred years.

There is evidence that the romance between Abelard and Heloise was well known at the time that it happened.

Historically, Melisende was the second or third abbess of le Paraclet after Heloise, from c.1179 until the early 13th century.

FLOIRE & BLANCHEFLEUR

Anonymous: *Floire et Blanchefleur*
France, c.1150–1160

There are four surviving Old French manuscripts of this story, revealing two different versions; it seems to have been adapted from a much older oral folktale. During the Middle Ages, it was also translated and adapted into English, German, Italian and Norwegian, indicating that its simplicity and happy ending made it popular throughout Europe. The opening quote is based on one of the original texts.

This story was first written down long ago,
and read by a cleric
who told it to a woman, who told it to her sister
who I happened to overhear
and I have now written it down for you to enjoy.

Old chronicles tell how the Muslim King Fenis of Spain sailed across the sea to attack a Christian kingdom. When he returned, his ships were heavily laden with plundered gold, gemstones, furs, silks and many foreign slaves.

The queen disapproved of the king's ceaseless warmongering so, to placate her, he gave her one of the slaves as a gift. She was a young Frenchwoman whose husband had died in the battle, leaving her pregnant. It so happened that the queen was expecting a child too. Since both women could speak the common Latin tongue, they became very friendly.

Early the next spring, the queen gave birth to a fine baby boy, who she called Floire because he was born in the season of flowers. On the very same day, the slave woman also gave birth – to a daughter, who she named Blanchefleur.

King Fenis was glad to have a son and heir. He ordered his wife to ensure that Floire was raised as a devout Muslim, in accordance with his kingdom's tradition. The queen pretended to comply with this; but secretly put the little boy in the care of her trusted slave woman, although she was a Christian. So Floire grew up alongside Blanchefleur, who was also allowed to live in the queen's apartments.

They were both good-natured, beautiful children who soon became inseparable. When they reached the age when Floire must start school, he dug in his heels and fell into a rage, refusing to go – until the king agreed that Blanchefleur could attend school with him.

Time sped by and they grew up. By now, they were regularly writing secret letters to each other – *love* letters. Gossip about this reached the king, who was outraged. 'This must stop,' he told the queen. 'Order Floire to end all contact with that slave's child at once. It's imperative that we find a suitable king's daughter to be his bride.'

'He'll refuse to stop seeing her,' the queen retorted.

'If he does,' said the king, 'I'll have Blanchefleur slain.'

'No!' cried the queen in horror; for in truth, she loved Blanchefleur almost as much as her son. 'If you do that, Floire will die of grief. Let me think…let me suggest…I know. Floire's a fine young man now, so send him away to finish his education in Montorio, where my sister is the duchess. She always has a selection of princesses staying in her palace, and she'll help him choose one to marry. To ensure that Blanchefleur doesn't try to follow him, I'll order her to stay here to help her mother.'

Floire fought fiercely against this proposed change, refusing to leave Blanchefleur behind. But the queen made empty promises, saying, 'My dear boy, in a couple of weeks we'll let Blanchefleur follow you to Montorio.' Thus he was persuaded to go, but not until he had kissed Blanchefleur passionately in full view of his parents, which did not please the king at all.

Once Floire was installed in his aunt's palace, he found himself surrounded by many beautiful princesses and other noble young ladies. However, he did not notice any of them, for he was still obsessed with Blanchefleur. He counted the days carefully until the appointed time for her to join him; but she failed to arrive. Floire fell into a deep melancholy, unable to sleep, eat or even drink. The duchess sent urgent word of this to her sister, the queen, who quickly shared the alarming news with King Fenis.

'This proves it beyond doubt,' the king declared. 'Blanchefleur has bewitched our unfortunate son with love spells, to bind him to her. The only way to overcome her evil influence is to have her killed.'

'My lord, no!' the queen cried. 'I assure you that Blanchefleur isn't a witch. She's just an innocent girl who suffers as much as Floire does. She's been weeping constantly since he was sent away. It would be shameful to kill her.' She thought desperately, trying to devise some way to save the girl's life, even if she could not spare her suffering. 'My lord, since her mother is a slave, why not get rid of Blanchefleur by selling *her* into slavery too.'

The king thought that an excellent idea. So Blanchefleur was wrenched away from her devastated mother, bound in chains and handed over to two wily slave traders. Because she was of exceptional quality, they willingly paid the king the full price he demanded for her: one hundred pounds each of gold and silver, one hundred webs of silk, one hundred horses and three hundred falcons and hawks. They also threw in a splendid golden cup which, they claimed, had once belonged to mighty Caesar himself. The king was well satisfied with this payment, particularly with the cup.

The traders travelled all the way to distant Babylon. There they sold Blanchefleur to their most highly valued customer: the Emir of Babylon himself. He was so excited by her beauty, grace and innocence that he willingly paid the traders ten times Blanchefleur's weight in gold.

Now, the emir had a very macabre habit. He liked to take an endless series of wives and concubines, then kill them one by one as he grew tired of them. Whenever he obtained a new young woman for this purpose, instead of enjoying her at once, he would titillate himself by locking her away for a year to mellow at the top of a very high tower, attended by twenty-five lesser maidens. Together, these young women were strongly guarded day and night, by a band of brawny eunuchs under the command of a brutal watchman. No 'whole' man, apart from the emir himself, was ever allowed anywhere near them.

Thus Blanchefleur, shocked and terrified, found herself forced into a chamber at the top of the emir's tower alongside twenty-five equally distressed companions.

Meanwhile, back in Spain, the queen feared that, when Floire discovered they had sold his sweetheart into slavery, his grief would know no bounds. To silence her on this matter, the king suggested that they tell their son that Blanchefleur had died. To make this deceit convincing, they had a marvellous marble tomb built, inscribed with the words, *Here lies Blanchefleur who loved Floire with tender heart and true.* Inside it, they placed an empty golden coffin. The whole court was ordered, on pain of death, not to whisper a word that the girl was actually still alive.

When all was ready, the queen sent Floire a message to return home at once. He did so eagerly, anticipating that Blanchefleur would be waiting to welcome him. Seeing no sign of her, he hurried to his mother's chamber and demanded to know where she was.

'Alas, dear son,' said the queen, 'Blanchefleur has died from lovesickness.'

Floire swooned. The queen screamed, which brought the king running, and together they managed to revive their son. Floire begged to see where his sweetheart was buried, so they took him to the tomb and showed him the inscription. 'Oh, Blanchefleur!' he wept. 'We were born on the same day, so it's right that we should die together. I am coming to join you in Paradise!'

He reached into his shirt and drew out a golden writing stylus, brandishing it ready to stab himself in the heart. But the queen snatched it from him, saying, 'Don't be a fool. If you kill yourself you will never reach Blanchefleur in Paradise.'

She took the king aside. 'Unless we stop this deceit,' she whispered urgently, 'Floire is bound to take his own life. That would leave no heir to your kingdom, thus putting it into terrible danger.'

The king saw the sense of this. So the queen confessed to Floire what they had done, adding, 'We did it with the best of intentions. We could not let you continue an affair with a *slave*-child who follows an alien religion...'

But Floire was not listening. For now he knew that Blanchefleur was still alive, he was already planning how to find her and bring her home.

Floire disguised himself as a merchant selling valuable hides and silks. The king now realised it was impossible to stop his wilful son, so he decided to help him instead. He told him the name of the harbour where he had sold Blanchefleur to the slave traders, and gave Floire the priceless golden cup of Caesar that the traders had paid for her. Then the queen gave Floire a magic golden ring, saying, 'So long as you wear this, my son, no one can refuse you anything.'

Floire thanked them both, rode to this harbour and there hired a room for the night. When his host joined him for supper, he remarked on Floire's mournful demeanour. 'Doesn't that remind you,' said the host's wife, 'of another guest who recently stayed here?'

'Yes indeed,' exclaimed the host. 'It was that poor young slave girl brought here by her captors. They let her sit and eat at the table with us, but all she did was sigh and repeat the name "Floire, Floire!" as if her heart was breaking.'

'Good people,' cried Floire, 'where were her captors taking her?'

'We heard they were bound for Babylon,' said the wife.

Floire jumped up, paid them generously for his meal, said he had no need of lodgings after all and hastened down to the harbour. There he booked a passage on a ship due to sail eastward at first light on the morrow.

He landed many weeks later and continued his journey overland, through vast deserts, sweeping plains and looming mountains. Everywhere he went, he heard more gossip about the sorrowful French slave maiden weeping over her lost Spanish sweetheart.

At long last, Floire reached the walls of fabulous Babylon and took lodgings with the city gatekeeper. As he sat at supper there, the gatekeeper noticed his guest's melancholy and said, 'Young man, the style of your clothes and the dust coating them show that you have travelled from a far distant land. Where are you from, where are you heading; and, most importantly, what are you grieving for?'

'Husband, can't you guess?' the gatekeeper's wife interrupted. 'He's surely the lover that girl was weeping for, when the slave traders took her to the emir.'

Floire cried, 'This girl – was she called Blanchefleur?'

They nodded.

'Then you know the truth,' sighed Floire. 'I am the son of the King of Spain. I've travelled all this way across seas, deserts, plains and mountains to rescue Blanchefleur. I beg you to help me.'

'You're crazy,' said the gatekeeper. 'You're risking your life, and what you want to do is impossible. The emir has imprisoned your sweetheart in an impenetrable white marble tower, thousands of feet high, protected by locked steel doors thicker than your arm is long. It's impossible to break in, and any man who even dares approach it is seized by his guards and castrated.'

'Will Blanchefleur be imprisoned there forever?' said Floire in despair.

'Not if the emir follows his usual custom,' said the gatekeeper. 'When spring comes – very soon – he'll kill his current wife and marry Blanchefleur. He'll ravish her brutally for a year, then have her publicly beheaded – like all the others before her.'

Floire let out an anguished groan.

The gatekeeper pondered in silence for a moment. Then he said, 'Listen prince, I know how you could get the tower watchman onto your side. But don't tell a soul I suggested it.' And he revealed to Floire a very cunning plan.

Early the next day, Floire walked through the city, carrying a measuring rod and set square. He stood at the base of the tower, stared up at it and walked carefully all around it. When he got back to his starting point, a burly man accosted him. 'What are you spying on?' he snarled.

'I am a prince from a distant land,' said Floire politely, 'come to admire the buildings of your celebrated city. I am so impressed by this magnificent tower, that I would like to build a copy in my own city as a treasure store. Would it be possible to see the interior, so I can fully understand its structure?'

'Not without the emir's permission,' growled the watchman.

'I'm sure he won't hesitate to grant it,' said Floire pleasantly. 'For my father is even richer and more powerful than he is.'

The watchman looked him up and down, taking in Floire's magnificent clothes and soft leather boots. 'Well…I can see that you're both wealthy and well bred. The emir's a very busy man, so I won't be able to get hold of him for a while. But in the meantime – come in to play chess with me. I'm bored out of my mind with this job, and I haven't had a game for ages.'

He led Floire into his little hut. The watchman produced a chess set made of ebony and ivory, and they agreed stakes of a hundred coins for whoever won. As they sat down to play, Floire made sure that the magic ring his mother had given him was clearly visible. Its bright gleam distracted the watchman so much that he quickly lost the game, thus owing Floire a hundred coins.

However, following the gatekeeper's advice, Floire declined the winnings, and instead offered a return game to even things out. The watchman readily agreed. So the following morning, they sat again at the chessboard, this time playing for double stakes. Again, the magic ring enabled Floire to win easily. This time, he not only refused his winnings, but said, 'Here, *you* take them from *me* instead – and have the winnings from our last game too. To be honest, I'm so rich that this money is nothing to me; but I can see that it would really improve your life.'

The watchman was so grateful that he asked what he could do for Floire in return. Floire said he only wanted to continue their game. So he returned the next day, won again, and again gave the watchman the prize. The following day, Floire said he had run out of coins for stakes, and instead brought the golden cup from Caesar's treasury. The watchman's eyes almost popped out of his head.

'Friend,' said Floire, 'I'm fed up with chess. There's something else I've come for today. If you'll help me – totally in secret – this cup shall be yours.'

'Whoah!' said the watchman licking his lips. 'What do you want for it?'

'First, swear an oath to do whatever I ask you.'

'All right,' the watchman agreed. 'I promise that in return for this cup I'll do whatever you want.'

'Excellent,' said Floire. 'Now then. You must help me get up to the top of the tower, to visit Blanchefleur, who's imprisoned there.'

The watchman turned very pale. He sat down and cursed obscenely. 'What an idiot I am!' he cried. 'This will be the death of us both.' He glanced back to the gleaming golden goblet. 'But I can't lose the chance of such a treasure. Just... give me a moment to think out a plan...Yes, I know. Come back in three days' time. But not as you are now; you need to dress from head to toe in red – *rosy* red. If you manage that, I should be able to smuggle you up to Blanchefleur's prison.'

Floire sent his servants to buy a rose-red suit, hat and boots. On the third day he put them on and hurried back to the watchman's hut. There he saw a great basket of red roses, gathered from Babylon's most splendid gardens. The watchman looked him up and down, nodded then growled, 'Crouch in the bottom of the basket and don't move.'

Floire did as he was told. The watchman scattered more red roses on top of him, until the prince was completely concealed. The next moment, two strapping eunuchs hurried in. 'We heard you wanted us?' they said.

'Take this basket up to that Blanchefleur girl,' the watchman ordered. 'The emir's sent it to sweeten her up before he has his way with her. Dump them in her room, make sure you lock up properly, then come straight back.'

The porters did as they were told, grumbling loudly at the weight of the basket. They unlocked the tower, carried the basket up the spiral staircase to the top, unlocked the top level, knocked on the nearest door and yelled, 'Open up! The emir's sent flowers for Blanchefleur!'

Now, the room behind this door was not Blanchefleur's; it belonged to one of the other incarcerated young women, a good friend of Blanchefleur's who was called Clarissa. She admitted the porters. They deposited the basket, then went out and locked up behind them.

Floire stayed motionless in the basket until he heard the porters turn their key in the outer lock. Then he pushed aside the suffocating, sweet-scented roses and sprang out.

Clarissa stifled a scream. She stared at Floire, who immediately realised his mistake and tried hopelessly to burrow back into the flowers.

'You...' Clarissa whispered, 'surely you're not...you can't be...but... Are you the Spanish lover Blanchefleur moans for day and night?'

Without waiting for an answer, she ran to another door which connected to her friend's room and called, 'Blanchefleur, come quickly! The emir's sent you flowers.'

'I don't want them,' sobbed Blanchefleur. 'I suppose he thinks they'll make me go to him quietly, but I won't. I'll scratch and kick him; I'll let him *kill* me rather than betray my own true love.'

At the sound of Blanchefleur's voice, Floire leaped from the basket again. He burst through her door, ran to her, took her in his hungry arms and kissed her frantically.

With a cry of joy, Blanchefleur returned his kisses. Then she closed the door tightly and took him to her bed. For a short while they just sat quietly, telling each other everything that had happened since they were parted.

Then Blanchefleur drew the curtains around the bed and they spent the rest of the day in bliss.

Clarissa had never had a friend as true as Blanchefleur, and she promised to do everything she could to keep the lovers' reunion secret. None of the other young women imprisoned in the tower had any inkling of what was going on. The three stayed quietly in their rooms, eating and drinking together, and for several days everything went very well.

However, the prisoners were not allowed to be idle. Every day the emir spent time in the pleasure garden surrounding the tower, and they had to take turns in pairs to attend to him there, performing his most intimate ablutions. Soon it was Blanchefleur and Clarissa's turn. The latter rose in good time, and knocked on Blanchefleur's door to be sure she was awake. Blanchefleur, who at that moment was lying ecstatically in Floire's arms, called out, 'You go to the garden now, Clarissa; I'll catch you up.'

So Clarissa got the guards to let her out. At the bottom of the spiral staircase, she took a golden basin, filled it at a spring, then waited for Blanchefleur. When her friend failed to appear, Clarissa assumed she was already in the garden. So she fetched a towel, mirror and comb, then hurried out to the emir, who was waiting there impatiently.

'Ah, it's you two today is it, Clarissa,' he said lazily. 'Where's the lovely Blanchefleur?'

'Oh sir,' said Clarissa quickly, 'I...I believe she overslept because...um...she stayed up late last night praying for you.'

'I'm glad to hear she values me so much,' said the emir lasciviously, 'but she mustn't keep me waiting.' He snapped his fingers at one of the eunuchs. 'You! Go and tell Blanchefleur to hurry up.'

The eunuch soon returned, prostrated before the emir and cried, 'My lord, I found Blanchefleur *lying in the arms of a stranger!*'

The emir let out a terrible bellow. He pushed Clarissa away, scattering the basin, towel, mirror and comb. Drawing his sword, he pounded up the spiral staircase, then kicked open Blanchefleur's door.

He found Blanchefleur and Floire cowering in the bed together, completely naked.

'You squirming little wretch!' bellowed the emir. 'How dare you make sport with my private property? I paid ten times her weight in gold for her, yet you dare to sully her before I've had a single taste of her virginal delights. I'll have you both dragged around the city by wild horses, until your skin is flailed to pieces and your bones ground to dust!'

Floire swallowed and sat up. 'Sir,' he said boldly, 'you *lust* crudely for Blanchefleur, but I have *loved* her since the day when we were both born, within hours of each other, in the royal palace of my father, the king of Spain. I have travelled across the world to save her from you. Kill me if you must, but I beseech you to spare my innocent Blanche…'

At that moment, Blanchefleur interrupted him, crying, 'No, sir – I beseech you to spare my beloved Floire. Kill me instead. I am only a slave's daughter whilst he is a prince. His life is far more valuable than mine.'

Thus the two lovers argued, each defending the other, while the emir drew his sword. At once, Blanchefleur leaped out of bed and offered her neck to the sword. But Floire pushed her away, offering *his* neck instead. Before the emir could strike him, Blanchefleur stepped before him again…

But Floire pushed her away and fell to his knees, crying, 'Sir, listen!' He began to tell the whole story that you have just read, from the very beginning to the moment when they were caught together in the tower. He spoke so eloquently and with such passion about their unflinching faithfulness and suffering, that even the emir's ice-cold heart was moved. He stood above Floire uncertainly, his sword hovering; and his eyes became very moist.

'…And so, my lord,' Floire concluded, 'if this story pleases you, I beg you to pay for it – not with treasure – but by granting me permission to live with Blanchefleur.'

The emir gulped. A few tears actually fell from his eyes. With trembling hands, he slowly sheathed his sword. Then he took Floire and Blanchefleur's hands and joined them together.

'All right,' he said, 'your extraordinary story has persuaded me. I will let you both go free. Even more, Floire, I will make you a knight of my realm, and… Ach, take her! I grant you permission to marry Blanchefleur.'

Shortly afterwards, their wedding was held in the heart of the emir's city. As part of the celebrations, all the other captive young women were also set free from the tower and allowed to return to their families.

In the middle of the feast, a messenger arrived hotfoot from Spain, with grave news: both King Fenis and his queen – Floire's parents – had died. The country was in mourning and desperate for the late king's only son and heir to return.

At this, Floire brought the celebrations to an abrupt end, declaring that he and Blanchefleur must return to his country forthwith. Nothing the emir said or did could dissuade them. So in good time, Floire and his beloved Blanchefleur returned to be crowned the new king and queen of Spain. They ruled together well and in tender love until they were both a hundred years old.

Much of Spain was under Islamic rule from the early 8th century to the late 15th century. It is believed that Christian and Jewish communities lived separately but relatively peacefully within it, suffering neither forced conversion nor enslavement, although there is much scholarly debate about how much equality was allowed.

The ancient city of Babylon (located in modern Iraq) was capital of a major kingdom in ancient Mesopotamia from the 18th to 6th centuries BC. It was one of the largest cities in the world, with a population of up to two-hundred-thousand. To medieval European storytellers, it would have been a place of exotic legend.

The imprisonment of a heroine at the top of a tower was a common motif in medieval legends, as was the return of an absent crown prince to claim his kingdom after his father's death. The idea of a cruel ruler taking a series of wives, and killing them as soon as he tires of them, may be derived from *Shahrazad*, the well known frame-story of the ancient Arabian book, *One Thousand and One Nights*.

FENICE & CLIGÉS

Chrétien de Troyes: *Cligés*,
France, c. 1160–72

Chrétien was a French poet from Troyes in northern France. He worked under the patronage of Countess Marie de Champagne, daughter of King Louis VII and Eleanor of Aquitaine. The latter is widely credited with spreading the concept of 'courtly love' through France and England. In many medieval stories of chivalry and romance, this was expressed as a highly stylised form of sexual desire and fulfilment outside marriage. It was characterised by illicitness, secrecy, passion, humiliation and jealousy; but also extreme self-discipline and sometimes spiritual transcendency.

The particular story retold here survives in eight medieval manuscripts and various fragments. It is considered one of Chrétien's most important works, alongside four other chivalric epics: *Erec et Enide, Yvain, Lancelot* and the unfinished *Perceval*.

Chrétien composed his stories as extended narrative poems, using eight-syllable rhyming couplets. His style is typically leisurely and very long-winded, with very detailed descriptions of the characters' beauty, clothing, jewellery and surroundings; particularly elaborate are his accounts of hunting, battles, skirmishes and the resultant injuries. All this reflected the leisure pursuits of his aristocratic readers.

Chrétien is believed to be one of the first European writers to create literature about chivalry and romantic love. This was in stark contrast to earlier French epic poems, which celebrated virility and war inspired by religion, with little romance, and indeed scarce mention of women. He is said to be the originator of the concept of King Arthur's court as a centre for questing knights and leisurely ladies seeking amorous adventures, particularly the illicit love affair between Sir Lancelot and Queen Guinevere. He is also the first known writer to mention the Holy Grail (see p.168).

In the passage reproduced at the beginning of this retelling, Chrétien states he did not invent the plot himself, and his narrative gives a sense that the characters are already familiar to his readers. Some scholars believe that the story originated in Celtic folklore.

> The story which I intend to relate to you, we find written in one of the books of the library of my lord St Peter of Beauvais. From there I drew the material to make this romance. The book in which the story is told is very old, and this adds to its authority. From such books which have been preserved we learn the deeds of men of old and of times long since gone by. Our books have informed us that the pre-eminence in chivalry and learning once belonged to Greece. Then chivalry passed to Rome, together with that highest learning which now has come to France.

This story is about fair Fenice, the daughter of a German emperor who named her after the fabled phoenix bird.

When Fenice reached marriageable age, another emperor, old Alis of Greece, wrote to her father, asking for her as his bride. The German emperor immediately agreed. Fenice herself had no say in the matter.

In truth, Alis had no legal right to make this marriage proposal. For after the previous emperor died, Alis's elder brother, Alexander, should have acceded to the throne; but he had gone missing. By the time he reappeared, Alis was already installed as emperor. So the brothers reached a compromise: Alis would continue to rule, but he promised not to marry or father any children. In this way, Alexander's son, Cligés, would be his sole, uncontested heir.

Shortly after making that agreement, Alexander died. This emboldened Alis to break his promise, and take a wife after all. Being long starved of sensual pleasures, he could not wait to get his hands on the beautiful young Fenice.

As soon as Alis arrived to claim her, the German emperor summoned Fenice to meet him. 'Come out as you are,' he ordered, 'with your head uncovered and no veil, so he can see your full beauty.' Though Fenice shuddered at the thought of being ogled by an ageing lecher, she dutifully obeyed. Emperor Alis was immediately dazzled and besotted by her, even though she lowered her glance and refused to look at him.

However, as she walked slowly down the room, her attention was caught by a light that shone as brightly as her own. She glanced up – and her eyes met those of a handsome, well built youth. It was only for the briefest moment; but at once her heart began to race with the madness of love. Moreover, she saw her secret yearning reflected in the young man's own eyes. No matter that Fenice was already claimed: somehow they must find a way to overcome this. But how?

This was made even more difficult, because the youth was the very one who would be deprived of his rightful inheritance when Fenice bore Emperor Alis a son. He was Alis's own nephew, Cligés.

Fenice had a beloved old nurse called Thessala, who was a skilled enchantress. It did not take long for her to notice that something was troubling Fenice. So she called the girl to her side, saying, 'My dearest child, why have you stopped laughing and turned so pale? Come, you know you can confide in me. Don't I always keep your secrets? Do I ever pass judgement? Let me guess: you are suffering from lovesickness, eh?'

Fenice nodded and whispered, 'But I don't even know his name.'

'*I* do though,' said Thessala, wiping away her charge's tears, 'for I saw what happened when your father paraded you before the Greek visitors. The young man you yearn for is none other than Cligés – your future husband's nephew!'

Fenice gasped.

'Don't look so shocked,' said Thessala. 'It makes things quite a bit easier. For since he's a member of your future husband's household, it will be easy to meet up with him.'

'But when I marry Emperor Alis,' wept Fenice, 'I will have to yield my body to him. And I can no more share my body between two men than I can share my heart.'

Thessala sucked on her toothless gums and considered the problem carefully. Then she said, 'I know exactly what to do. On your wedding day, I shall brew a special potion, rich with charms and spices, irresistibly delicious, and arrange for your husband to drink it. He will guzzle it down – little realising that with every sip he is becoming more and more impotent. By the time he has satisfied his thirst for it, he will never be able to consummate your marriage.' She chuckled. 'But there's more to it than that. Each night when you go to bed with him, he will immediately fall into a deep slumber, enjoying endless erotic dreams about you. He will awake every morning, believing that these dreams have really happened, thus giving him great happiness and satisfaction. You, meanwhile, will preserve your precious chastity for the one you truly love.'

Shortly after that, the dreaded wedding took place. As the guests sat down to the feast, Thessala beckoned Cligés aside.

'Young man,' she said quietly, 'to celebrate your uncle's marriage to my beloved charge, Fenice, I have this mouthwatering drink for him. Take it to him now, saying it comes with the compliments of...er...a special incognito guest. Assure him that the royal samplers have approved it. But do not taste even a single drop of it yourself.'

'Why?' asked Cligés. 'What is it?'

She winked at him. 'Ask no questions. One day, you will be very glad you followed my advice.'

She poured some of the potion carefully into an exquisitely cut crystal goblet. Cligés carried this to his uncle, Emperor Alis, who was already pleasantly drunk. The emperor swallowed the potion in a single gulp, smacked his lips in delight, then sent Cligés to fetch some more. This was duly done, several times over. By the end of the evening, Alis's blood had absorbed so much of the potion that he would never be free of its influence. From that time until the day he died, every night he believed himself to be wide awake when, in fact, he slept. And while he slept, he always dreamed of Fenice lighting his fire, then thrillingly quenching it.

Despite Thessala's promise, Fenice followed her new husband to the marital bed with great trepidation. Drunkenly, Emperor Alis beckoned her between the sheets beside him. Warily, speechlessly, ashen-faced, she obeyed. But before he could even reach out to her, his eyes drooped and he began to snore. Fenice slipped from the bed, opened the curtain to the moonlight and stood watching him. She saw him fidgeting and twitching, wrapping his arms around his pillow and caressing the empty air; she heard him groaning and his fat lips making loathsome sounds of kissing. Not once did he realise she was absent. Nevertheless, when he woke in the morning he was utterly content, believing that the dream he so vividly recalled had really been true.

This continued night after night. Though Fenice was by no means happy, she too had her dreams; and her precious chastity remained intact.

Alis took Fenice back to Greece with him and established her there as his empress.

Shortly after this, Cligés told Emperor Alis that he was going to Britain for a while. 'Before my father died,' he said, 'he advised me to visit the court of my great-uncle, King Arthur, to prove myself to him and thus become a knight. Now I am ready to fulfil his last wish.'

Fenice was greatly distressed to see him go. Cligés was absent for two years or maybe three; and all that time Fenice yearned for him. However, eventually he returned, telling his uncle that he had distinguished himself in many tournaments before King Arthur, who had knighted him eagerly; and since then he had performed some outstanding deeds of chivalry.

One day, when Empress Fenice was sitting with her maids in her private chamber, Cligés paid a call on her. He entertained the ladies with tales of his knightly exploits, then asked to speak with Fenice in private.

As soon as they were alone, Cligés said, 'My lady, long ago I lost my heart to you. Although you are married to my uncle, I yearn to serve you in secret as your knight.'

'Likewise, ever since I first set eyes on you, my heart has always been yours,' Fenice replied.

'That is what I always hoped and believed,' said Cligés.

'And just as my heart belongs entirely to you, so does my body,' Fenice confided to him. 'For I am Emperor Alis's wife in name only; in truth, I am still a chaste virgin.' Then she told Cligés about Thessala's potion, and how, though he did not realise it, her husband had never actually consummated their marriage.

Cligés recalled how Thessala had ordered him to give his uncle the potion at the wedding. He was jubilant. 'Now all we need do is find a way to be together!' he cried.

'Indeed,' said Fenice. 'But to avoid gossip, you must leave me for now. Come back tomorrow; and meanwhile let us both try to think of a way to free me from Emperor Alis so that I can live with you.'

Cligés returned the next day and sat chatting to all the ladies for a while, until Fenice found an innocuous excuse to take him aside.

'Have you come up with anything?' she asked quietly.

'Yes, indeed,' said Cligés. 'The best course is the simplest one. I will go back to Britain – and take you with me. When I left King Arthur, he urged me to return soon; and his queen, Guinevere, will be delighted to have you join me.'

But Fenice said at once, 'No! That will not do at all. Imagine the cruel gossip if we were to run away together! People would be shocked and disgusted; they would disparage our love. No one would believe that I was still a virgin when I left your uncle, and thus never lawfully married to him. I would be condemned as a whore, and you would be mocked as a weak and gullible fool. I have a much better plan, one that will totally avoid malicious rumours: we must pretend that I am dead.'

'What?' cried Cligés. 'I could not bear for you to die!'

'Hush, keep your voice down,' whispered Fenice. 'Remember, anyone who sees us talking must believe this conversation is about trivialities. Now listen. I have it all worked out, and Thessala has already agreed to help me, just as she did before. Very soon, I will pretend to fall seriously ill. Shortly afterwards I will feign my own death. In the meantime, you must prepare a sepulchre for me.'

'A sepulchre?' he hissed in horror.

'Yes. Arrange it secretly in advance. After my apparent death, tell my husband that you know the perfect stonemason to fashion a final resting place for a woman of my status. It must be designed so that air can freely enter it, thus preventing me from suffocating when I am laid inside. The night after my funeral, you can come to the sepulchre and release me – then take me to freedom! I don't care where we go, Cligés, so long as we end up together; I'm sure you can find a suitable place. Everyone will believe that I am mouldering in the ground, and neither of our reputations will be sullied.'

Cligés was impatient to carry out Fenice's audacious and extraordinary plan. He knew the very man to help: a serf called John, who worked for him as a farmhand, but who also had a talent for stone carving. Cligés sought him out, saying, 'I have always found you exceptionally capable and trustworthy. If you can carry out an important task for me, and keep it totally secret, I will set you free, alongside your wife and children.'

'Only a fool would refuse an offer like that,' said John. 'I'll do whatever you ask.'

So Cligés told the serf everything about his romance with Fenice, and about their bold plan, sparing no detail. John did not bat an eyelid. 'Come at once to my workshop,' he said. 'For not only can I help you with the sepulchre, but I can also assist with your beloved's long-term concealment.'

He led Cligés out to a very remote part of the countryside, far from any city, village or other dwelling. On a piece of wild, unclaimed land, the serf had built himself a fine wooden house, surrounded by a walled garden. He showed Cligés proudly around it, then took him into his workshop.

'This is where I will make a sepulchre befitting your lady's status,' he said, 'and also as a monument to her great beauty. I will ensure plenty of ventilation, so that she may lie safely within it, alive. When the time comes to smuggle her away from it, sir, I suggest that you bring her straight here.'

'Here?' said Cligés.

'Yes,' said John. 'For if it suits you both, sir, your lady is welcome to live in this house. No one will ever find her here, for no one even knows this house exists, not even my wife or sons. You have seen with your own eyes what a wilderness of forest and scrub it stands in, with no road leading to it. No one would ever find it without my help. Besides, you have not yet seen the best of it. Follow me.'

He pointed to a heavy oaken door. Taking a set of keys, he turned several in its row of locks, then beckoned Cligés to follow him down some steps. These led into a splendid vaulted apartment, containing beautifully worked furniture including a large bed, spread with white linen and ermine coverlets. Opening an inner door, he revealed an exquisite mosaic bath with pipes fixed to it. 'When I light the stove in my workshop,' he said, 'it heats water which flows into this bath. I built and furnished these rooms for my own entertainment. But would it not make the perfect apartment for your lady? She can enjoy its comforts and luxury far from prying eyes. Even if someone were to stumble upon the house here, once I hand the keys over to you, no one else will be able to unlock the door; and since the apartment has no windows, no one can peer in. Sir, I am happy for all this to be hers, in return for my family's freedom.'

'I will take it!' cried Cligés, and he clapped his hand upon John's shoulders. 'Good man, as soon as my lady is safely installed here, you and your family shall be released from bondage.'

They went outside. John locked the door behind them, and then the garden gate, and pressed the keys into Cligés' hands. Then he led his former master back to the city, taking care to point out all the landmarks he would need to find his way back to the lonely house. As they went, the two men discussed the sepulchre for Fenice's feigned death in detail. Then, for the time being, they parted.

Cligés managed to see Fenice once more, and told her everything he had arranged. Fenice shared this news with her old nurse, Thessala.

'This is excellent,' Thessala cried. 'I will brew a potion to make you appear cold, colourless, pale, stiff and speechless. But that will only be an illusion; in truth you will be totally unharmed, though for a while you'll be unable to feel any sensations. As you sink under its influence, everyone except myself and Cligés will believe that your soul has departed. The emperor will wish you to be buried in grand style. Since I am your oldest companion, he is bound to ask my advice about your funeral. I will refer him to Cligés, saying he knows all the best craftsman and can recommend one to build the perfect tomb. The emperor has great respect and affection for his nephew...' she chuckled merrily '...little suspecting that he is planning to cuckold him! Assuming all goes to plan, they will inter your apparently lifeless body – and you will awake the following day in your new home, completely mindless of your night in the sepulchre. After that, my dear, your happiness will finally begin!'

A few weeks later, the citizens of Greece were dismayed to hear that Empress Fenice had fallen seriously ill. Cligés swallowed his excitement, composed a sombre face and hastened to the palace. There he learned that Fenice was apparently close to death, and that no one but her husband was permitted to enter her bedchamber. She refused to let any doctor examine her, but had allowed Thessala to collect samples of her urine for the royal physician to examine.

The cunning nurse had previously made enquiries around the city until she found a woman who was genuinely suffering the advanced stages of a mortal disease. Pretending she had come to help, Thessala collected urine from *her*, then delivered it to the royal doctors, claiming it was Fenice's. They analysed it with growing horror, and confirmed that the empress's death was imminent. The emperor, who believed from his dreams that Fenice was his perfect lover, swooned in despair.

At this, Thessala crept into Fenice's chamber and administered the second dose of her potion. As soon as she swallowed it, Fenice totally lost consciousness. Thessala rushed out of the room, crying: 'She's gone! My beloved Fenice is dead!'

At once, all the courtiers crowding outside set up an anguished wailing. The emperor came round from his swoon and summoned Cligés. 'Good nephew,' he groaned. 'As you can see, I am too beset with grief to do anything. So I put the funeral arrangements in your good hands. I wish you to erect a sepulchre to honour my late wife's beauty and status.'

Cligés immediately sent for John. As a pretence for the courtiers gathered around him, he greeted his former serf as if he were a stranger who had been recommended by an acquaintance as an excellent stonemason. He asked if John could possibly construct a suitably grand tomb quickly enough for the state funeral. John played along and replied that, by good chance, he had built one some time ago, simply to practise his skills, never dreaming that it might be used to inter the empress. Cligés went with John to inspect it, then returned to tell the emperor that the sepulchre was even more splendid than he could have desired, and it was already on its way to the royal cemetery.

It was put in place, to the mournful tolling of bells and chanting of masses for the dead. Fenice's apparently lifeless body was carried there and gently laid on a featherbed inside it, strewn with flowers. As the crowd grieved for her, John sealed the sepulchre tightly. No one noticed the copious air vents he had subtly cut in its walls.

That night, by moonlight, Cligés and John returned to the cemetery. Finding the gates secured against intruders, they helped each other over the high wall, and ran straight to the sepulchre. John took a long knife and carefully cut open its sealed door. Even in the shadows, Cligés could see that his beloved Fenice was indeed still alive, very weak, but with dark eyes shining. He stooped inside, gathered her into his arms and carried her out. Then John re-sealed the sepulchre, leaving no sign that it had ever been touched.

Between them, the two men carefully lifted Fenice back over the cemetery wall. Their horses were waiting nearby. Cligés lifted her gently onto his own horse's saddle, and climbed up behind her. Holding her steady, he rode after John out of town, into the wilderness, on and on through the night, until they reached his secret house.

Thessala was already waiting for them there. She helped them lay Fenice on the bed in the underground chamber, then administered an awakening potion, bathing her weakened body with special ointments. Within no time at all, Fenice was fully recovered. She gazed around her new home in amazement and delight, for John had prepared it splendidly in readiness for her arrival.

'My love,' said Cligés, 'I must leave you now, to avoid any suspicion about my absence. However, I have the perfect excuse to visit you here every day. For I recently bought a new hunting falcon, and everyone knows I must come out to the wilderness regularly to exercise and train it. That is my pretext. But after I have dealt with the bird, I will be free to spend all my time with you.'

'I will be waiting for you, my own love,' Fenice smiled.

And so it was. Under the smokescreen of his falcon, Fenice now gladly sacrificed her long-guarded chastity to Cligés, without hindrance or restraint. There is no doubt that the lovemaking of this besotted couple was far better than anything the cheated emperor enjoyed even in his dreams.

It was late spring when Fenice first arrived at the secret apartment. She spent over a year concealed inside it, living in candlelight, enraptured by her daily visits from Cligés. But she badly missed the outside world and fresh air.

One morning, after she and Cligés had taken their pleasure of each other, she said, 'My love, I am so happy seeing you here every day, but I never anticipated how hard it would be to stay in hiding. If only I could step out for a brief moment to enjoy the sun, and see the trees and flowers! I long to feel soft breezes on my face, and grass beneath my feet.'

Cligés answered, 'My own love, this house is surrounded by a very beautiful garden. I will ask John to make it safe for you to come outside and spend some time in it.'

Another month passed, with Fenice daily repeating her longing. At last, Cligés came in one morning and said, 'The garden is all ready for you. John has raised the height of its wall, so that even if some stranger happened to pass by – which is most unlikely in this wilderness – they would never catch even a glimpse of you. Come.'

He took her hand and led her up the steps, through the main part of the house and out through a door. She was overjoyed to taste the pure, sunny air of a summer's morning. The garden was full of fragrant shrubs and brightly coloured flowers; but its centrepiece was a blossom tree, with a spreading top and many long branches hanging almost to the ground. Under its dappled shade, they spread out fresh linen and there discovered new sweet joys in their union.

A few months later, during the bird-hunting season, a young knight called Bertrand was chasing game through the wilderness. Suddenly, his falcon flew right off, and over a distant wall. He galloped after it and clambered up the wall, hoping thus to entice the falcon back to his glove. As he sat astride the top, he saw a beautiful garden on the far side; and under a central spreading tree, a naked young couple lying fast asleep in close embrace.

Bertrand was not prudish, so he leaned forward to take a proper look – and was astonished to recognise the naked man as his fellow knight, the emperor's nephew, Cligés. 'Whah-hoah!' he thought, 'he's certainly having fun. But I wonder who his girlfriend is.' He leaned closer – and almost fell off the wall with shock. 'That's extraordinary! She looks just like the late empress…in fact, if she wasn't dead and buried, I'd swear that it was her!'

Unfortunately, as he wriggled about to keep his balance, he knocked the branch of an overhanging pear tree, sending a fruit crashing down into the garden below. The noise woke Cligés – who looked up and recognised Bertrand. He shook

Fenice awake, hissing, 'My dear, we are in terrible danger! Stay here while I try to save us.'

He seized his sword, which was lying in the grass beside him, ran to the wall and scaled it. At once, Bertrand slid down the far side. Cligés jumped down after him into the wilderness and gave chase. Within moments, he had caught up with Bertrand, and succeeded in striking off the knight's leg, just below the knee. But Bertrand's horse was close by; somehow, despite bleeding heavily, he managed to mount it then gallop away towards the city.

There, the wounded knight staggered to the palace, demanded an audience with the emperor and related what he had seen. Some of the emperor's councillors dismissed Bertrand as a gibbering fool, reminding him that Empress Fenice was long dead and buried; but others pressed for a full investigation.

So the emperor sent a search party to the wilderness house. The men broke in and scoured every room, but found no sign of Fenice or Cligés. For Thessala had already smuggled her young friend away with the help of enchantments, and Cligés had fled.

However, John was soon identified as the owner of the house and taken prisoner. When the emperor offered him the choice of confessing or being burned alive, he revealed himself as a treacherous coward after all, and admitted everything. But in an attempt to save face, he concluded: 'I helped Cligés, sir, to make amends for the dreadful crime that *you* committed against him. For you broke your promise to your own brother, never to marry, in order that Cligés could inherit the throne after your death. And I'll reveal something else to you, sir: your whole marriage to fair Fenice was actually a sham.'

Then John told Emperor Alis all about the anti-love potion that Thessala had sent him on his wedding night, and how the pleasure he believed he had received from his wife was no more than a dream. 'Fenice always despised you,' he went on. 'But she loves Cligés so much, she feigned her own death because it was the only way she could be with him.'

Shocked, the emperor turned his thoughts back to his wedding night, and to all the other times he had shared his marital bed with Fenice. He recalled the delicious brew that he had so eagerly imbibed at the marriage feast, and how his lovemaking had always seemed like a shadowy dream. He realised that John spoke the truth.

Desperate for revenge, he sent out a whole army of search parties to scour the world from one end to the other until for Cligés and Fenice, and bring them back to be punished.

However, this was all in vain. For old Thessala still had plenty of tricks left in her brewing cauldron, and now she concocted an enchantment that made Fenice and Cligés invisible until they reached the coast. There they resumed their normal shapes and found passage on a ship that took them across the sea, to the court of King Arthur in Britain. When he heard of Cligés' deep love for Fenice, Arthur took the young man's side at once, and prepared a large fleet of ships with thousands of soldiers, to vanquish Emperor Alis.

But before they could set out, messengers arrived from the court of Greece. The remorseful John had directed them to King Arthur's court, guessing that Cligés might find sanctuary there. Speaking to Cligés in the presence of the high king, they announced:

'Emperor Alis of Greece has died of fury and a broken heart. On his deathbed, he acknowledged that you, Cligés, are his rightful heir. The throne of Greece is yours, sir. We beg you to return and claim it.'

So the new Emperor Cligés hurried home with his beloved Fenice, whom he now married and crowned empress for the second time. The people were all delighted to see her alive and well, and gave her a wonderful reception.

After that, Cligés loved Fenice as no man had ever loved a wife before and gave her all the freedom that she could wish for.

This retelling is based on the second part of *Cligés*, which actually comprises two quite separate though intricately related stories.

The first part describes the adventures of Cligés' father, Alexander. His absence from Greece loses him the throne to his younger brother, Alis; who, however, promises not to marry or have children so that Cligés remains Alis's heir. Here, Fenice is originally betrothed to the Duke of Saxony before Emperor Alis asks for her hand. The two men engage in extensive warfare before Alis wins her, with Cligés establishing himself as a promising warrior on his uncle's behalf.

The incident in which doctors use urine to assess the severity of Fenice's supposed illness is verified by medieval manuscript illustrations of the process, with diagnostic coloured charts.

At first sight, Fenice's role seems to validate proactive women. However, Chrétien's conclusion unfortunately suggests that it is more correctly a cautionary tale for powerful men who allow their wives too much freedom, saying:

> For never since has there been an emperor who did not stand in fear of his wife, lest he should be deceived by her upon hearing [this] story. Therefore, every empress, however rich and noble she may be, is guarded...as in a prison, for the emperor has no confidence in her... He keeps her constantly guarded in her room, nor is there ever allowed any man in her presence, unless he be a eunuch.'

From
THE LAIS OF
MARIE DE FRANCE

England, late 12th century

A 'lai' is a lyrical narrative poem composed to be sung by minstrels, accompanied by a harp or rote (a five-stringed harp), usually comprising tales of adventure and romance. Marie used this form to retell twelve oral folk tales from Brittany, a Celtic region of north-west France. There is also a verse prologue, and the entire collection is around six thousand lines long, each line containing eight syllables.

She explains the stories' provenance thus:

> The Bretons, who lived in Brittany, were fine and noble people. In days gone by these valiant, courtly and noble men composed lais for posterity and thus preserved them from oblivion. These lais were based on adventures they had heard and which had befallen many a person.

Little is known about Marie except that she was a Frenchwoman who lived and worked in England, and wrote in the Old French language. She is believed to have composed her lais for an aristocratic audience who relished hearing her emotionally charged narrative poems read aloud. It is claimed that she and her work were known at the court of King Henry II of England (reigned 1150–1189); and she may have been a contemporary of the Arthurian writer Chrétien de Troyes (see p. 46).

Marie was described by Denis Piramus in *The Life of St Edmund the King* (1180) as follows:

> Dame Marie...who wrote lais in verse which are not all [*or* not at all] true... The lais are accustomed to please the ladies: they listen to them joyfully and willingly, for they are just what they desire.

The complete set of lais survives in a 13th century manuscript. Some of the same poems appear in four other, less complete, manuscripts. Marie reveals her own identity by stating at the beginning:

> Hear, lords, the words of Marie who in her time does not neglect her obligations.

and at the end:

> At the close of this text, which I have written and composed in French, I shall name myself for posterity. My name is Marie and I come from France.

She also makes her presence as the narrator known by peppering the text with phrases such as 'I believe' and 'as I understand it'.

Marie is also widely credited as the author of a collection of fables; some are translated from Aesop, but others may be her own work and portray female cunning. In addition, she may have written some works with a religious theme.

64

Love Knots
(Guigemar)

My lords and ladies, I shall tell you a true adventure which happened in Brittany long ago. It is the inspiration behind *The Lai of Guigemar*, which is often sung to the harp with a very pleasing melody.

There was a very beautiful, courtly and clever lady – I do not know her name – who was married to the lord of a large city. Her husband was much older than her and, like all elderly men with young wives, he lived in constant dread of being cuckolded. Because of this, he kept her shut away under lock and key in a very remote, one-roomed house by the sea. It was surrounded by a garden, which in turn was surrounded on three sides by an impenetrable, green marble wall. The wall had but a single gate. This was guarded day and night by an old priest – a eunuch – who recited prayers in a small chapel beside the house, and also served the lady at table. Apart from the gate, the only gap in the the marble wall was filled by a very steep, rocky crag overlooking a lonely stretch of ocean. Thus the lord felt confident that no one else could enter the grounds, and that the lady could not possibly escape.

The lady was forced to spend all her days there. But she did have one companion: her husband's young niece, a noble and intelligent damsel. Fortunately, the lady was very fond of her.

One day, the lady and the damsel were taking some air in the garden, and paused by the crag to watch the waves breaking on the tiny beach below.

'Oh, my lady,' the damsel suddenly cried, 'look, there's a ship down there!'

Sure enough, a fine ship built of pure black ebony wood, with a white silken sail, had come to rest in the shallows at the bottom of the rocks. It was the first time they had ever seen such a thing.

'It seems to have been abandoned,' said the lady. 'I wonder if it's possible to somehow clamber down and take a proper look at it.'

'Please, do let me try,' begged the damsel, who was glad of any excuse to relieve their boredom. The old lord would have been shocked to see how easily she managed to descend the rocks to the little beach at the bottom, then wade out and pull herself up onto the ship. At first sight, there seemed to be no one aboard at all. But then the damsel saw an enormous bed in the stern. It was finely crafted from cypress wood inlaid with ivory and gold, spread with silken sheets and sable coverlets. On this bed lay a half-naked knight. His breeches were thickly stained with blood, and he looked so pale and lay so still, that she feared he was dead.

She stifled a scream, hastily climbed back up and told her lady what she had found.

'We must do our duty and arrange a proper burial for this poor dead knight,' said the lady. 'Let us try together to lift the body out of the ship and haul him up here.'

She too managed to make her way down the rocks without hindrance, and followed the damsel back onto the ship. When she saw the knight...well! In all her life, she had never even imagined such a handsome man.

The damsel began to weep for his untimely death. The lady hushed her, gingerly placed a hand upon the knight's bare chest – and cried, 'He's not dead at all! He's still warm, and I can feel his heart beating.'

Sure enough, at her touch, the knight stirred and opened his eyes.

'Noble sir,' the lady said, 'who are you? Where are you from?'

He sat up, cleared his throat and said in a hoarse voice, 'My name is Guigemar.'

'Who is your father?' asked the damsel. 'Who is your wife, or which lady do you serve?'

'My father is a lord in Brittany,' he answered. 'I have neither wife nor lover. Indeed, I have no interest whatsoever in women, for I have never met any who attracted me.'

'How did you get here?' the damsel persisted.

The knight shook his head, as if trying to free himself from confusion. 'It's a long story,' he said. 'I was out hunting. I had fallen some way behind my companions, when my dog flushed out a pure-white hind from a thicket. Naturally, I shot an arrow at her. She fell at once; but unfortunately, the arrow rebounded and struck me too. The blood you see seeping through my breeches is where it penetrated my thigh. I tumbled from my horse, landed beside the injured hind and almost swooned. While I was in that state, I heard the hind speak to me in a human voice.'

'Truly?' said the lady. 'Is that possible?' Her eyes were fixed intently on Guigemar. 'What did the hind say?'

He went on, 'She said that, in revenge for me mortally wounding her, she cursed me never to recover from my own wound – until I fall in love with a woman. I objected that this was impossible, since I have no interest in either women or love. However, she assured me that, one day, I would surely succumb to love, despite my intentions. Then she added a further curse: that this love will cause unimaginable anguish.

67

'When I came to, I removed my shirt and managed to bind the wound with it. I could not face rejoining my companions, fearing their taunts if I tried to tell them what had happened. So I rode down a narrow track through the forest, which eventually led to a harbour. The only ship moored there was the one you have just found me on. It was fully prepared for sailing, so I staggered aboard in search of someone to help me; but there was no sign of any crew. Then I saw this bed. By that time I was feeling dizzy with pain, so I lay down on it – and immediately drifted off to sleep. I woke briefly to find that the ship had set sail in a fair wind, then I dozed again. The next thing I knew, you two were standing over me here. I have no idea where I am; but in God's name, I beg you to help me.'

'Sir,' the lady replied, 'I shall gladly take care of you until you recover. But it is vital that your presence here is kept totally secret.' She explained how her jealous old husband had isolated and imprisoned her, forbidding her to have any dealings with men apart from the eunuch priest.

Guigemar thanked her courteously and accepted her offer. With some difficulty, he managed to rise from the bed. The lady and her damsel helped him stagger ashore, up the steep rocks and through the garden. In the lady's one-roomed house, they laid him on the damsel's bed and drew the curtain around it. They washed his wound from a golden basin, bandaged it in clean white linen and nursed him with gentle care. When the priest brought their meal, they kept the knight concealed, then gladly shared their food with Guigemar.

Later, the lady lay in her own bed, tossing and turning, completely unable to sleep. For she was smitten with love for Guigemar.

The next morning, the damsel quickly realised the cause of her mistress's affliction, and resolved to help things along.

So, when the lady went into the chapel for her morning prayers, the damsel slipped along to the bed where the knight lay, and sat down beside him. He was sighing loudly and groaning.

'Sir,' she asked, 'is the pain from your wound no better?'

'Ah,' he answered, 'it is not the wound in my leg that hurts me now, but quite a different wound – in my heart. I am in agony, for I have never experienced anything like it before.'

'I'm sorry to hear that, sir,' said the damsel. 'Tell me what kind of pain it is, for I may be able to advise how to relieve it.'

'If only you could,' said Guigemar. 'I do not understand it, but I keep thinking about your lady. This causes me the most terrible pangs, as if I had been stabbed in the heart. At the same time, her face constantly floats before my eyes as in a wonderful dream.'

'Oh, that's easy to understand,' the damsel smiled. 'You have fallen in love with my mistress.'

'But that's impossible,' he cried. 'No woman has ever had this effect on me before.'

'That's because there is no woman in the world equal to my lady,' said the damsel. 'Well, sir, you'll be pleased to hear that she is in love with you too! What a perfect couple you are: you're as handsome as she is beautiful. Now then, if you wish to relieve your pain, I advise you to confess your feelings to her at the first opportunity.'

Soon after that, the lady returned from mass, and went straight to see the knight. At first, Guigemar was too nervous to say anything, fearing rejection; but at last he spoke up, saying, 'My lady, I am dying for love of you. I beg you to save me!'

The lady did not have the courage to admit her own feelings at once. So she answered carefully, 'Sir, as I told you,

I am in a very difficult situation. I need time to consider your request.'

'In God's name, fair lady,' Guigemar replied, 'do not tease me; my condition is so serious that I may not have much time left. I am asking you straight out: will you accept my love? If so, have mercy and tell me at once.'

The lady blushed and said, 'I would be very glad to accept it. But I worry about both my jealous husband, and the curse that hangs over you; I fear that your proposal will lead us both into trouble.'

'So be it,' said Guigemar. 'But before this ill-fated trouble strikes, let us enjoy our love while we can.'

Without further ado, he took her in his arms. She did not resist. The damsel discretely hurried out, leaving her lady and the knight alone. They began to talk, kiss and embrace freely; and it was not long before the ultimate act was accomplished, with the very greatest enjoyment on both sides.

Guigemar lived happily in hiding with his lady for a year and a half.

They almost forgot the curse. But one summer morning as they lay together, they began to discuss what would happen if some crisis suddenly forced them to part. Each promised undying love for the other.

To express this, the lady took Guigemar's shirt and tied a knot in its tailpiece, so complex and tight that it seemed impossible to release without scissors or a knife. 'Beloved,' she said, 'in case we are ever compelled to separate, I beg you to promise not to love any woman except one who can untie this knot with her bare hands.'

In return, Guigemar fastened a silken girdle gently but firmly around the bare skin of the lady's waist, tying it with a similar knot. 'And you, beloved,' he said to her, 'must promise not to love any man except one who can untie this knot with his bare hands.'

Perhaps they had a premonition of what lay ahead. For the very next day, the lady's jealous husband ordered the eunuch priest to take a message to her. The priest was surprised to find that he could not gain entry to her house, so he climbed a ladder and spied through a window to discover the reason. In this way, he saw the lady making love with Guigemar. He immediately reported what he had seen to his lord who, in a frenzy of rage, summoned three guards to accompany him to the chamber and break down the door. The old lord interrogated Guigemar, then had him dragged back into the ship on which he had arrived, and cast out to sea.

As for the lady, her husband now built a cold, dark tower beside her lonely house, and imprisoned her right at the top. Up there she languished for over two years, mourning her lost love with indescribable anguish.

But one day, when she tried the door – as she had done every single day since the tower became her prison – she found that the priest had forgotten to lock it behind him when he last brought up her food. She crept out tremulously, descended the narrow, winding stair and thus made her way into the garden without hindrance. She ran to the crag overlooking the sea – and there was astonished to behold the very ship that Guigemar had been cast adrift on.

'Alas,' she thought, 'he must have fallen overboard and drowned, in which case, everything is lost and I have nothing left to live for. I may just as well end my own life in exactly the same way.'

So she made her way down the rocks, and for the second time boarded the ebony ship. This time she intended to throw herself into the seething water. However, before she could do so, she fell into a swoon. And as she lay on the deck unconscious, the wind blew into the silken sail and carried her out to sea.

After a very long journey, the ship reached Brittany, and entered a harbour below the castle of a lord called Meriaduc. It so happened that Meriaduc was in the middle of fighting a fierce war, and had risen early that morning to look out for his enemy approaching. When he saw the ebony ship arrive, he sent some men to it to investigate. On board they found no one but the lady who was still in a swoon, pale and lovely as a fairy. They carried her up to the castle – where Meriaduc immediately fell in love with her.

He entrusted the lady to the care of his own younger sister, who nursed her back to health. But though the lady's body was healed, her mind was afflicted with endless sorrow.

Meriaduc often went to sit with her, and offered to marry her many times over; but she always silently shook her head and refused. When he became even more insistent, she finally broke her silence. She told him about the girdle she wore beneath her gown, explaining that only a man who could unfasten it would be able to win her love.

'You are as ridiculous as a notorious knight I have heard of in a neighbouring kingdom!' Meriaduc exclaimed. 'He will only marry a lady if she manages to untie an impossible knot in his shirt. Well, it's one thing for a knight to avoid marriage if he so wishes, but a lady has no right to turn down an honourable suitor for such a preposterous reason.' Then, ignoring her screams, he seized her, unlaced her gown by force and attempted to untie the girdle knot; but he could not do it. Nevertheless, he continued to harass the lady with proposals and pleadings.

This added greatly to the lady's distress. However, one small hope now saved her from dying of heartbreak: Meriaduc's revelation about the knight in a neighbouring kingdom with a similarly knotted shirt. Could this possibly be her beloved Guigemar? Had he miraculously survived?

Sometime after that, Meriaduc challenged his enemy to a new battle, summoning knights from far and wide to fight on his side. Amongst those who answered his call was Guigemar himself, who arrived with a hundred men to support him.

For in truth, he had not drowned as his lady had feared. Instead, the ebony ship had carried him safely back to the harbour where he had first boarded it. From there, he had returned home and tried to settle back to his old life; but like the lady, he suffered from constant sorrow. His friends tried to persuade him that the best cure for this was to marry. However, though Guigemar no longer claimed to despise all women, he now insisted that he would only marry the one who could untie the impossible knot in his shirt. Many very beautiful and noble young women from all over Brittany came to attempt this, but none succeeded.

When Guigemar arrived with his fellow knights to join the battle, Meriaduc's sister brought the lady into the castle hall to join the merry company, hoping this would cheer her. As soon as the lady entered the hall, her eyes were drawn to Guigemar. She was so overcome that she stumbled into the arms of the sister. Guigemar heard the commotion, turned to see the cause – and saw her too. After his long despair, he thought it must be an illusion – for how could she have possibly have escaped her tyrannical husband to come here? Nevertheless, when the lady was taken to a seat to recover, he went to sit beside her, and kissed her hand.

Lord Meriaduc was outraged, and resolved to belittle both the stubborn lady and the arrogant Guigemar. So he said mockingly, 'Well, Guigemar, you self-denying wretch, since this lady pleases you so much, why don't you get her to untie your famous knotted shirt?'

To everyone's surprise, Guigemar agreed to this at once, and sent a servant to fetch it. Of course, the lady immediately recognised it, for her own fingers had long ago tied that very knot. Though she dreaded what Meriaduc would do when she succeeded, she pulled it loose at once.

Guigemar was overjoyed by this, but feared it was merely a cruel and tantalising dream. To test its reality, he said, 'My sweet lady, do you still wear the girdle that *I* once tied around *you*?'

'Keep away from her!' Meriaduc roared.

But the lady ignored him and unlaced her gown in full view of everyone. She took Guigemar's hands and placed them on the girdle that circled her waist. Within moments he had undone it.

They fell into each others' arms, and while all the company listened in astonishment, each related to the other everything that had happened since they were forcibly parted.

When they were finished, the lady rose to her feet and cried, 'Beloved, now we have found each other again, I beg you to take me away!'

'I forbid that!' Meriaduc cried, even though he had no legal right to her. '*I* found her – so I shall keep her. I will fight you, Guigemar to defend my claim.'

Guigemar did not argue. Instead, taking his beloved by the arm, he immediately called on all his knights to ride away with them, thus abandoning Meriaduc in the coming war. The next day, Guigemar's company joined Meriaduc's enemies, fought against him and besieged his castle, until Meriaduc and all his men were starved to death.

In this way, Guigemar finally rescued his beloved lady to keep her permanently by his side. All their trials were now over, and they lived happily together forever more.

By the time Marie wrote this particular story, she must already have been a celebrated writer, for she introduces it with a strongly worded defence of her work. It is an intriguing declaration, which implies that some medieval people were philistines, who despised creative success and responded to it with malicious gossip:

> When there exists in a country a man or woman of great renown, people who are envious of their abilities frequently speak insultingly of them in order to damage this reputation. Thus they start acting like a vicious, cowardly, treacherous dog, that will bite others out of malice. But just because spiteful tittle-tattlers attempt to find fault with me, I do not intend to give up. They have a right to make slanderous remarks.

Interestingly, she makes no mention of receiving worse treatment than a man might have done.

In this story, the heroine is partly victim, partly proactive – as, indeed is the hero. It is the lady's husband who gets the most critical treatment, for Marie says:

> All old men are jealous and hate to be cuckolded; such is the perversity of old age.

Werewolf
(Bisclavret)

In past days, there were many tales of men who became possessed by a madness that transformed them into the shape of wolves. Some claim that these were not mere stories, and that it really used to happen.

There once lived an admirable and very noble baron called Bisclavret, who was a close confidant of the king. His wife was equally worthy, and they loved each other well. However, one thing caused the lady a great deal of concern. Every week Bisclavret would disappear for three days in a row without telling her – or anyone else – where he was going, or why.

One day, when he had just returned from one of these absences, she said, 'My dear husband, I long to ask you something: please don't be angry.'

'My lady,' he replied, 'put your question to me at once, and I shall answer as truthfully as I can.'

'That's a great relief to hear,' she said. 'You see, I get so anxious and miserable when you are away. I worry that you have a secret lover, or that one day you won't return. So please tell me the truth: where do you go each week, and what do you do there?'

For a long moment, her husband sat in silence, staring into the distance. Then he said, 'In God's name, wife, don't press me. If I tell you the truth, I am bound to lose your love, which I treasure greatly – and I will also be destroyed.'

The lady immediately realised he was hiding something serious, and she determined to worm it out of him. So she questioned him over and over, nagging and coaxing, until in the end he gave in.

'My lady,' he said, 'this is the truth: I am a werewolf. When I go away alone each week, I transform into my wolf shape, then hunt in the forest for other animals to eat.'

At first, she was too shocked to speak. But at last she whispered, 'In your wolf form, how do you dress?'

'Like any other wolf,' he said. 'Naked, except for my fur.'

'Then...' she stammered, 'wh...where do you leave your clothes?'

'I'm not telling you that,' he said quickly. 'For then you might steal them – and as a result, I would have to remain in my wolf form for ever.'

'But husband,' she protested, 'you know how much I dote on you; I've never hurt you or done you any wrong. So why won't you tell me *everything*?'

She continued to badger him until, to silence her, he said, 'Close to the path that I take into the forest, there stands an ancient chapel. Beside it is a bush, and under the bush is a broad, hollow stone. That is where I leave my clothes until I am ready to transform back into human shape.'

This brought the unsettling conversation to an end. Naturally, the lady was greatly alarmed by what she had learned. The thought of lying with Bisclavret now repulsed her. She began to consider how to get rid of him for good.

It happened that the lady had a secret of her own: a local knight was deeply in love with her. So far, she had never returned his affection or made any promises, but that had not stopped him from wooing her with great passion. She decided that he offered the best way to escape her awful situation. So, when her husband next went away, she sent a message to this knight, inviting him to come to her urgently.

As soon as he arrived, without beating about the bush, she repeated the horrific things her husband had told her. 'So, my friend, rejoice!' she declared. 'I no longer feel any loyalty to Bisclavret; he revolts me. I will happily be your mistress.'

The knight thanked her warmly, and they pledged themselves to each other. Then they discussed her situation in depth. She told the knight the path that Bisclavret used to enter the forest, and about the hollow stone by the deserted chapel where he concealed his clothes. Then she hastily sent the knight to steal them.

In this way, she committed a double sin, by both cuckolding and betraying her lawful wedded husband.

After her lover stole the clothes, Bisclavret was unable to resume his human form, just as he had warned. He was condemned to live permanently as a wolf. News soon got around that he had gone missing; search parties were organised and many enquiries were made far and wide. But no trace was ever found of him.

Soon after that, the lady – who now claimed to be a widow – married the knight who had been courting her for so long.

A year after this, the king was hunting in the forest. His hounds picked up Bisclavret's wolf scent, followed him, surrounded him and began baying excitedly, in anticipation of tearing him to pieces. But before they could do so, the king rode up. The wolf saw him, dodged the hounds and ran up to the horse. He pawed the stirrup urgently, like a dog, and started licking the king's boot. The king was astounded, and very touched by this unusual behaviour from an animal with such a savage reputation.

'Call off the hounds!' he shouted to his men. 'This is no ordinary wolf. His eyes are full of intelligence, and he seems to be begging for mercy – almost like a human. I can't bear to refuse him. No more hunting for me today: I'm going to take this fine creature home with me and keep him as a pet.'

When the king rode off, the wolf followed eagerly back to the palace. The king delighted in his new companion. He considered the wolf to be a great wonder, and treated him with kindness, ordering all his servants to do the same. They fed him well, and every night he was allowed to sleep by the king's bed, like a faithful dog. The wolf was so gentle and well behaved, that he won everyone's affection. He was totally loyal, following the king wherever he went.

Now, just hear what happened next.

The king held a festival at court for all his barons and knights. Amongst those who attended was the knight who was now married to Bisclavret's former wife. Of course, the couple had no idea that Bisclavret was still alive – let alone that, in his wolf form, he was close at hand in the palace.

But the wolf certainly knew who the knight was. For he could still understand everything that people said, and had overheard plenty of gossip about his wife and her new husband. He made a beeline for the knight, then pounced on him, sank his teeth into his leg and dragged him to the floor. Fortunately for the knight, the king was standing by. He rushed forward, threatened the wolf with a stick and ordered him to behave. The wolf withdrew, but as soon as he got another chance, he again snarled menacingly at the knight. So for the rest of the festival, the wolf had to be shut away.

The king was very upset, and everyone in the royal household was quite bewildered.

'Whatever has got into the wolf?' people wondered.

'He's always been as gentle as a lapdog until now. He's never threatened anyone else.'

'He must have come across that knight before and been hurt by him; he's behaving as if he wants revenge.'

The king was determined to get to the bottom of this curious affair. So a short while afterwards, accompanied by the best men from his household, he took the wolf back into the forest where they had first met, to search for clues.

Their overnight lodgings in the forest happened to be very close to the house where Bisclavret's former wife now lived with her new husband. When she heard that the king was close by, she decided to try and win his favour by paying homage to him. So she dressed up in her best clothes and went to call on the king, bringing an expensive gift.

The wolf smelled her coming even before she arrived, and started to work himself up into a frenzy. The king and his companions tried their best to restrain him, but before they could do so, the innkeeper brought in Bisclavret's ex-wife.

The wolf let out a bloodcurdling yelp. He flung himself at her with with bared teeth – and bit off her nose!

At this, everyone in the room started shouting:

'Sir, that wolf is dangerous!'

'You can't keep him as a pet after this!'

'Kill him on the spot before he does any more harm!'

The king was very upset for he had come to love the wolf dearly. The wolf, now very subdued, came cringing to his side.

The king's wisest councillor was amongst the men there. 'My lord,' he cried, 'please listen. Ever since you first brought this wolf to the palace, we've all observed him in a variety of situations. He's normally as gentle as a lamb. He's never attacked or even threatened anyone apart from this poor lady here, and that knight who came to your festivities – who is the lady's second husband. That suggests something has happened in the past, giving him a grudge against them both. Perhaps when the lady feels a little better, she'll be able to throw some light on what is going on.'

So after the innkeeper's wife had bandaged the lady's nose, the king questioned her. At first she refused to say anything. But the king could tell that she was concealing something and threatened to torture her – which quickly persuaded her to confess. She told of her first husband's strange, shapeshifting habit. The king, who had known Bisclavret well and been fond of him, was shocked. Before he had a chance to pass comment, she then admitted that she had betrayed Bisclavret to her secret lover, whom she had since married, and persuaded the lover to steal Bisclavret's clothes while he was in his werewolf form.

'Are you saying that this wolf is actually your first husband?' the king cried in astonishment.

'I think he must be,' she wept, 'because after my lover took his clothes, Bisclavret never came back. The wolf certainly seems to know who I am – and to have it in for me.'

The king ordered her to fetch the clothes, sending a guard to accompany her back to her own house so she could not give him the slip.

When she had brought them, the king commanded, 'Put them down before the wolf.'

She did so, snivelling and shaking. The wolf ignored them.

The wise councillor spoke up again, saying, 'My lord, this isn't the right way to do it. Think how humiliating it would be for the wolf to transform while everyone is watching. Let him go into your bedchamber with the clothes, and leave him alone for a while.'

The king himself led the wolf away, spread the clothes before him, then came out of the bedchamber and closed the door.

They waited for a long time, but nothing happened. So the king went back to the bedchamber, with two of his barons, and quietly opened the door. Inside, they saw no sign of the wolf. But a man was lying on the bed, fast asleep. When they went closer, they all immediately recognised him as the long lost Bisclavret!

Bisclavret was soon restored to his former position, and the king rewarded him for his loyalty with countless treasures.

As for the woman who had doubly betrayed him, Bisclavret in his wolf form had already given her one just punishment by biting off her nose. Now the king added to that by banishing her from his realm, alongside her second husband.

They stayed together in exile and had many children – all of whom were born without noses.

The adventure I have just described actually took place – do not doubt it! This lay was composed to ensure that the story would always be remembered.

In her prologue to this story, Marie says that Bisclavret was the Breton name for the hero, but that the Normans called him Garwaf; this implies that the same story was also told in other regions of France.

Belief in werewolves goes back to ancient Greece. In medieval Europe, wolves were normally feared and hated; and in some medieval codes the term 'werewolf' was used to mean an outlaw. Although Marie asserts that there were many werewolf stories in circulation, only sparse references to werewolf lore have survived from her time.

The Hawk
(Yonec)

This adventure tells of the sorrow and grief that must
sometimes be suffered for love.

The lord of Caerwent, in Wales, was extremely wealthy; but
he had no wife or heir. So he persuaded a nobleman to let
him marry his daughter. She was much younger than the
lord, and such a beautiful and charming lady that he quickly
became obsessed with her. His greatest fear was that some
other man would steal her away, so he locked her up at the
top of a very high tower, under the guard of his elderly,
widowed sister.

The lord had his way with her up there every night, but
she never produced the desired heir. Apart from his visits,
she had no contact with anyone except for the old widow.
Naturally, the lady grew more and more distressed. With
nothing but death to look forward to, she wept and sighed
so much that her beauty faded away. Thus the poor lady
languished for seven long years.

One April morning, the jealous lord rose early and set out to
go hunting in the forest. The widow secured the doors
behind him, then went to a lower room to mumble over her
psalter.

The lady stayed in her bed, making her habitual lament:
'Why does the grizzled old brute treat me so cruelly? Why
won't he let me mix with other people and enjoy some fun?

Curse my father for giving me to him! How I wish that one of those old wives' tales could come true, and a valiant knight would somehow find his way here and rescue me!'

The very next moment, the window was darkened by the shadow of a huge bird. It alighted on the sill, then squeezed through the bars and flew into the room.

The lady screamed.

The bird landed gently on the floor by her feet and folded its wings. It was a hawk, perhaps five or six moultings old, with straps on its feet. As she gazed at it in wonder, its feathers dissolved away...until, in its place, she saw a very handsome and lusty looking knight.

'Do not be afraid, my lady,' he said. 'I promise you are safe with me. I have known of your loneliness and admired you from afar for many years; but I had to await your summons before I could leave my own country and come to you. Now, at last, you have wished for me – so I can ask you to accept me as your lover.'

The lady had never met such a handsome and worthy man. 'Sir,' she said, 'I would gladly accept you, but first I must make sure that you are a good Christian.'

'My lady,' he said, 'of course I am. To prove it, ask for a priest and watch me take communion.'

'I cannot call a priest,' she said. 'For I am allowed no visitors except my hateful husband. And if I managed to persuade him to bring a priest to me, he would discover you.'

'That will not happen,' said the knight with a smile. 'You have already seen that I have powers beyond your dreams. So this is what we will do: you will hide – and I shall transform into your likeness! In your shape, I shall pretend to be mortally ill, then receive communion and recite the Credo. After that, you will have no cause to doubt me.'

Just then, the elderly widow pushed open the door and called to the lady, 'Surely you're not still abed? Get up, you lazy thing!'

The lady took up the deceit at once. 'But I can't,' she groaned. The knight nodded at her, and she began to cough and splutter. 'Oh, I feel so ill, I fear I am dying! Quickly, fetch me a priest to cleanse my soul before it's too late.'

'You know perfectly well I can't do that,' grumbled the widow. 'Your husband is the only man permitted to enter your room.'

'But my need is urgent,' insisted the lady. 'Can't you get my husband's permission just this once?'

'That's impossible,' said the widow. 'He's away hunting until tomorrow.'

At a nudge from the knight, the lady pretended to gasp and convulse. This caused the elderly widow such alarm that she decided to ignore her brother's orders, and rushed out to find a priest at once.

Meanwhile, the knight swapped his hiding place with the lady, then transformed himself into her shape. Thus, when the priest arrived, it was actually the knight who received the holy wine and wafer. He did this in full view of the widow, but she had no idea what was really going on. Once this private mass was over, the widow bustled the priest out and locked the lady in again, leaving her, she supposed, to die.

But as soon as the lovers were safely alone, the knight transformed back into his true shape. The lady came out from her place of concealment, and the knight drew her willingly onto the bed beside him. 'You see, my love,' he said, 'I have proved myself a respectable man.' They shared much merriment about his trick. Then they began to sport together; and after they were both satisfied, they talked of many matters. For the first time in her life, the lady understood the meaning of happiness.

All too soon, the knight said, 'I must leave you now and return to my own country.'

'Very well,' she said sadly, 'and it is vital that you depart before my husband returns. But please come back to me often.'

'Whenever you wish for me, I will be here within the hour,' he promised. 'But we must take great care. For if your guardian ever discovers me here, she is bound to betray us to your husband – and I will be doomed to die.'

That ominous warning failed to spoil the lady's continuing happiness after he had left. The next morning, she rose from her bed and told the old woman that she felt much better, attributing her sudden recovery to the priest's holy ministrations.

From that time on, whenever she was sure that neither her possessive husband nor the widow would intrude, she wished for her lover to return and pleasure her; and every time, her wish was granted. Night or day, early or late, he was hers whenever she wanted. Now she was happy, her lost beauty was not only restored, but positively glowed.

Her husband also still visited her regularly to force himself on her, and his suspicious mind noticed the change. So he called his sister. 'What's going on?' he demanded. 'Why is my wife suddenly always smiling instead of bawling and complaining?'

'I have no idea,' the old widow replied. 'I too have noticed something strange about her, as if there's something suspicious going on. But I always keep a close eye on her, and ensure she's securely locked up.'

'This needs to be investigated,' said the husband. 'After I've gone out tomorrow, pretend to lock her up as usual, but instead hide in her chamber and spy on her.'

The widow willingly agreed.

So the next morning, the husband rose from the lady's bed, saying, 'Wife, I'll be away all day until midnight.'

As soon as he had departed, the widow made a fuss of securing the door; but while the lady's back was turned, she slipped back inside the chamber and concealed herself behind a heavy curtain.

The lady remained in her bed, muttering to herself. The widow could not make out her words, so she had no idea that the lady was making her regular wish for her lover. But within moments, listening and peeping from behind the curtain, she discovered the lady's secret. For the great hawk appeared at the window, squeezed through the bars and transformed into the handsome knight! The widow, keeping totally still, listened in astonishment to their animated conversation, and watched in shame as they sported together. Then she saw the knight turn back into his hawk shape and fly away. She was not only disgusted at the lady's infidelity, but also horrified by the supernatural nature of her lover.

The widow slipped out, unnoticed by the lady, and waited for her brother. When the jealous lord heard what his wife was up to, he fell into a rage. He ordered his blacksmith to make a set of large, razor-sharp iron spikes with pointed tips, and fit them to the lady's window, exactly where the hawk had been seen to enter.

The lady did not despair, assuming that her lover's special powers would enable him to avoid the deadly trap set for him. Even so, she debated with herself whether it was best for him now to keep away; but in the end, she could not stop herself wishing for him. Her husband was out hunting again and the widow was busy elsewhere, so it was a perfect time for her lover to come.

As she made the wish, she added a warning, but to no avail. For her lover was so eager to fulfil her desire, that he assumed his hawk shape and came to her at once without caution. When she saw the hawk at the window, she again tried to warn him, but he flew to her so fast, that he hit the spikes with full force. One pierced his body, in a cascade of scarlet blood.

He managed to free himself and staggered into the room, where he at once assumed his human shape. In this form too, he was bleeding heavily. He stumbled to the bed and sat down, covering the sheets in blood.

The lady wept and tried desperately to staunch the bleeding. But the knight pushed her away, saying, 'Hush, my sweet beloved, this was fated to happen. I told you at the outset that if ever our love was discovered, I would be destroyed.'

'I'm sorry, so sorry!' she cried.

The knight, regardless of his own pain, comforted her tenderly. 'Please do not grieve for me. Instead, listen carefully. You are carrying my child, our son.'

She gasped, for as yet, she herself did not know this.

The knight went on, 'When you give birth, you must name him Yonec. He will be a fine boy who will bring you much comfort. In the fullness of time, he will grow into a valiant man – and then he will avenge my death.'

His wound was bleeding profusely, but he did not linger for the lady to bandage it, or to answer any of her frenzied questions. Instead, he used the latch to open the barbed window, changed back into a hawk and flew falteringly away.

The lady was almost naked except for her shift. But she did not hesitate to jump down from the high tower after him. By a miracle, she somehow landed unharmed.

She followed her lover's trail of blood to a hill. There, a bloodstained door in the side opened at her touch. She passed through it and felt her way along an unlit path, right through the hill, to another opening on the far side. This led out onto a beautiful meadow, where the trail of blood continued, gleaming on the grass like red dew. It led all the way to a city. Above the high wall that enclosed it, she could see the tops of houses, all built of solid silver. On one side of the city were marshes, forests and paddocks; but the blood trail led the opposite way, following a riverbank where hundreds of sailing ships were moored. At last, she reached the city gate. It stood wide open, so she hastened in. The streets were deserted. The blood trail led straight through them to the palace. Its doors stood ajar, also covered in blood. Still, she saw no sign of any other people.

She walked into the palace, looked around and tried the first door that she came to. It opened into a chamber where a knight was lying on a bed, fast asleep. But it was not *her* knight. A similar sight greeted her in the next room that she peeped into. But when she entered the third room – there was her beloved! He was lying on a bed covered in priceless linen, and lit by golden candelabra worth more than all the rest of the gold in that entire city.

The lady ran up to him with a shriek, and swooned beside him. He who loved her as deeply as she loved him, awoke at once and took her in his arms. As she came round, he comforted her and wept with her over this tragic change in their affairs. But then he said, 'My fair beloved, in God's name, you must flee from here! I do not have much life left in me: I shall be dead before dawn. If my people find you here, they will realise that I died for your love, and in their distress they will torture you.'

'My own beloved,' the lady answered, 'I would rather stay here and die beside you than return to my cruel husband. Besides, what use would that be? As soon as he had hold of me, he would kill me anyway for my unfaithfulness.'

'I will not let you die,' the knight promised. 'Take this magic ring: as long as you wear it, your husband will be a changed man. He will remember nothing of what happened today; moreover, he will free you from your long imprisonment.'

She put the ring on to please him. Then he unbuckled his sword in its scabbard, and placed it in her hands.

'Do not let any man take this from you or even touch it,' he said. 'I put it into your keeping, for Yonec, our son who will soon be born. Listen. You must live to care for him and raise him well. One day, after he has grown into a man and been dubbed a knight, your husband will ask you and Yonec to accompany him to a feast. On the way, you will stop off at an abbey, where you will see a tomb. Then you will know the time has come to tell Yonec that I was his father, and give him my sword. My own beloved lady, can you remember everything I have told you? Can you carry out my instructions?'

She said that she could.

The dying knight gave the lady a splendid and very expensive gown, and told her to put it on. The two said their final farewells. Then she walked out, wearing the gown and the ring, and carrying the sword.

When she was on her way back, only half a league from the city, she heard bells ringing to announce her beloved's death. She swooned four times with grief, then passed back through the hill and returned to the tower.

Thanks to her beloved knight's magic ring, her husband now acted completely differently towards her. He no longer kept her locked up, forgot everything that had happened and even began to treat her with the courtesy due to a wife.

In time, the lady gave birth to the son she had conceived from her true beloved, and called him Yonec. The lady's husband believed himself to be the father. The boy grew up to be exceptionally good-looking, valiant and generous. As soon as he came of age, he was dubbed a knight.

Now listen to what happened that very same year.

Just as the dead knight had predicted, the lady's husband was invited to a feast along with his wife and son. It was to be held in Caerleon, which was some distance away, so they broke the journey by taking lodgings at an abbey next to a splendid castle. There the abbot offered to show the family around his establishment. When he took them into his chapter-house, they were greatly struck by the sight of a splendid tomb covered with a cloth of brocade and gold, surrounded by twenty gleaming candles, richly scented by incense burning in amethyst censers.

'Whose tomb is this?' her husband enquired.

At this question, the monks gathered in the chapter-house broke into a dirge. Then one spoke up saying, 'This is the last resting place of the best knight ever born; the strongest and fiercest, the fairest and most beloved. He was once our king. Never has there been a ruler as noble as he was. He was slain for the love of an unknown lady at Caerwent. Since his death, this city has had no ruler, for his last words commanded us to wait for the arrival of his son, born of his beloved lady, who is his rightful heir.'

The lady turned to Yonec. 'My son,' she said softly, 'this is *your own true father* who lies here. I was once his lady. The man who killed him was my jealous husband, who is standing here beside us now. As my own beloved knight was dying, you were growing from his seed in my womb. Your father entrusted his sword to my keeping for you. Now the time is ripe for you to receive it.'

Her husband shook his head in astonishment.

The lady went to her bags, drew out the sword that she had guarded for all those years, and placed it into Yonec's hands.

'But how can this be?' Yonec cried.

The lady's voice now grew louder, and she spoke up so that everyone gathered around the tomb could clearly hear. She told how her beloved knight – who she had only just discovered was a great king – used to come to her in the shape of a hawk, of how her husband had discovered their affair and of how he had killed her lover.

In the stunned silence that followed, she suddenly collapsed onto the tomb and died.

At this, Yonec took a grip on the sword she had just bestowed upon him, rushed at the lord who was his stepfather – and struck off his head. In this way, he justly avenged the sorrowful deaths of both his true father and his mother.

The lady was laid with great honour in a magnificent tomb of her own, beside that of her beloved.

As for Yonec, once news of what had happened spread across the city, he was welcomed as his father's heir and crowned as the new king.

The name of Yonec's father was Muldumarec.

With its lady imprisoned in a tower and a shapeshifting lover, this story has the feel of a fairy tale, yet it is firmly set in real-life Wales. Caerwent, where the lady's jealous old husband had his castle, is located in Monmouthshire. The town dates back to Roman times with a pre-10th century monastery and was an important medieval centre. It was connected by road to Caerleon, where the story tragically ends. Caerleon was also founded by the Romans and, during the Middle Ages, was at the centre of the Kingdom of Gwent. In Arthurian legend, Geoffrey of Monmouth's *Historia Regum Britanniae* (History of the Kings of Britain), also written in the 12th century, claims Caerleon as King Arthur's capital. The two towns are less than ten miles apart, suggesting that Marie, and the original lai composers whose material she worked from, had little idea of Welsh geography.

As birds of prey, hawks were commonly tamed and trained for hunting small animals in the sport of falconry, which was popular amongst the nobility of medieval Europe.

AUCASSIN & NICOLETE

Anonymous, France, late 12th century

This story was originally written in prose with verse interludes, a format that was commonly used by Spanish writers in Arabic and Hebrew (see *The Prince of Beauty*, p.183), but is very unusual in European languages.

The only surviving manuscript is contained in a miscellany of verse narratives. Scholars believe it was composed in northern France; but both its folk-tale plot and its narrative style suggest origins in Moorish Spain.

It seems to be a cheerful parody of the type of melancholy love stories popularised by Marie de France.

> Pray listen to this charming lai
> Of how two lovers met:
> Aucassin the coward
> And fearless Nicolete.
> If you are feeling weary,
> Sickly, worn or sad,
> May this story cheer you up
> And help you to feel glad!

There was a war being fought and Count Bougars of Valence was easily winning. He had almost vanquished Count Garin of Biaucaire, and was busy destroying his land. This should not have happened because, although Count Garin was very old and frail, he had a strong young heir: his son, Aucassin. In theory, Aucassin should have been more than able to defeat the enemy. However, he was an idle shirker who refused to be dubbed a knight and had never fought a battle in his whole life – not even a friendly tournament.

One morning, Count Garin summoned his son in great agitation. 'The enemy's right at the city gates!' he cried. 'Get off your backside, go out and defend us!'

But Aucassin just shook his head like a spoilt child and said, 'I'm not fighting any battles until you let me marry Nicolete.'

'*Nicolete*?' his father was horrified. '*Marry* her? Surely you're not still chasing after that worthless, infidel Saracen slave? She'll warp you with her foreign ways and blasphemous pagan beliefs. She'll send your soul to Hell…'

'I'm very happy to end up in Hell,' Aucassin retorted. 'I've heard there's great company there, much better than all the sanctimonious priests and martyrs in Paradise.'

'*Please* go to war,' his father begged. 'Then I'll find you a pretty Christian wife from a rich noble family…'

'No thank you,' said Aucassin. 'Even if you offered me the queen of France, I'd turn her down. Nicolete's the only one for me.'

In despair, Count Garin rushed round to Nicolete's owner, who was the city governor. 'Friend,' he said, 'my son's so obsessed with your wretched slave girl that he refuses to carry out his duties. I order you either to send her away at once or kill her.'

'Don't blame me,' said the governor. '*I've* never encouraged Aucassin to pester her. I paid a fortune for that girl, and she's turned out so fine that I recently adopted her.

I've got a respectable working man lined up to marry her, so I'll happily protect her from your good-for-nothing son.'

The governor forbade Nicolete to have any more contact with Aucassin, and banished her to the top room of his house, locking the door tightly. There she was kept under the guard of a very fierce old woman, eating and sleeping up there, not even being let out for fresh air.

> The key was turned within that door,
> and Nicolete was seen no more.
> From the window up on high
> She would often gaze and sigh:
> 'Aucassin, my love so bright,
> I know that I'm your heart's delight.
> So why, for your sake, must I dwell
> Locked within this chamber cell?'

Rumours about Aucassin's passion for the slave, and her sudden disappearance, spread rapidly. Some said she had been banished overseas; others that the count had ordered her to be killed. Aucassin marched round to the governor, demanding to know where she was. 'If you've killed her,' he threatened, 'I'll die of heartbreak. Then my father will execute you for causing my death.'

'I don't care,' said the governor coldly. 'I'm not telling you where she is.'

Aucassin went back to his chamber in the castle, weeping profusely – until old Count Garin burst in, his face puce with anger. 'Son, the enemy's all over the streets and about to break into the castle!' he roared. 'How many times do I have to tell you? Get outside and defend us, you lazy lump!'

Aucassin said slyly, 'I'll go and fight if you bring me Nicolete afterwards – and let me kiss her – as my reward.'

'Oh...all right then,' said Count Garin wearily.

> Lured by this promise of a kiss,
> The youth did not now wish to miss
> The war! He dressed in armour bold,
> And seized a sword with hilt of gold.
> Then, dreaming of his lady dear,
> Rode off to fight, shunning fear.

Out in the fray of the battlefield, face to face with the enemy, at first Aucassin's bravado melted away and he stood helplessly rooted to the spot. But then he thought, 'If I die, I'll never see Nicolete again!' So he forced himself to find some courage and, to his own astonishment, quickly demolished a good number of the enemy.

He even managed to capture their leader, Count Bougars. 'Look,' he crowed to his father, ' I've taken your arch-enemy prisoner!'

'Well done,' said old Count Garin, with a sigh of relief.

'So you've got to fetch me Nicolete now,' said Aucassin.

'Never!' said Count Garin.

'But you promised,' said Aucassin.

'The only reason I'd fetch that slave would be to burn her,' said Count Garin.

Aucassin turned to his captive. 'Did you hear that, Count Bougars? My own father has broken his word to me! Well, I'm going to take revenge on him – by setting you free.'

Before his father could stop him, he loosened Count Bougar's bonds, gave him back his horse and let him gallop away.

Naturally, this achieved nothing, because Count Garin had his guards seize Aucassin and throw him into a deep dungeon. And there he pined away for Nicolete all day long, without further interruption.

News of his incarceration eventually reached Nicolete, up in her lonely locked room, where she was busy making a secret plan to escape.

One night, while the old woman guarding her slumbered, Nicolete knotted her bedsheets into a long rope, opened the window, fixed the rope firmly to the frame and slid down it into the garden. There she hitched up her petticoats, unbolted the gate and slipped out into the city streets. She ran through them, until she found the building where Aucassin was incarcerated in the dungeon. She knew it was the right place because, through a grille in the wall, she could hear her lover far below, hopelessly calling out her name.

'Aucassin my love,' she whispered excitedly. 'I'm here!'

There was a long pause. Then he called back, 'Nicolete? Is it really you?'

'Yes,' she replied. 'You must free yourself and come away with me.'

'I don't know how to,' he answered.

'Well, I managed to escape,' she said, 'and I'm only a slave girl.'

'But there's no way out of here,' he whined. 'Anyway, it's no use: my father will never let me marry you.'

'Are you absolutely sure?' she said. 'Is there no chance you could change his mind?'

'My situation is totally hopeless,' Aucassin groaned.

'Then… Oh well, I might just as well just leave this city and start a new life on my own,' said Nicolete.

'No!' cried Aucassin.

'It's best if I go at once before they recapture me,' said Nicolete. 'Here, I'll leave you something to remember me by.' She pulled the needlework scissors from her purse, snipped off all her long, golden curls and thrust them down through the grille into the dungeon.

Aucassin seized the hair and clasped it to his breast. 'Don't go!' he begged. 'I know exactly what will happen: you'll meet another man and let him seduce you. Then I'll have no choice but to dash my head against this wall!'

'But surely you want me to find happiness?' she said. 'If not, you obviously don't love me as much as I thought...'

In this way, they argued on, completely forgetting the joy there should have been in their meeting. Their voices rose in anger, so that neither heard the sound of heavy footsteps approaching. Count Garin's soldiers were coming along the street – searching for Nicolete, to kill her!

Fortunately, however, the sentinel who guarded the dungeon *did* hear them, and he was a kindly man. To avoid attracting the soldiers' attention, he strolled past Nicolete and disguised his warning in a song:

> 'Sweet maid! Although you know no fear
> There is danger lurking near.
> Soldiers from the city's lord,
> Sent to slay you with a sword,
> Are drawing close as close can be.
> Stop your chatter – quickly, flee!'

Nicolete heard this, whispered a hasty thank you, called down through the grille – 'Farewell, Aucassin!' – and shrank into the shadows. She slipped past the soldiers and ran to the city wall. She clambered up it, scrambled along the top, crossed herself for luck, slid down into the deep fosse beyond, crawled through it and heaved herself over the next wall, landing on the far side. Here the forest was only two crossbow shots away – full of dangerous wild beasts no doubt. She put herself in God's hands, made a run for it and plunged into the trees, walking deeper and deeper through them until she was too tired to go any further. Then she hid in a thicket, lay down on the soft moss and dropped off to sleep.

By the time she awoke, dawn was breaking and she could hear voices. She peered through the branches and saw a group of young shepherds on their way through the forest with their flock. They saw her too and stared at her in astonishment.

'Where have you sprung from?' one said nervously. 'Why is your hair all shorn?'

'She looks uncanny, like a faery,' said another.

'Whoah, watch out,' said a third, 'faeries are shifty creatures.' He flicked his fingers at her. 'Keep away from us, weird one.'

'I'm not a faery,' said Nicolete. 'Um… Do any of you know who Aucassin son of Count Garin is? If so, would you take him a message?'

'Everyone knows the count and his son,' said the first one. 'What's it worth?'

'I'll give you five sous,' she said. 'I just want you to tell him that there's…um…a rare wild creature waiting for him in this forest. Say it's got power to heal his torment, but he must come for it within three days – or it will vanish.'

'She *is* a faery,' whispered the second.

But the third held out his hand. She pulled the promised coins from her purse, he snatched them from her and the shepherds ran off.

Nicolette walked on. Soon she came to a pleasant clearing, surrounded by flowering trees. She broke off a pile of branches, then used them to build a cosy little hut, which she decorated with rustling leaves and fragrant blossom. When it was ready, she went and sat inside it.

'If Aucassin's love is true,' thought she,
'He'll escape and come to me,
And share this hut and simple life
Just like wedded man and wife.
If he doesn't, no more sighs:
I'll know his love's just empty lies.'

Down in his dungeon, Aucassin heard passers-by gossiping about Nicolete's strange disappearance. It made him so ill with worry, that his father had him removed from prison. He even attempted to cheer up his son by throwing a special feast for him. But all through it, Aucassin just sat wretchedly in a corner by himself.

At length, he slipped away from the merrymaking, fetched his horse and rode off aimlessly. In this way, he stumbled upon the young shepherds, who were on their way to find him.

'Hail, sir,' said one. 'You're Count Garin's son, Aucassin, aren't you?'

'So what if I am?' he replied.

'We've got a message for you,' said another.

'Who's it from?' said Aucassin.

'From a dangerous faery,' said the third one darkly. 'So it's likely a matter of life and death that you heed it.' He grinned at his fellows. 'But we won't tell you what it is unless you give us ten sous.'

Aucassin immediately handed over the coins. The shepherd shared them out with his companions, then repeated Nicolete's cryptic message.

Aucassin at once guessed who the message was from and what it meant. He spurred his horse into the forest, desperate to find Nicolete. He galloped so fast, brushing against thorn trees and briars, that he tore his clothes to tatters and badly scratched himself. As dusk fell, he turned down an ancient, overgrown track, hoping against hope that *she* might be at the end of it. But instead, he came face to face with a monstrous giant.

'Oi, you scabby little namby-pamby runt,' the giant roared. 'You can't pass this way unless you help me find the four oxen I've lost. Otherwise, my master will throw me into prison, leaving my poor, sick mother...'

Aucassin swallowed and said tremulously, 'Um... How much are these oxen worth?'

'Twenty whole sous!' groaned the giant.

'If I give you the money to pay your master compensation,' said Aucassin, 'will you let me pass?' With quaking hand, he pulled out the coins and offered them to the giant – who pocketed them with a roar of laughter – but still did not budge. Even so, Aucassin managed to squeeze past him, and continued along the overgrown track.

The darkness deepened and the moon came out. Suddenly, his horse stopped short in front of a strange little hut, built of roughly woven branches and flowers. Inside, he could hear a maiden singing.

He leaped down from the saddle. But he missed his footing and fell hard, tearing his shoulder against a rock. 'Aargh!' he hissed. 'Ow!' He staggered back to his feet, rubbing his wound – just as Nicolete emerged from the hut.

'You've passed the love test,' she cried, 'you managed to come to me!'

Then they forgot their tiff and fell into each other's arms. However, Nicolette squeezed Aucassin so tightly that he almost screamed with pain from his scratches and injured shoulder. He had no choice but to admit his clumsiness to her, fully expecting her to mock him, as his father would have done. But Nicolete only tut-tutted, skilfully applied some healing leaves to his injuries, then said:

'It really is not safe to bide
Much longer here. We must hide
Lest your father's men should find us
Imprison us, and with chains bind us.'
Her lover answered, 'I don't care
Which way we go, here or there
Through wilderness or gusty weather –
So long as we are close together!'

They rode through the night side by side, out of the forest,
up hills, down dales and across a great wide plain. By dawn,
they found themselves at a harbour. Aucassin approached
the captain of the nearest ship and, without bothering to find
out where it was going, asked if he would take them as
passengers. When he offered a large quantity of coins, the
captain eagerly beckoned them aboard.

Soon after the ship set sail, a terrible storm arose. It blew
them wildly around the ocean, hither and thither, casting
them into the sea. At last, they were swept ashore to a
strange country.

They sought sanctuary at its royal castle, feeling confident
that a king would treat two young lovers kindly. However,
they were told that the king could not see them because he
was in bed – not with illness, but because he was in the
middle of childbirth! As for his queen, she was busy out on
the battlefield, commanding the army.

'I'll wait here with the horses,' said Nicolete. 'You go and
sort out these crazy people.'

Aucassin wheeled his way into the king's chamber.

'Go away, don't disturb me!' the king groaned. 'I'm lying-
in, for I've just given birth to a baby son.'

'But that's impossible,' Aucassin cried. 'Stop this nonsense
or I'll beat you!'

He did not need to actually carry out his threat, for simply pulling the king's bedsheets out from underneath him and tossing them around the chamber did the trick. The king immediately dropped his bizarre claim and offered to take Aucassin to see how the war was going. He led the way outside, where Nicolete let them take both horses, then went to make herself comfortable in the queen's chamber.

When they reached the battlefield, there were more surprises in store. For there was the queen dressed as a warlord, resplendent in full shiny armour! As for the weapons both sides were using, they were absolutely extraordinary. There was not a sword, spear, lance or pike in sight; instead the soldiers were throwing:

> Baked apples and fresh cheese,
> Any kind of food they please;
> Piles of mushrooms, soft and grey –
> Less like battle, more like play!
> When he asked who might win
> The king's blithe answer made him grin:
> 'He who splashes most in the ford
> Will be declared victory lord.'

Laughing heartily, Aucassin jumped down and joined in the fun. Aha, this was the kind of fighting that really suited him! But after a while, he started to feel guilty for enjoying himself in the name of war, without facing any real danger. So he said to the king, 'Would you like me to win this battle for you?'

'With all my heart I would,' declared the king.

So Aucassin drew his sword and ran into the fray, smiting it left and right. It was so easy...

But the king yelled, 'Hey, stop that! You mustn't *kill* anyone. That's not the custom in this land.'

Not that it mattered, for the enemy was so terrified of Aucassin's ferocity that they all fled anyway.

The king took Aucassin straight back to the castle. And there they had quite a to-do. Because instead of rewarding Aucassin for his valour, the king announced he was going to banish him – but keep Nicolete there to marry his son. Naturally, she refused, because she loved Aucassin very much; besides, the king's son was the new-born baby! Her arguments were so eloquent that the king quickly capitulated.

So, at last, amidst the luxury of the castle, Aucassin and Nicolete were able to settle down and live together completely openly.

However, their idyll did not last long. For out of the blue, a troop of Saracens arrived from across the sea. They attacked the castle and seized all the inhabitants – including Aucassin and Nicolete, who were taken and held on two different ships. Shortly after they set sail, a violent windstorm blew up, just as on their previous voyage; only this time, Aucassin's ship was blown in one direction, and Nicolete's ship went completely the opposite way.

When Aucassin finally reached land, he found himself back home in Biaucaire – his own country. His first thought was that he was in for a good rollicking from his father. However, up at the castle, he discovered that both his parents had died – so *he* was now the count!

He soon set himself up on the throne, and the first thing he did was announce that he had no intention of fighting any more wars, ever. So all his father's enemies withdrew – for there is no point in a battle if the other side won't join in.

Though Aucassin was glad to be his own master at last, he was not in the least bit happy, for he missed Nicolete terribly. Each day he went to sit alone up in his tower, singing this wistful song:

'Sweet Nicolete, so fair of brow
Where in the world are you now?
I'll send my men to search for thee
In every land across the sea
And trust that they will bring you back,
My dearest love – alas, alack!'

Unfortunately he never actually got around to organising the intended search for her.

Meanwhile, Nicolete's ship was blown in the opposite direction, all the way to Carthage. Fortunately, none of the sailors molested her, thinking her so beautiful and dignified that she must surely be precious cargo. When they landed, they immediately took her to the king.

The king looked at her in wonder, for he felt there was something very familiar in her face, though he could not put his finger on it. So he started to question her, saying, 'Who are you?'

'My name is Nicolete,' said she.

'That's a beautiful name,' said the king. 'I once had a daughter called Nicolete, but I lost her many years ago. Who is your father, where are you from?'

'I was originally the daughter of a king,' she replied, 'but I don't remember him, or where I lived, for I was stolen by pirates when I was very young, and sold into slavery.'

'What a coincidence,' said the king, 'for my own daughter, Nicolete, was also abducted by pirates at a very tender age.' He gazed at her thoughtfully, then said, 'I believe I must be your father, and you must be my long-lost only daughter! Welcome home, my dearest!'

He threw his arms around her and she embraced him back. Then the king at once arranged a magnificent feast to celebrate her unexpected and most fortuitous homecoming.

But Nicolete's happiness was short-lived. For the king had a good friend, another ageing king, who was on the lookout for a young bride. Her father made sure he came to the celebration feast, and as soon as the friend saw Nicolete, he decided she would make him the perfect wife. Her father immediately agreed to the marriage, without even considering that he should first consult Nicolete herself. Naturally she was not at all happy, because:

> She still longed for Aucassin
> That gentle, lovely, hapless man,
> Who always was to her so true.
> One thing certainly she knew:
> That even though they dwelt apart
> 'Twas Aucassin who had her heart.

The date of her unwanted wedding was set for four days ahead. She wasted no time but went straight out and bought herself a viol, then found a music teacher to instruct her how to play it. She practised so diligently, that within four days she was a veritable maestro.

By then, of course, it was time for her wedding. Before the servants came to dress her for it, she crept out of the castle by a secret passage, and ran away to a seaport. There, keeping quiet about her true identity, she found lodgings with an elderly fishwife. This good woman asked no questions – not even when Nicolete returned one evening dressed in a man's smock, hose and mantle, in the style of a travelling musician. Nicolete paid off her rent, then hastened to the harbour. There she made friends with an unsuspecting sailor, who persuaded his captain to give her free passage in return for entertaining the crew each night with her viol.

The ship sailed over calm seas without hindrance, and eventually arrived in Biaucaire. Here bold Nicolete went ashore and travelled across country, earning her keep with her music, until she reached the castle where:

> Count Aucassin sat in his tower
> Weeping softly by the hour
> For the loss of Nicolete
> His only love! His one regret.
> Suddenly, a violist came in,
> Played a tune, began to sing:
> 'Your long lost love will rise anew!
> Be patient and this will come true.'

Aucassin, having no idea that this musician was really his sweetheart in disguise, paid generously for the prophesy and begged for more information. But the musician hurried away without another word, and ran through the city streets to the house of the governor who had once adopted her. To her sorrow, he too had died; but his wife, her foster mother, recognised her and took her in joyfully.

Nicolete stayed there in secrecy for eight days, while her foster mother helped restore her beauty with baths and potions. At the end of this time, Nicolete dressed in a splendid silken gown and waited in the best chamber, while her foster mother went to fetch Aucassin. His servants led the woman to the top of his tower where, as usual, Aucassin was weeping over his lost sweetheart.

'My lord,' the foster-mother cried, 'for goodness sake, stop this childish bawling and pull yourself together. For Nicolete has come back! She's waiting for you in my house!'

When Aucassin did hear tell
That Nicolete, safe and well,
Was back in his own country
He was cock-a-hoop with glee.
He hurried forth to see his love,
His angel, darling, sweetest dove.

Together for ever, thus at last,
Arms about each other cast,
They kissed and held each other tight,
Then sported happily all night.
Next morning after that fine bedding,
They formalised it with a wedding.
No more sorrow, no more tears,
Lived happily for many years.
With not a single least regret
'Twixt Aucassin and Nicolete.

With many words, both spoke and sung,
This story now is blithely done

Even hundreds of years after this story was composed, it is easy to appreciate the satire in which all the roles and rules of normal romance are turned on their heads. The 'hero' displays no heroism at all and succumbs to the most unmanly trait of weeping, while being dependent on his shrewd sweetheart to find a solution to their problems.

One might speculate that the manuscript was a script for oral performance by a duo of storyteller and singer, or maybe for a larger group, for it contains instructions each time the narrative switches from one form to the other: 'So they say, they speak, they tell the tale' and 'Here one sings'.

THE ULTIMATE SACRIFICE

Hartmann von Aue: *Der arme Heinrich*
Germany, c.1195

Hartmann was a nobleman from Swabia, southwestern Germany. He has been described as the first major courtly poet in the German language. He also wrote adaptations of two of Chrétien de Troyes's stories (see p.46), lyric poetry and a narrative that explores the relationship between chivalry and religion.

This story survives in three complete manuscripts, and three small fragments, with some inconsistency between the texts. It is written in verse, and is around fifteen thousand lines long.

Hartmann stated that his work was retellings of older stories that he had found in books. The original source of this one has not been identified; though his mention of the biblical story of Job suggests that may have been an inspiration.

There was once a Swabian nobleman called Earl Heinrich, whose wealth, gallantry and hedonism won him fame far and wide.

But alas! In Fortune's balance, such a sensuous, worldly life hangs by a fine thread. One night as Heinrich slept, God cursed his body with the spreading sores of leprosy.

News of his illness quickly circulated. Beforehand, knights and ladies had all adored his company; but now they shunned him, and heartlessly mocked his downfall. In this way, his previously sunlit life was eclipsed by endless night. He knew in his heart that, for the good of his soul, he should follow the example of Job in the Bible and accept God's punishment meekly. However, he was too proud to do so, believing that his unlimited wealth should easily purchase him a cure. He consulted doctors from north, south, east and west, promising unprecedented payment to whoever could heal him. Unfortunately, none of them could.

Must he then resign himself to unbearable pain, loneliness and rapidly approaching death? No! For now he heard of a doctor in distant Salerno, Italy, who was reputed to have healed many hopeless cases. So, despite his debility, Heinrich rose from his bed, saddled his horse and made the long journey to that doctor's town. As soon as he reached the great man, Heinrich subjected himself to examination, saying, 'I beg you to find a way to save me.'

The doctor said at once, 'I do know a certain cure for your condition.'

'Then speak up and tell me what it is!' cried Heinrich. 'However much you normally charge, I will pay double.'

The doctor hesitated then said, 'Let me be plain, sir: you cannot actually *buy* this cure.'

'Then… just *give* it to me,' Heinrich pleaded.

'I cannot give it to you either; nor can any man,' the doctor replied. 'You will have to fetch it yourself; yet I urge you not to. My cure is an astonishing and very gruesome formula that I happened upon by accident during my long years of study. Now then, listen carefully, Earl Heinrich. You must find an innocent virgin, a girl who is not only chaste, modest and pure minded – but also willing to sacrifice her own young life to save yours. She would need to *freely volunteer* to let you bring her to me. Then you would have to wait close by as I cut out her pure young heart, even while she

111

was still alive; after which, you would have to drink some blood from it. For the particular way in which your leprosy has manifested itself, that is the only certain cure I have ever heard of.'

Heinrich said wretchedly, 'No young girl would freely give up her life to save anyone, let alone a repulsive invalid like me. Besides, it is an appalling sin even to hope that I might find such a volunteer. Doctor, I have made a wasted journey; I wish you good day.'

Thus Heinrich returned home, overwhelmed by thoughts of death.

However, death operates by its own laws, and the more that Heinrich prayed for it to come quickly, the longer it lingered. Back in his earldom, he resigned himself to his sorry fate. He put all his affairs in order, disposing of his estates and giving away most of his wealth to the poor. He kept nothing for himself but one small cottage with a byre and a field, where a kindly peasant lived with his wife and family. In return for generous payment, they took him in and cared for him.

Heinrich's troubled soul was greatly comforted by the good peasant-woman's ministrations, and the cheerfulness of their children. Amongst these little ones was a girl of ten years old, with innocent eyes and an angelic smile. She greatly pitied the frail earl. Though her siblings feared his increasingly loathsome appearance and kept their distance, she willingly spent long hours sitting at his feet, soothing him with childish chatter. Heinrich was enchanted by her guileless affection. Whenever a pedlar passed the door, the earl bought her a trinket: a ribbon, a ring or a looking-glass, just for the delight of seeing her pleasure. Sometimes he even teased her by calling her his 'little wife' – which pleased her even more.

Three years passed. Still Heinrich survived, though his distress and torment increased day by day.

One day, the peasant couple were sitting talking quietly with this particular daughter, who had now grown into a lovely damsel.

The woman said, 'I'm so glad we're able to ease poor Heinrich's suffering. Although he's an earl, he's such a decent fellow and treats us all so civilly, as if we were his equals. I wonder how long he has left to live.'

'Judging by how he's declined, not long surely,' her husband replied. 'And when he departs this world, my dear, I fear for our own fortunes. For then, no doubt some heartless crony of his will take over our cottage and throw us out to be destitute.'

'Then for our sake as well as his,' said the woman, 'we should pray even harder for his speedy recovery.'

Her husband got up and went across to Heinrich, who was dozing in his chair.

'Master,' said the peasant, 'I'd like to ask a question that greatly puzzles us. Why don't you seek help from a renowned doctor? You can well afford to pay for it.'

To his surprise, tears welled up in Heinrich's eyes. 'Good man,' he said, 'before you became my carers, I consulted every doctor in this land and far beyond, but none could do anything for me.' He sighed. 'No doubt it's my rightful divine punishment for wasting all my early life on worldly vanities, worshipping wealth instead of God.'

'I can't believe there's no cure at all for a rich man like you,' said the peasant woman boldly.

Heinrich answered wretchedly, 'Since you persist in your questions, forgive me if I share with you something horrific. There was indeed one doctor, who revealed to me a single

113

path to certain recovery. It would require an innocent young woman to volunteer to have her heart cut out by him – while she was still alive so that I could drink its blood – thus killing her in the most abominable and excruciating manner. He assured me this was the only possible cure. Obviously, I cannot even contemplate going ahead with it.'

The peasant couple were both struck dumb, and hastily hustled their daughter away. But the girl was greatly affected by what she had heard. That night she could not sleep for thinking about it; and her restlessness awoke her parents, who demanded to know why she was disturbing them.

She whispered, 'I am weeping for Earl Heinrich's misery, and for our uncertain future when he passes away.'

'There's no point in brooding on these things,' said her mother. 'God decides all our fates.'

But though they silenced her lament, they could not still her thoughts. For the rest of that night, and for many nights afterwards, she lay awake, pondering Heinrich's revelation about the only possible cure. Slowly, her resolve sharpened. At last she went to her parents saying, 'Do you recall how Heinrich said that he could be cured by the heart blood of a virgin? Father, Mother, I wish to give him that blood.'

'No!' her father cried in horror. 'You speak like a reckless, ignorant child. Surely you are old enough to have more sense. Fortunately, you have never yet had any direct experience of death; but one day you will look into the depths of someone's grave and quake at that grim monster. I forbid you to say any more about this.'

'Father,' she answered quietly, 'I do understand what death means, through watching dear Earl Heinrich's decline. It upsets me more than I can describe. Everyone must die one day, so why delay the inevitable? If I give up my earthly life for his sake, I will gain the blessing of *eternal* life with

God all the sooner – which is what I long for more than anything. It will enable the earl to recover. Then he is bound to reward our family, by granting you the security that you fear losing when he passes away. I assure you, I have thought this through very carefully. It will benefit us all, so don't scold me for it.'

'Daughter,' said her mother, 'look me in the eyes. You talk of rewards. Well then, think of the pain I suffered when I carried you in my womb and delivered you into the world. Does your own mother deserve to be rewarded with yet more pain? Besides, you would be disobeying God's commandment to honour your parents.'

'Mother,' the girl replied, 'how can you begrudge me wishing to reach God as soon as I can? My life here on earth feels like no more than dust and empty smoke. I understand that you're upset by my proposal, so I'm not seeking your permission; all I ask is that you don't stop me. That's the greatest gift of love you can ever give me.'

Her parents could not understand how their child could speak so blithely about wanting to die. But in the end, her weeping mother embraced her and nodded as her father said hoarsely, 'Well, daughter, if you truly believe this is God's will, you'll have to ignore our feelings.'

The next morning, the girl hurried to Heinrich's sickbed, saying, 'Dear lord, are you awake?'

'What, nagging me again, little wife?' he teased her affectionately. 'Why are you up so early?'

'Because I have been thinking long and hard,' she answered, 'and I have come to a conclusion. Some days ago, you revealed that you could be cured by a maiden willingly sacrificing her life for yours. I wish to do this for you.' Her words were chilling, yet she smiled as she spoke them.

Heinrich stared at her in wonder. 'God forbid!' he cried. 'The last thing I would ever want is for you – my most precious friend – to sacrifice your innocent spirit for me. My dear, I have witnessed death many times in my past life on the battlefield, and I tell you, it is more terrible than you could ever imagine. And think how such a deed would hurt your parents. After all their care and kindness to me, is this what they deserve in return? Besides, if it actually came to it, you would never dare to do it.'

Just then, her father came up and interrupted, saying 'Master, she's spent the whole night imploring us to agree to this. Though it breaks my heart to say so, my wife and I realise that, if she truly believes it is God's will, we have no right to stop her.'

As his voice faltered, they all began to weep. Such anguish! The parents were distraught that their beloved daughter wanted to extinguish her life in this way; yet at the same time felt compelled to beg Heinrich not to oppose her. No words could describe his own torment at the sweet girl's desire to sacrifice herself for his unworthy sake.

But in the end he gave in to their pressure and agreed.

Heinrich pulled himself together and prepared for the long journey back to the doctor in Salerno with his young companion. He ordered a dress to be made for her, finer than she had ever expected to own, richly trimmed with silk embroidery, sable and shimmering jewels. He gave her a splendid horse to ride. She smiled her thanks at these gifts, but remained composed. She sat on the horse in a serene flush of saintly beauty, yet as excited as a bride. Her parents did their best to conceal their distress.

Heinrich and the girl rode to Salerno as fast as they could, stopping only when necessary. All through the grim journey, she spoke to him cheerfully, trying to lighten his sorrow. When they finally arrived, she begged to be taken to the great doctor's house without delay.

They dismounted. He took her arm and led her inside, where the doctor greeted them. Heinrich did not beat about the bush but said, 'Sir, a few years ago, you told me I could be cured of leprosy by drinking blood from the heart of a virgin, if she would willingly give up her life for that purpose. My dear young friend here is determined to carry out this cure. Neither I nor her parents can dissuade her.'

The doctor groaned. 'Sir,' he replied, 'when I put this wild idea into your head, I never expected you would actually return and ask me to carry it out.' He turned to the maiden. 'Who pressed you into doing this, young lady?'

'No one,' she said, loud and clear. 'My dear lord here has done his utmost to try and change my mind, and so did my parents. But I am absolutely certain that I want to do it.'

The doctor took her hand and led her into the privacy of an inner room. 'You poor, innocent young fool,' he said softly. 'You mustn't die for him! Your whole life still lies before you, whereas he has already enjoyed much time on earth. No doubt he mostly wasted it on futile, unsavoury pleasures. I warn you: it is impossible for your heart's blood to cure the earl unless you sacrifice yourself completely freely. So now is the time to admit that you are being forced to do it.'

'But I am not being forced,' she said. 'Everyone has begged me *not* to do it. I offer myself completely of my own free will.'

'Very well,' sighed the doctor. 'Then let me give you a further warning: you will suffer indescribably before you die. Firstly, you must experience the shame of stripping

117

completely naked before me. Then I will bind you around your heels and arms, so tightly that it will cut your skin raw. Finally, you will feel unbearable pain as you watch my knife enter your chest to cut out your heart while you are still fully conscious. Furthermore, if at any point you regret your decision, even silently, even by a hair's breadth – the cure will fail. Then you will have given up your own life in vain.'

'Sir,' the girl said, 'I appreciate your frankness. Be assured, I have fully communed with God about this and have no doubts or fear at all. I believe it is *you* who are really frightened. Find courage, good doctor! I say it again: I offer myself in all eagerness to enable Heinrich's recovery – for I know this act will immediately bring me the joy of eternal life. With the promise of such good things for each of us, why should I even hesitate?'

The great doctor went back to Heinrich and said wretchedly, 'Sir, she has convinced me that she wishes to go ahead.'

Heinrich was too troubled to answer.

The doctor went back in to the girl, locking the door tightly behind him, for he did not wish Heinrich to see or hear her ordeal. He told her to undress. She did so at once, not in the least discomfited to stand thus before him. The doctor thought there was surely never such a pure and beautiful creature in all the world. At his command, she lay upon the table and let him bind her to it with rough cords. He picked up a broad, long knife and began to sharpen it, wanting her death to be achieved as quickly as possible.

In the outer room, Heinrich heard the sound of the blade against the whetstone and was overwhelmed with horror. He sprang to his feet and rushed to the door – but found it locked. He began to pound upon it with his feeble, wasted hands, then slumped against it, cursing the frailty of his illness, his mind racing. 'Where is your faith in God?' he asked himself. 'If He has fated you to die, nothing anyone does can prevent it; and if He wishes you to survive, you will do so anyway, so there is no point in *her* dying. To let her sacrifice herself will provoke God's anger – and thus lead you even further away from redemption.'

He took a deep breath, summoned up some strength and began to strike the door more powerfully, roaring, 'OPEN UP!'

'Don't disturb me,' came the doctor's reply. 'I am in the middle of your treatment.'

'Then STOP!' Heinrich yelled. 'DO NOT KILL HER! Open up at once and let me in, to save your soul as well as mine.'

The key turned in the lock. Heinrich pushed at the door again, and this time managed to fling it wide open. Before him, lying bound to a table in the middle of the room, he saw his young friend, quietly awaiting death. The doctor, still holding his sharpened knife, looked at Heinrich questioningly.

'Give that knife to me,' said Heinrich. 'Loosen her bonds at once. Let my beloved live.'

Even after she was unbound, the girl remained prostrate on the table. She began to wail and tear her hair, sobbing, 'You have prevented my soul from receiving its longed-for reward. You have snatched me away from Heaven. Why, why? Heinrich, I always believed you to be honourable, but now I see that was all a deceit. You are really a weak coward, and don't care about my own suffering. I beseech you – I *order* you – let me die!'

But now Heinrich had made up his mind, nothing could move him. Eventually she gave in and allowed him to dress her back in her finery with his own hands. Heinrich gave the doctor the generous payment he had promised, then the pair set out to return home. The girl was in a fever of confusion and dismay. She refused to let Heinrich comfort her, or even to listen when he spoke.

Heinrich knew that the whole world would soon hear what had happened, and that then he would be severely humiliated by malicious gossip and insults. But rather than being daunted by this, suddenly he felt a great weight lift from his soul. For his adventure with the girl had finally cured him of all the sins of arrogance and pride.

That night they lodged at an inn. In their separate rooms, each prayed fervently, he thanking God for turning him away from the path of selfish wickedness, she imploring God for a sign that she was still in his grace. The Father, who comforts all His faithful children, heard them both.

While the earl slept, he was miraculously cured of leprosy. He awoke at sunrise, to find his body whole and unblemished again, and his long-lost vigour returned.

He rose from his bed and knocked on the girl's door. When she saw him, fully restored to health, she recognised it as a divine sign that he had been right to save her after all. Ah, how she cried out her thanks to God!

Earl Heinrich took the girl straight back to her parents. No words can describe their relief to see their daughter still alive and well. They clung to her for ages and smothered her with kisses, first laughing, then crying with joy.

Earl Heinrich returned to his own house. Every day he felt stronger and better. He told everyone, friends and strangers alike, how God had saved him from both affliction and damnation. Those who had seen him struck down by leprosy, and presumed him either dying or dead, were astonished by the strange story of his recovery. He was a totally changed man, constantly thinking of God.

Heinrich rewarded the long kindness of the peasant couple, and the zeal of their daughter, by giving them a proper farm of their own, with a herd of cattle, and servants to work for them. Thus they never feared for their home or livelihood again.

His kin advised him to marry and suggested many fine brides. However, he had already vowed to marry no one but his dear friend, the peasant girl whose devotion had cured him of both his bodily and spiritual sins. All who knew his story agreed that she was the perfect choice; and of course, the girl herself was very willing. So a priest came and bound them together in wedlock.

They enjoyed many long and happy years together until finally they rose to Heaven, hand in hand.

Leprosy is a chronic bacterial infection which can damage the nerves, respiratory tract, skin and eyes; and cause muscle weakness and poor eyesight. It is often characterised by disfiguring skin lesions. Since nerve damage may cause inability to feel pain, some sufferers fail to notice injuries, resulting in the loss of hands or feet. In the modern world, leprosy can be cured with drugs, but in the Middle Ages it was incurable. Medieval lepers were disparaged as being unclean and morally corrupt, and because of this they were often segregated. The disease seems to have been widespread in 12th century Europe, with thousands of special hospitals built for sufferers in association with the Church.

Belief in miracles was widespread in the Middle Ages. Many thousands of examples were recorded by the Church, as part of the process of deciding whether someone should be canonised as a saint. To qualify, they were supposed to have done one or more of the following: healed someone who was sick, saved someone from danger, enabled someone to escape from unjust imprisonment or punished wrongdoers.

Detail from a drawing in a miscellany,
England, late 13th century

13th
CENTURY

Western Europe enjoyed population increases and flourishing economies, helped by the spread of new technologies ranging from paper to the spinning wheel.

The popular romantic works of this century followed in the footprints of the previous one, drawing particularly on Arthurian legends and the conventions of courtly love. It also saw publication of the iconic *Romance of the Rose*, which maintained its status as a bestseller for several centuries.

FERGUS & GALIENE

Guillaume le Clerc: *Fergus,*
Scotland, c.1200

Guillaume is believed to have come from north-eastern France. He wrote this book in Old French, presumably for a Scottish patron. It has survived in two 13th century manuscripts, written in rhymed couplets, each line containing eight syllables.

At this time, Scottish culture varied according to location. Galloway was a Celtic region. The lowlands were dominated by Anglo-Norman culture, with a number of French settlers, and links to mainland Europe through aristocratic marriages, politics and the Church. Argyll, the Western Isles, Orkney and Shetland were allied to Norway.

The author was clearly very knowledgeable about Arthurian legends – particularly the work of Chrétien de Troyes (see p.46), from whom he borrowed many characters, motifs and ideas. Indeed, the story has been described as a pastiche of Chrétien's *Perceval* romance.

According to the story as I have heard it told, in the land of Galloway there lived a peasant called Soumillet. Unlike most men of his lowly status, he was unusually wealthy, with his own castle and a noble lady for his wife. They had three strapping sons, the eldest of whom was called Fergus.

One day, when Fergus was ploughing his father's fields, King Arthur came riding by on his way back from a hunt, followed by a grand retinue of knights and squires. Fergus was so impressed by the sight of them, that he ran straight home to the castle, flung down his tools and exclaimed, 'Father, get me a suit of armour and some weapons. I need to be off at once to serve at King Arthur's court.'

'Who gave you that crazy idea?' his father retorted. 'Get back to the fields, you wretched son of a whore!' He grabbed a massive stick and made to hit Fergus.

But his noble wife pushed between them, saying, 'Husband, stop that foul language at once. You know perfectly well I'm not a whore. My family has a long tradition of knightly service, so it's natural our boy should have grand ideas. He's so good-looking, he'll probably do very well for himself.'

'Sorry, madam,' Soumillet muttered. 'You know best.'

The father opened up a storage chest and brought out a set of armour: a hauberk, leggings and a helmet. They hadn't been touched for years, and were all as red as an Ethiopian sunrise – not from paint, but from rust. Never mind; the links were still strong. Fergus put them on, then his father gave him a short, broad sword, and brought him a fresh horse from the stables. Fergus leaped briskly into the saddle, leaned down to kiss his mother a hundred times over, then galloped off.

Over the hills and through the valleys he went, all the way to Carlisle, where King Arthur was holding court. He rode straight into the royal hall without dismounting, and announced to the king, 'My lord, my name is Fergus and I've come to serve you.'

Before the king could return this brazen greeting, his ill-tempered steward, Sir Kay, let out a loud guffaw. 'Just look at your rusty armour, Fergus,' he said sarcastically. 'I can see you're the kind of fellow we desperately need. You'd better go off at once to vanquish the infamous Black Knight. To prove you've done it, bring back the horn that hangs from the neck of his lion.'

Fergus nodded eagerly.

But King Arthur chided Kay: 'Now, now, stop goading the lad.' He turned to Fergus. 'You are very welcome here, my friend, but don't bother trying to carry out Kay's ridiculous challenge.'

'But I want to prove myself,' said Fergus.

Without further ado, he rode out of the hall and into town, where he took lodgings with the king's chamberlain. The next morning, the chamberlain gave Fergus a set of splendid new clothes. Wearing these, he returned to Arthur's hall and announced he was going straight off to slay the Black Knight. Nothing Arthur said could dissuade him.

The first day of Fergus's quest passed without adventure. At sunset he came to Liddel Castle where, on the bridge below the gate, he saw a white-haired man holding a hawk on his wrist. Walking beside him was a damsel with laughing eyes and a face paler than white lilies. Let me share the truth as I heard it: she was as clever as she was beautiful.

Fergus asked if they could give him lodgings for the night.

'You're most welcome, young man,' the lord of the castle replied. 'This is my niece, Galiene. Come in and make yourself at home.'

The damsel came up and held the stirrups while Fergus got down from his horse. She watched intently as a squire helped him out of his armour. How handsome and proud he looked in the new silk tunic that the chamberlain had given him! Galiene could not take her eyes off him.

The god of Love – who is always on the lookout – quickly noticed this, and immediately shot a gold-tipped bolt from his crossbow. It struck her right in the heart and lodged there securely. She turned pale. Then she blushed and began to tremble. Hastily, she lowered her face, hoping neither man would notice.

They went into the hall and sat down upon couches. Fergus and Galiene found themselves seated side by side, but neither said a word to the other: Fergus did not know how to, and she did not dare. They were served an excellent ten-course supper. After the ebony tables were cleared away, the lord asked Fergus where he came from and what he was seeking. Fergus told him everything about himself, how he had succeeded in impressing King Arthur, and how Sir Kay had taunted him to fight the fearsome Black Knight.

'You are an impressive young man,' said the lord. 'But I urge you to give up this foolhardy quest. Didn't Sir Kay warn you? Thousands of men have already attempted it, and all have died on the way.'

'Even so,' said Fergus. 'I'd rather risk my life than refuse the challenge.'

Thus the talk continued between the two men, with Galiene sitting there in silence.

When it was time for bed, the damsel could not get to sleep for thinking about Fergus. In the privacy of her chamber, she moaned and sighed, tossed and turned. She sobbed, scolded herself, yawned, called out Fergus's name – and occasionally even burst out laughing. 'I'm a fool to love a stranger who will go off tomorrow and not even remember meeting me,' she thought. 'He's shown no sign of interest in me at all. Anyway, there's no point in thinking about him, since Father insists I must marry a powerful lord, to protect our land after he dies. Oh, oh! But this is probably my only chance with Fergus; I'll never get another one!'

In great agitation, she jumped out of bed, with her hair all disheveled and only wearing her lightest shift. No matter, she pulled on a fur-lined mantle, took a candle, tiptoed to the room where Fergus was lodging, and crept up to his bed. He was fast asleep. She hesitated, then tremulously lifted up the coverlet and gently placed a hand upon his bare chest.

At once, he woke up and stared at her in alarm. 'What are you doing here?' he cried.

'Oh, good sir, forgive me,' she whispered meekly. 'I'm suffering the most terrible torture because you've stolen my heart. Please give it back!'

'Your heart, my lady?' Fergus whispered back sleepily. 'What do you mean? I haven't got it.'

'But how can you not have noticed?' wept Galiene. 'My heart has placed itself totally at your service. You are so handsome, so brave and clever... You hold my life and death in your hands.'

Fergus sat up, rubbing his eyes. 'My lady,' he said, 'as you know, I am currently engaged on an important quest. I've got no intention of delaying it; but if I achieve it, I might come back here and see you again some time.'

Such callous words! Galiene jumped up, ran back to her own chamber and threw herself onto the bed, sobbing violently. She hated herself; but even more, she hated the man who had stolen her heart.

After a while, she calmed down a little. Her thoughts turned to her father, the king of Lothian. She had left him over a year earlier, when she had come to stay with her uncle. 'I'll go home and see him,' she thought. 'That'll take my mind off things.'

The next morning, she rose early. Fergus was already outside, mounted on his charger. He bid her farewell, adding, 'Perhaps I'll return if I succeed in my quest.'

Galiene lowered her face and said nothing. Then Fergus rode away.

He travelled through wild country, and at last reached the mountain where the Black Knight lived. At its foot, he dismounted and climbed to the top. Here he found himself standing before the lion Kay had spoken of. It turned out not to be a real lion, but merely a marble statue. The horn he had been challenged to bring back was hanging round its neck. He seized the horn easily and blew it three times, expecting it would summon the Black Knight. But no one appeared. So he retreated down the mountain. As he reached the bottom, he heard the drumming of hooves. The next moment, he was confronted by a colossal knight, clad in armour as dark as a blackberry.

'How dare you blow my horn, you pathetic little toad!' the Black Knight roared. 'I suppose you're another of King Arthur's cronies, sent to trespass on my land, eh? Well I'll soon cut off your head, just like all the others.'

They fell to a fierce battle. Fergus quickly got the upper hand and had his opponent on his knees, begging for mercy. Initially, Fergus refused. But then he remembered how he had heard the knights at court talking about the rules of chivalry, and realised that being merciful was a vital way to enhance his reputation. So he spared the life of the Black Knight, on condition that he presented himself to King Arthur as a prisoner.

With his quest was completed, Fergus rode back to Liddel Castle, as he had promised. He was looking forward to seeing Galiene again, for he had decided it would be a grand adventure to be her lover. He arrived at sunset and found the white-haired lord pacing about the bridge on his own.

'Where's your niece this evening?' said Fergus as he dismounted.

'Oh, alas, alack,' groaned the lord. 'I don't know. Nobody knows. All of us here, old and young, tall and short, are terribly worried, for she mysteriously vanished on the very same morning that you left here. She told no one where she was going. I miss her terribly, for as you saw with your own eyes, she is the most courtly, intelligent maiden in all the world. But never mind, my friend, come in.'

Fergus followed him into the castle despondently, for now that Galiene had vanished, he could not stop thinking about her. 'What a fool I was to rebuff her,' he thought. 'If only I'd told her there and then that I was willing to return her love. Then she would have waited here for me, and we could have got to know each other properly.'

The lord saw that he was distracted and asked what was wrong. Sheepishly, Fergus confessed his feelings. 'I know it's foolish to dabble in love,' he said, 'but I can't help it.'

'It's foolish indeed,' said the lord. 'She's my niece, so it's right that I should mourn her disappearance; but to you she is nothing.'

Fergus could not be comforted. He took brief refreshment, then donned his armour, got on his horse and set out on the road again. 'Good host,' he said, 'I cannot rest until I have found fair Galiene.'

He had no idea where to go. Nevertheless, he soon encountered new adventures, in which he vanquished numerous villains. As with the Black Knight, he sent each of his conquests to King Arthur.

This noble behaviour greatly enhanced Fergus's renown, making the king and his knights eager for him to join them at the Round Table.

However, no one had any idea where to find him. For Fergus, maddened by his lost love, now turned his back on the world and went to live in the depths of the wilderness. He survived on raw venison, which he gobbled up like a wild dog. His hair and beard grew long and straggly, and he became so emaciated that he almost wasted away.

After existing like this for a year, Fergus found himself riding through a dappled woodland, weak with thirst. He was greatly relieved to see a clear spring bubbling up beside the path, and got down to scoop up some water. As soon as he began to drink it, a miraculous change came over him: all his troubles drained away and his normal vigour returned.

He gazed around in wonder, and saw a dwarf coming out of a nearby chapel and sauntering up to him. 'Ahah, it's Fergus isn't it?' said he. 'I've been expecting you. You're trying to find fair Galiene, aren't you? I know you regret refusing her your love.'

'If you know where Galiene has gone, I beseech you to tell me, sir,' cried Fergus. 'Even if God has consigned her to the darkness of Hell, I'll gladly descend there and suffer any torments just to find her.'

'Don't waste your time going to Hell,' chuckled the dwarf. 'It's Dunnottar Castle that you need to head for.'

'Is Galiene there?' Fergus asked.

'Not so hasty,' scolded the dwarf. 'When you arrive at Dunnottar, you must overcome the hairy hag who guards its gate with a gigantic steel scythe. Then you must seize the radiant shield hanging in the castle tower. Use it well, and this shield will light up the sky for you, protect you from being unhorsed in battle, save you from death…and eventually win you fair Galiene.'

With those words, the dwarf turned on his heel and went back into the chapel, locking the door noisily behind him.

So now Fergus journeyed north to Dunnottar Castle. He suffered many difficulties, and found no sign of what he was seeking for two whole months. At last, however, he noticed a radiant light in the sky ahead, so dazzling that even the most learned man in the world could not describe a tenth part of its beauty. He spurred his horse towards it, and soon reached a grand castle, separated from the mainland by a long causeway.

In the middle of this causeway stood the most gigantic, monstrous-looking old woman he had ever seen. Long, plaited grey whiskers dangled from her chin, her eyes were set two whole feet apart, and her brown fangs were sharply pointed. She was brandishing her deadly scythe, standing legs astride and hissing loudly. The causeway was so narrow that Fergus was forced to dismount and face the hag on foot; but it did not take him long to stab her dead. Then he passed through the gate and climbed up nine steps, each as high as he was. At the top, he entered a large hall. It was brightly lit by the radiance of a splendid shield, hanging from the top of a marble pillar and guarded by a massive, flame-breathing dragon. Though the dragon lunged at Fergus, he easily sliced it in two with his sword. Then he reached up, removed the radiant shield from the pillar and carried it away.

He ran out and back over the causeway, retrieved his horse, galloped south to the coast at Queensferry and took a ship across the water. On the far side, he rode on again, through a strange, deserted land.

Eventually, he met a shepherd. 'Good fellow,' Fergus called to him, 'I'm a stranger here and find myself in these parts by accident. What country is this?'

'It's the kingdom of Lothian,' the shepherd replied.

'And who is its king?'

'Ah sir,' said the shepherd, 'our king died only this past month. Now the land is ruled by his heir, the noblest lady who ever lived, Queen Galiene.'

'So Galiene has become a queen!' cried Fergus.

'Yes, sir,' said the shepherd, shaking his head, 'but her position is not a happy one. For a powerful king from a neighbouring realm is trying to overthrow her and seize her land. He has besieged her fortress at Roxburgh Castle, and burned down all the towns, villages and farms around it. Most of her own warriors have been slain; the rest have abandoned her. So she's shut up in the castle with just thirty loyal knights, and they have almost run out of food and wine. Unless something drastic happens to change her fortunes, within a fortnight she will have to surrender.'

Fergus thanked the shepherd for this information, asked directions to Roxburgh and set off there at once. However, his mind was in such turmoil at his beloved's plight, that he took a wrong turn. As night fell, he found himself standing before a castle ruled by the wicked giant of Melrose Mountain – the husband of the hideous hag who Fergus had killed at Dunnottar. When the giant saw the radiant shield, he realised at once what Fergus had done, and attacked him in revenge. After a long struggle, Fergus succeeded in killing the giant too.

He went into the castle, where two maidens greeted him in great distress, because the giant had killed their two lovers only the night before. When they heard that Fergus had just slain the villain, they threw themselves at his feet and promised to do everything they could to help him in return. They healed his wounds, bathed him, gave him a fine new set of white linen clothes, served him a hearty meal and showed him to a splendid bedroom.

The next morning, Fergus awoke feeling greatly refreshed. He looked out of the castle window and saw the entire realm of Lothian spread out before him. It was dominated by Roxburgh Castle, where Queen Galiene was besieged. The castle was completely surrounded by the enemy camp; and all the land around the camp had been burned to a cinder and laid to waste.

Fergus rushed downstairs to the hall and told the two damsels how Galiene had loved and lost him, saying 'To make amends, I must hasten to Roxburgh and save her from this terrible siege!'

The damsels unlocked a chest and produced the most splendid armour and weapons that Fergus had ever seen. He clad himself in them and took up the radiant shield, then fetched his horse, and galloped out through the gates to Roxburgh. Even as he went, he heard the enemy bugles announcing their latest assault, and saw them manning the catapults and placing ladders against the fortress walls.

Meanwhile, inside Roxburgh castle, Queen Galiene had climbed to the top of the tower in despair. As she gazed down on the hostile troops below, her eye was suddenly caught by a strange light in the distance, moving fast towards the battlefield. At first she thought it was some kind of supernatural creature.

But then she saw the Knight of the Radiant Shield sweep into the enemy camp! The warriors there were completely taken by surprise. The knight struck out in all directions with his lance, slaying every man who tried to obstruct him.

Word of this terror spread through the tents like wildfire. The enemy king ordered his men to abandon the castle assault, and concentrate on getting rid of this extraordinary opponent. A terrible battle ensued. By sunset most of the enemy lay dead – and the Knight of the Radiant Shield had vanished into the forest.

As Galiene descended from the tower, her hopes raised just a little, a messenger came running up to her. 'My lady,' he said courteously, 'I bring you word from the Knight of the Radiant Shield. I am to tell you that everything he achieved today was done out of love for you.'

The next day the battle resumed. Again, the Knight of the Radiant Shield fought single-handedly against all the enemy troops and slew countless warriors, whilst remaining virtually unscathed himself.

At sunset, another messenger came to Queen Galiene. This one was an uncouth, aggressive fellow sent by the enemy king. 'Keep quiet, lady, and listen,' he growled. 'My king says he'll withdraw all his troops, on condition that you put yourself at his mercy. By which he means that he'll seize you for his own pleasure and when he's had enough of you, he'll toss you to his serving lads to use.' He sniggered lewdly.

'A thousand curses upon you and your king!' Galiene replied. 'I'll have nothing to do with with his offer.'

'Only a woman would answer so stupidly,' sneered the messenger. 'You'd better look out, because if the king wants something, he always gets it.'

The next day, Queen Galiene found herself surrounded by a bunch of her angry nobles. 'What is the matter with you, my lady?' their leader exclaimed. 'Do you think it's beneath you to marry the enemy king? It's the only way to save your people from total destruction. For their sake, you must accept his offer.'

'Hold your tongue, you stinking slanderer!' she retorted. 'May Jesus Christ torment you for such a suggestion. *You* go and grovel to the enemy king if you wish, because you'll certainly never see a wedding between him and me.'

That night, alone in her chamber, she wept bitterly: 'I'll never submit to that brute. If only Fergus had agreed to become my knight, I'm sure he would have protected me… I wonder if he ever returned to Liddel. Perhaps I should have waited there… But now it's too late, for tomorrow I shall have to throw myself to my death.'

She rose before dawn, went to mass, then slipped out alone and climbed up to the top of the highest tower in the keep. She stood by a window, measuring the leap with her eyes, gathering her skirts together to stop the wind catching them and thus impeding her fall. She crossed herself, then thrust out her head, ready to climb out and throw herself down.

But God would not allow it. For at that moment, she seemed to hear a voice – though where it came from, she had no idea: *Damsel, look towards the woods!*

She looked – and thought at first that the whole forest was on fire. But no, it was a light that she recognised: the radiance of the mysterious knight who had already destroyed so many of the enemy. He came galloping out of the forest, the sun reflecting brilliantly from his shield, and circled the tower as if hoping a special lady might look down and see him.

Then the final battle began. This time it was quick, for the Knight of the Radiant Shield quickly unhorsed the enemy king.

Galiene saw him standing over the king, sword held aloft to behead him. She heard the enemy king begging for mercy, and the knight saying, 'I will spare your life on condition that you withdraw from this lady's realm and restore all her land. Then you must present yourself to King Arthur as my prisoner.' She heard the enemy king meekly promise to do this.

The Knight of the Radiant Shield handed over the vanquished king to Galiene's men; then vanished again into the forest.

Shortly after that, on Ascension Day, King Arthur's court was making merry at Carlisle when the defeated king arrived. He put himself at Arthur's mercy, and confessed his defeat at the hands of the incognito Knight of the Radiant Shield.

'Where is that knight?' asked Arthur. But the defeated king had no idea.

There was much discussion at the Round Table of how this secretive knight could be persuaded to emerge from his self-imposed exile and reveal his identity.

Noble Sir Gawain spoke up: 'My lord, why not hold a grand tournament on the plains near Jedburgh in four weeks' time? Announce that the overall champion will be granted the prize of marrying whichever lady he chooses, and also be crowned king of a realm. Such a contest is bound to lure the Knight of the Radiant Shield out of hiding to take up the challenge.'

Thus it was done. Word of the tournament spread throughout the land, soon reaching Queen Galiene. Although she had now regained her lands and was safe for the time being, she knew her security would not last long without a husband to protect her. So she resolved to go to the tournament, and offer herself to Arthur as the prize bride for the winner. Her heart was still wholly given to Fergus, but now she was willing to sacrifice her personal feelings for the safety of her people.

What more should I tell? The first day of the tournament dawned and the jousting began. An amazing body of knights assembled on the field, waiting to begin.

Suddenly, out of the forest, face hidden by his helmet, there came the Knight of the Radiant Shield! The arrogant Sir Kay was the first to challenge him; within moments, he found himself knocked off his horse into the quagmire. After that, many other knights tried their luck against him. Each one suffered a similar ignominious fate, even the invincible Sir Lancelot. And so it continued all day and every day in exactly the same way. By the end of the week, everyone was loudly praising the Knight of the Radiant Shield. He was declared the indisputable victor.

Just as it was time for the end of tournament celebrations to begin, the exquisite Queen Galiene arrived at court, to ask King Arthur to arrange her marriage. She told him everything, concluding, 'If the champion will become my husband, and thus take over my realm, saving it from future trouble, I will gladly accept him.'

'My lady, I will be delighted to help,' Arthur replied. 'The champion of this tournament is a knight with a shield so radiant that it even outshines the sun.'

'But that must be the very same knight who defeated the evil king who besieged my realm!' she cried. 'He will be a perfect match.'

'There is just one problem,' said King Arthur. 'No one knows his name or where he dwells. He should be here now to claim his prize and celebrate with the rest of us; but as is his custom, he has vanished.'

Gawain spoke up. 'May I intervene, my lady? I am the only one who has not yet jousted with the Knight of the Radiant Shield, and I believe he may return tomorrow to try himself against me. I will go out alone to meet him, and see what I can do for you.'

So the next morning, when the Knight of the Radiant Shield emerged from the forest, Gawain was waiting for him. 'Friend,' he said, 'do not think me a coward; but rather than jousting with you today, I would like to take you to speak with King Arthur.' He threw back his helmet to show his face.

'Sir Gawain!' exclaimed the Knight of the Radiant Shield. 'King Arthur's own nephew and his most valiant knight! How can I refuse you?'

'Now *you* must reveal who you are,' said Gawain.

'I am Fergus,' said the Knight of the Radiant Shield.

Gawain rushed forward and flung his arms around him. 'So it's you!' he cried. 'We have all been searching for you everywhere for years. King Arthur will be overjoyed.'

He seized Fergus's hand and led him over to a juniper tree, where Arthur was sitting alone with Galiene. Arthur was delighted to see the radiant shield at close quarters, and even more so to discover that Fergus was its owner.

'So, Fergus, we meet again at last!' he cried. 'A thousand welcomes. Now, to business. As the acclaimed champion of this tournament, the prize for winning is both a wife and a kingdom. By lucky chance, this noble lady sitting beside me has come here to offer herself as your bride. She is also willing to give you power over her realm of Lothian, for she urgently needs a valiant husband to protect it. If you accept this prize, both your wedding and your crowning will take place tomorrow, at the festival of St John.'

When Fergus saw Galiene sitting beside King Arthur, he was overwhelmed, for being apart had made his love grow deeply. Nevertheless, he answered cautiously, saying, 'As far as I am concerned, I will obey your command, and not refuse this lady. But is she is willing to have me? You must ask her to state freely whether that is her wish.'

Arthur turned to Galiene with a smile. 'My lady, are you prepared to take this man?'

'Good sir,' Galiene replied, 'I happily place my mind, my heart, my sentiments and my entire person at his disposal.'

Fergus was overjoyed. He would not have given up this chance – even for the entire empire of Rome!

The very next day, the wedding was held. The celebrations resounded throughout the town, with drums, trumpets and horns; everyone in the whole country was invited. After mass, Fergus and Galiene were crowned side by side, and there followed a sumptuous wedding feast. The celebrations lasted twenty whole days, and were just as excellent on the last day as on the first.

Afterwards, Fergus returned to Roxburgh beside his beloved Galiene. There, as king and queen, he loved her as his tender sweetheart, and she loved him as her noble lord.

Here Guillaume le Clerc comes to the end of his composition, for he has never found any man anywhere who could tell anything further about the knight with the splendid shield. So this concludes the romance. May great joy come to those who hear it!

As in most Arthurian legends, Arthur's status of a 'high king' or emperor gives him benevolent power over other lesser kings.

Fergus was a real-life king of Galloway, who died in 1161, though his life and marriage seem to bear little relation to Guillaume's hero, since the real Fergus may have married a daughter of Henry I. The places mentioned in the story are all real ones: the ruins of both Liddel Castle and Roxburgh Castle can still be seen in the modern Scottish Borders; Dunnottar Castle is in Aberdeenshire.

GUINEVERE & LANCELOT

Anonymous: *Lancelot of the Lake*
France, early 13th century

This narrative is one of many contemporary Old French romances about King Arthur's court, often grouped together under the name of the 'Vulgate Cycle', 'Lancelot-Grail Cycle' or 'the Matter of Britain'. Their roots lie in oral tradition and they employ many common folktale motifs. They form the major building blocks of the great body of medieval Arthurian literature, which began in the 12th century with the work of Chrétien de Troyes (see p. 46), and reached its climax with the publication in 1485 of Sir Thomas Malory's monumental *Le Morte d'Arthur* (p. 400).

Lancelot of the Lake was written in prose. Some two hundred manuscripts survive. It was copiously copied in French and various other European languages during the following centuries.

The opening is similar to that of *Fergus & Galiene* (p. 124). However, it soon develops in a very different direction, following the highly stylised conventions of 'courtly love' between an older married noblewoman and a younger subservient knight.

King Arthur – best of all earthly kings – was holding court at Camelot when the door suddenly burst open and an exceptionally fair youth came in. He was dressed in white, fully armed and leading a white horse. He strode brazenly up to the king and cried, 'Greetings, sir! I go by the name of Handsome Foundling, for I am an orphan and do not know my real name or who my father was. These are my credentials: I am an excellent archer and horseman; I can think fast; I have mastered many skills such as chess and singing. I wish you to make me a knight.'

'God bless you and give you health, young man!' cried King Arthur. 'But I cannot knight you until you have proved your worth.'

Now, Queen Guinevere was seated beside the king, and she was greatly taken by the youth. He had the most shapely body and limbs she had ever seen, a fine complexion glowing with natural ruddiness, perfectly formed features and shining, curly, chestnut-coloured hair. She reached out and took his hand, saying, 'Who has raised you to be so courteous, Handsome Foundling, and where have you come from?'

At her touch, the youth's confidence seemed to dissolve. He said falteringly. 'I...I was raised by my foster-mother, Niniane. She is the lady of a distant lake, and I have lived almost all my life in her care, far beneath its waters. I come here with her blessing.' For a brief moment, he locked eyes with the queen, then blushed deeply.

The queen guessed at once that he was entranced by her, and in truth, she was not sorry. But she had no chance to talk any further with him, for the court was suddenly distracted by a great noise and commotion outside. Everyone jumped to their feet and rushed out to investigate. They were greeted by the sight of two horses that had just stopped by the door, carrying a litter on which lay a badly wounded knight. He was bleeding profusely, for the broken shafts of two lances were protruding from his body, and a rusty sword blade was embedded in his head.

King Arthur himself went to remove the offending weapons. But the wounded knight groaned, 'Stop! Don't even try to heal me until you have sworn revenge against my enemy and all his kin!'

'How many of them are there?' Arthur asked.

'Hundreds!' the wounded one replied.' Thousands!'

At once, the Handsome Foundling called out, '*I* will take revenge for you, sir.'

'Don't be so reckless, you young fool!' someone shouted; and a murmur of agreement went up, led by the king.

But the youth ignored them. He glanced at Queen Guinevere, as if seeking her approval, then approached the wounded knight and carefully pulled out the lances and the sword.

King Arthur was so impressed that he dubbed Handsome Foundling a knight on the spot. After that, the youth went away to arm himself.

The queen was rather distressed, for she realised he had undertaken this foolhardy quest in order to impress her; she feared it would lead him to a quick and sorry end. She went to her chamber to brood on this, telling her ladies to leave her alone for a while. Shortly afterwards, there came a gentle but persistent knocking at the door. 'Enter,' she called.

In walked Handsome Foundling. He came hesitantly towards her and fell to his knees at her feet.

'Why are you kneeling before me, young man?' she said. 'It's obvious from your bearing that you are of noble birth. Stand up.'

'I can't, my lady,' he whispered. 'For first I must beg your forgiveness.'

'Whatever for?' said she.

'For...almost setting out on my quest without first bidding you farewell,' he answered.

The queen smiled. 'You are far too callow to be criticised for such a minor lack of courtesy. I forgive you gladly.'

'Then m...may I ask something of you, my lady?' he said. 'Would you permit me to be your own knight – to serve you, and you alone, no matter where in the world I should go?'

'Certainly,' she said, 'I shall be very happy with that.'

'Then, by your leave, I shall now go out to fulfil my promise of revenge.'

'May God protect you, dear friend,' said the queen with feeling.

'Thank you, my lady,' said the youth softly. Then he added, 'Especially for calling me your "dear friend".'

She smiled, took his hand and raised him to his feet. Then he was gone.

No news was heard of Handsome Foundling for months, then years. Queen Guinevere was greatly unsettled, for she yearned to know whether her young protégé was still alive and safe.

In fact, he was busy carrying out countless perilous and valiant exploits, always in her name. Gradually, news began to reach her of his great deeds, so that her heart swelled with pride for him.

One day, some pavilions were erected across the river from King Arthur's court. A knight rode out from them and requested a private audience with Queen Guinevere, introducing himself as Sir Galehot. 'My lady,' he said, 'I bring you important news. Do you remember a young, incognito knight who, some years ago, devoted himself to serve you?'

'I do indeed,' she said at once.

'In the long days since you last saw him,' Galehot went on, 'that knight's adventures have won him great renown. In

144

fact, many people now refer to him as the best knight in all the world. Tomorrow, with your agreement, I will bring him back to you.'

'Tell that knight,' said the queen, 'that I am most impatient for tomorrow to dawn.'

The next morning, Sir Galehot returned with the incognito knight. As they approached, the queen could see that Handsome Foundling had matured into a truly splendid man. However, as soon as he entered her presence, his whole demeanour changed: he turned pale and began to tremble violently. The queen smiled to herself, and invited both knights to join her company of ladies. After they had exchanged pleasantries for a while, she sent the other ladies to sit apart from them. Then she said to the incognito knight, 'I have heard that you are victorious in every battle. Also, that you treat every lady and damsel you meet with utmost courtesy and decorum.'

'What messengers say is often embroidered in the telling,' he said modestly.

'True,' said the queen. 'So I would far rather hear such tidings from your own lips. Tell me everything you have done since I agreed to let you serve me.'

He could not refuse his own lady's request; so very diffidently the incognito knight began to tell the queen about the countless villains he had defeated, and the endless mortal dangers he had overcome. She was astonished and greatly impressed; but at last declared she could not bear to hear any more about these trials and traumas.

Sir Galehot said, 'My lady, it is timely to ask this knight to reveal who he really is, and how he discovered his name.'

'I would dearly like to know that,' said the queen. She turned to the incognito knight. 'Speak on.'

'My lady,' he said, 'there is one important adventure I have not yet told you about. It happened when I came to a castle that bears the name of Dolorous Gard – a place of the most terrible cruelty and sorrow. I shall not trouble you with the unsavoury details; suffice to say that, at length, I succeeded in overthrowing the evil tyrant who ruled it. After my victory, the good inhabitants of the castle were so grateful, that they implored me to become their new lord; it would have been churlish to refuse them.'

'So, my knight of the lake,' said the queen, 'you have your own castle now! Please accept my congratulations. But what about your name?'

He bowed his head and went on, 'To calm myself after the long battle, I went to stroll around the adjacent castle graveyard. And there, inscribed upon one of the tombstones, I saw these strange, portentous words:

Here the new lord of this castle is destined to lie.
His name is Lancelot of the Lake,
son of King Ban of Benwick.

'Well, Sir Lancelot,' cried the queen, 'so you really are a king's son, just as I always suspected. Now you must explain why you were absent for so long, putting your life at daily risk.'

Lancelot replied, 'My lady, before I left, you called me your "dear friend". All my exploits are to justify that supreme honour.'

Guinevere threw him a teasing smile, saying, 'But as queen I allow many knights to serve me, and I address them all with affection. Anyway, you are only a young man, and I am far too old for you to serve. This court is full of lovely damsels; surely you would prefer one of them?'

'No, my lady!' Lancelot cried. 'As God is my witness, the only one that my heart has ever yearned for is you.'

'In that case, Sir Lancelot,' said she, 'why do you not ask me properly for what you desire?'

He shook his head. So Galehot spoke up saying, 'Madam, do you not realise that when a knight loves a lady, his greatest fear is rejection. So allow me to beseech you on his behalf: Give Sir Lancelot your love! Become his own lady for ever! That would truly make him richer than if you had given him the whole world.'

'Oh, I am delighted to do that!' exclaimed the queen. 'Let me declare it at once: Lancelot is entirely mine and I am entirely his.'

'Excellent,' said Galehot. 'But he needs you to prove this – by kissing him.'

The queen feigned coyness. 'I don't mind you watching,' she whispered, 'but my maids over there are constantly throwing glances at us, trying to divine what secrets we are discussing. If I kiss him now, they are bound to see it.'

'But your own knight is desperate,' protested Galehot. 'I tell you what: let the three of us move closer together, so that your ladies cannot see what is going on.'

'A good idea,' said the queen. 'For in truth, I desire this kiss just as much as he does.'

The three drew very near to each other; but still Lancelot was far too nervous to make a move. In the end, Guinevere herself took the initiative – and gave him a long and very loving kiss.

When at last they drew apart, she said, 'Now you know for sure that I am your lady. But Lancelot, my own love, take great care to keep this secret. For I am supposed to be one of the worthiest ladies in the world; and if anything were to sully my reputation, that would seriously taint our romance.'

For a long time, nothing prevented Guinevere and Lancelot from enjoying their affair. Even when King Arthur was in residence, they managed to meet secretly every night in the shadows of the castle garden, where they made up for lost time with much kissing and embracing. Be assured that King Arthur did not suffer from this in any way. For he had no idea that his most gallant young knight was cuckolding him; and besides, *he* was not averse to straying into faithless romances of his own.

It was such an adventure that got the king into potentially mortal trouble. For it happened that, during a grand tournament at a distant castle, Arthur was beguiled by an exceptionally lovely damsel. She invited him to visit her covertly that very night. Unlike the queen's secret lover, who was, of course, sincere beyond perfection, this damsel was actually a malefactor who had deliberately set out to deceive the king. Arthur had no idea of this, and eagerly kept the tryst.

Soon they were lying together between the silken sheets of a very fine bed. For a good long while, she allowed him to enjoy her favours and do everything he wished with her. But when he finally sank back, exhausted, onto the pillows – forty armed knights suddenly forced open the chamber door! They rushed in, brandishing swords and candles which lit up the chamber, leaving no chance to hide or escape. The king was unarmed and still entirely naked. He jumped up, attempted to don his breeches and fumbled for his own sword. But, debilitated by too much pleasure, he was no match for his assailants. Within moments, they had taken him captive and thrown him into a prison with a heavy iron door.

That very same evening, Guinevere and Lancelot had discovered new heights to their love. But the next morning, the queen was dismayed to wake to news of her husband's capture. Her grief was terrible to witness. For she loved King Arthur deeply too, though this was a different love from the passion she felt for Lancelot.

In the midst of her despair, a damsel came hurrying to the royal pavilion, asking for Sir Lancelot. He stepped forward. The damsel said, 'I've heard you're a great hero, sir. If that's true, I challenge you to come with me to the prison where King Arthur is being held, and rescue him.'

Naturally, Lancelot agreed to this at once. However, this was actually the very same damsel who had already entrapped Arthur. Once she had taken Lancelot some distance from the royal pavilion, her accomplices pounced on him and threw him into prison alongside the hapless king.

Arthur was glad to have the young knight's company. But Lancelot missed his beloved Guinevere so badly that he could neither eat nor drink. This lack of nourishment turned him violently insane. Their captors feared he would harm the king, who was a priceless hostage; so they decided to free the frenzied Lancelot.

Somehow he found his way back to Camelot, where the grieving queen had now returned. He stood outside her window, wailing and weeping, until she sent her ladies down to investigate who was in such distress. When she heard it was Lancelot, she ordered him to be brought to her own chamber at once, and laid upon her bed.

There she nursed him diligently, nourishing him with the finest meat and wine. Gradually his sanity returned. 'My lady,' he said, 'I am greatly ashamed that you have seen me so emaciated and deranged. I fear you must now be repelled by me.'

'On the contrary,' she assured him. 'It was my pleasure to heal my own true knight; the experience has increased my tenderness for you.' She smiled. 'But I see you now urgently need a different kind of treatment to nurture you back to perfection.'

Understanding her gratefully, he took her into his arms.

This final part of his cure lasted for nine full days, during which they shared every great joy that a lover can imagine, and even more. In the end, Lancelot was completely recovered in both body and mind. As for his heart, it was full beyond bursting – as, indeed, was the queen's.

Shortly after that, Lancelot managed to rescue King Arthur from prison. This valiant act sealed Lancelot's knightly reputation. Guinevere was overjoyed to have the king safely back at court. Pretending that she was scarcely acquainted with Lancelot, she asked the king if she might express her gratitude by kissing the young knight. Arthur, in his ignorance, warmly encouraged her to do so. He then offered Lancelot the accolade of a seat at the Round Table – which was reserved for only the greatest knights in all the land.

King Arthur moved his court to Carlisle for a while, and there a most dreadful calamity occurred, that almost caused the death of the queen.

Guinevere was sitting at the Round Table alongside the king and his company, when a beautiful damsel came in, attended by an elderly knight who introduced himself as Sir Berthelai. The king gave his usual hearty greeting, and asked what business had brought them there.

'We come from Guinevere, daughter of King Leodegran,' said the damsel.

A hush fell on the room, and everyone gazed around in bewilderment.

'How can you "come from me",' said Queen Guinevere, 'when everyone can see that I am already sitting here?'

The damsel looked the queen directly in the eyes. 'Because *you* are an imposter,' she said coolly. She turned to King Arthur. 'Sir, on your wedding night, many years ago, you left your new wife alone in the bridal chamber for a few moments. While you were gone, she was snatched away by enemies.'

Everyone gasped.

King Arthur cried, 'This is a lie! I don't believe it! I know my own wife.'

'You do not, sir,' said Berthelai. 'For the real Guinevere, the lady you married, is languishing far away in an abbey, where she was incarcerated after her enemies abducted her.' He turned to the damsel, saying, 'Give the king her letter.'

She did so.

With shaking hands, the king tore open the seal and read it aloud, as follows:

'To my lord and husband from your legally married
wife:
Why have you abandoned me to pine and waste
away for so many years? The good people who
deliver this letter do so in the hope of freeing me from
this injustice. I beg you to banish the wicked lady who
has usurped me, and install me in my rightful place
by your side. If you refuse to do so, you are morally
bound to return the dowry which my father gave you;
by which I mean, of course, the Round Table and its
original band of knights.'

King Arthur looked at Guinevere in bewilderment, and then around the table at his astonished knights. 'How can this possibly be true?' he said. 'It would mean that my entire marriage is a sham.'

Guinevere was weeping profusely. From across the table Lancelot threw her a sympathetic glance.

Berthelai said gravely, 'It is a sham indeed, as I can easily prove. Good damsel, show him the ring.'

The damsel brought out a box and passed it to King Arthur. He opened it, then exclaimed, 'But this is the very ring I gave to Guinevere on the day we were wed!'

'It certainly is not!' retorted the queen, holding up her hand. 'Look, here is the ring exactly where it should be, on my own finger.'

'My lord,' said Berthelai smoothly. 'Truth and righteousness are normally decided in battle, are they not? So let the proof of what I say be shown on Boxing Day at Camelot. Anyone who doubts that the lady sitting at your side is an imposter must fight my own knights to defend her.'

The king's only honourable course was to agree.

But that was not the end of his enemies' cunning. To fill the tense time before the battle date, Arthur went hunting each day in the forest. There these enemies waylaid him and, with subtle arguments, persuaded him to follow them to the abbey where the woman who claimed to be the real Guinevere was living in penury. Arthur swore that he had never seen her before and turned his back on her. His enemies shrugged and offered wine to sustain him on his return journey. Arthur was badly in need of refreshment and drank it thirstily – little guessing it was laced with a love potion.

By the time he had quenched his thirst, the potion had so befuddled his mind, that he saw the false Guinevere with new eyes. He suddenly became besotted with desire for her, and spent that night sharing her narrow bed in the abbey. Before he left in the morning, he promised the false Guinevere that he would shortly install her in his court.

He returned to Carlisle, and openly told the queen what had happened. 'I don't know how you managed to deceive me for so long,' he said, 'but I have now seen through your treachery. Unless anyone can disprove your guilt on Boxing Day, you will be severely and justly punished.'

He removed the false Guinevere from the abbey, dressed her in finery, lay with her every night and took her on a tour of his kingdom. Everywhere he went, he told of the supposed deceit and announced that the false Guinevere was the real queen. His subjects were taken aback, but none dared to question their mighty king. An announcement was made that the false Guinevere would be formally crowned the day after the real queen's trial by battle.

The real Guinevere was now able to spend unlimited time with Lancelot. However, their lovemaking was badly blighted by her despair. Naturally, Lancelot swore on his life to save her.

Meanwhile, the other Round Table Knights pressed for the real Guinevere to be given a *proper* trial, not by battle but by jury. The king accepted this – but allowed the devious Sir Berthelai to convene his own barons to carry this out.

As previously arranged, the trial was held on Boxing Day. It was no more than a token, for the barons instantly found the queen guilty. Berthelai advised the king to punish her in the following ways:

By removing her hair and scalp – as penance for falsely wearing the crown; by skinning her palms – as penance for having been falsely being anointed; by having her dragged to death behind a cart; and finally, by burning her body and scattering her ashes to the wind.

'But if any man present still doubts her guilt,' roared Berthelai, 'let him defend her now, by defeating the three fiercest knights in my service!'

At once, Lancelot stepped forward. Before his opponents had even drawn their swords, he launched an attack on them. The three came at him from every side, but Lancelot was so fired by his love for the queen, that he fought with supernatural strength. Within moments, he had overwhelmed and badly wounded all his opponents.

When King Arthur saw Lancelot's passion to defend the queen's innocence, the scales fell from his eyes and he realised he had been duped. He turned to question the false Guinevere – but she had already fallen to her knees in shame, and quickly confessed her crime. The king had her seized, alongside the treacherous Berthelai. Without further ado, they were both taken away to be burned at the stake.

Then King Arthur fell to his own knees before Guinevere, and humbly beseeched her forgiveness.

'I forgive you with all my heart,' she answered. 'But my lord, thank goodness for Sir Lancelot! For he has saved both me and our marriage, and rectified our disgrace.'

'He is the most loyal and valiant of all my knights,' agreed King Arthur.

'After all he has done, do you think I should reward him by offering to be Lancelot's own lady?' said Guinevere.

'You should indeed,' said the king.

So Guinevere turned to her secret beloved and said to him, loud and clear, quite openly before the king, 'Good sir, from now on you are my own knight and I am your own lady.'

King Arthur himself, not fully understanding the significance of what she was saying, applauded loudly and begged Lancelot to stay permanently as a member of his court. The king assured him that everything he had there was entirely at Lancelot's disposal – not denying that this even included his wife!

The 'real' Arthur – if he even existed – was probably not a king, but a charismatic Christian Romano-British warlord, who died early in the 6th century AD. A 9th century Welsh monk wrote of Arthur as a charismatic and invincible war leader. He was described as a king who lost his realm through treachery in the 12th century work *Historia Regum Britanniae* (History of the Kings of Britain) by Geoffrey of Monmouth, who claimed to have based his work on an earlier book.

Lancelot's formal designation 'of the Lake' is because his foster mother was the legendary Lady of the Lake, Niniane (also called Nimue, Nimiane or Viviane). She is one of the most important female characters of Arthurian legend. In one story, she is loved and sexually harassed by the wizard Merlin. Finally, she manages to escape and turn his spells against him, by locking him away for eternity in an enchanted cave. It is Niniane who presents the magic sword Excalibur to King Arthur; and after his death, she leads a mysterious group of dark-robed ladies who carry him away to be healed in the island of Avalon (see p. 410).

In the original text, there is a very long description of his physical beauty, which reflects the medieval ethos that good-looking people possessed similarly 'beautiful' inner qualities. Later Arthurian stories portray Lancelot as King Arthur's greatest knight, whose unswervable loyalty to the queen ensures he rejects a number of other ladies who seek his love.

An affair between a married woman and a much younger single man is a typical manifestation of the ritualised conventions of medieval courtly love. Often the woman is in an unhappy arranged marriage, but Arthurian legend is ambiguous about the true relationship between Guinevere and King Arthur. It is interesting to observe how the lighthearted romance of this source book, *Lancelot of the Lake*, morphed into Thomas Malory's tragic portrayal of the same affair in *Le Morte d'Arthur*, published almost three hundred years later in 1485. Malory identified the castle Lancelot wins in the present story, Dolorous Gard, as located in Northumberland – see *Arthur, Guenever and Launcelot*, (p.400).

GAWAN & ORGELUSE

Wolfram von Eschenbach: *Parzival*
Germany, c.1210

This story comes from *Parzival,* a vernacular German verse
narrative, written in rhyming couplets. It is divided into sixteen
books, each containing several thirty-line stanzas. It survives in
sixteen complete medieval manuscripts and over seventy
fragments; there is also a printed version, dated 1477. It is a
retelling of the 12th century book, *Perceval, the Story of the Grail,*
which was left unfinished by Chrétien de Troyes (see p. 46) and
completed by several other French authors after his death. In
Parzival, the romance of Gawan and Orgeluse takes up Books Ten
to Fourteen.

Wolfram wrote in a very complex, idiosyncratic style, with many
humorous and forthright asides addressed directly to his readers.
Little is known about him, though he makes various
autobiographical remarks in his text which may or may not have
been true. He is believed to have been a well-educated
professional poet with a chivalric background, who wrote for
various patrons.

Would you care to hear an ancient tale about a haughty lady
who rejected one of King Arthur's finest knights? It opens at
the time when the Knights of the Round Table were all

engaged on the fabled quest for the Holy Grail, each following his own path across the world, and facing countless perils.

Amongst these adventurers was Sir Gawan, riding his faithful horse, Gringuljete. For a long time, he was lost in the gloom of the great forest; but he emerged at last into a country of rich farmlands and orchards where he met many other travellers. Some were friendly and some hostile; he exchanged courteous greetings with them all, riding on until he reached the city of Logroys. Here he passed through the gates and followed the winding streets to the centre, where a clear spring was gushing out from a polished rock. A dazzlingly lovely lady was seated right beside it. At the sight of her, Gawan's heart was suddenly struck by excruciating pain, forcing him to an abrupt halt.

'Greetings, my beauty!' he cried. 'May I sit here with you for a while? That would make me the happiest knight in the world.'

'Well, it certainly wouldn't make *me* happy,' she retorted. 'For goodness sake, stop ogling me. I can't stand men who go on about how beautiful I am. I suppose you're propositioning me, but get it into your head, stranger: I'm not interested. Go away and find some other lady to harass.'

'I can't go away,' Gawan protested, 'because you've captured my heart. You'll either have to free it or accept my company.'

'If I were to accept your company,' she said coldly, 'that would only bring you shame and sorrow.'

'Just let me serve you,' begged Gawan. 'I don't care about the consequences.'

The lady sighed. 'Since you are so insistent, you might as well do something useful for me. Do you see that path across there? Follow it over the high bridge and into the orchard beyond, where there's a crowd of people singing and dancing. Ignore them and walk straight on until you see my horse, which is tethered to one of the trees. Untie it and bring it to me.'

Gawan strode away eagerly, overjoyed to carry out her command. As he entered the orchard, he saw the knights and ladies she had mentioned, making merry. They all turned to stare at him, nudging each other and shaking their heads.

'Have you come for Duchess Orgeluse's horse, eh?' one of them shouted.

'Keep away from that treacherous bitch,' yelled another. 'She'll only bring you trouble.'

Gawan pretended not to hear. He quickly found the horse, which was a fine palfrey with an expensive bridle. He untied it and led it out of the orchard. When he reached the lady – who he now knew was called Orgeluse – he offered to help her into the saddle; but she pushed him away scornfully and leaped up herself, snapping at him: 'Right, you lead the way.'

He mounted his own steed and they rode along together, out of the city and back the way Gawan had already come, to a heath. There he suddenly stopped, jumped down from his horse and ran to a patch of flowers. When he came back, he was holding a big bunch of them.

'Flowers!' Orgeluse scoffed. 'What do you want with those, you sissy?'

'They're herbs of healing,' he replied. 'They're for an injured knight I met on the way to your city.'

A little further along, they reached the knight in question, who was lying groaning in his lady's lap beneath a tree. Gawan went to him, applied the herb to his wound and bound it up. As he worked, the knight hissed, 'What are you doing with that she-devil? I had dealings with her myself recently: she made me fight the battle that got me these injuries. Get rid of her!'

Gawan paid no heed. He finished the bandaging, helped the other knight's lady onto her horse, then turned to lift up the injured knight behind her. But while his back was turned, that rogue made a miraculous recovery, leaped straight up onto Gringuljete, and galloped away on him!

Orgeluse laughed heartily at his dismay. But Gawan simply shrugged and mounted the old nag that the injured knight had left behind. 'Your turn to lead the way,' he said to Orgeluse.

The nag stumbled along behind Orgeluse's high-trotting palfrey, while she continued with her taunting: 'Ha ha, you look like some ne'er-do-well pedlar pestering me to buy your moth-eaten wares!'

Gawan didn't care about her jibes; at least he had her attention. But even that didn't last much longer, for soon they came to a river that ran past the jousting meadow of a splendid castle. Here Orgeluse said, 'Right, I'm leaving you here, because you've got to fight a battle. Oh, and be careful, because there's a crowd of ladies watching from the windows up there – and if you split your breeches, they'll see everything!'

With that, she dismounted, thrust her reins into his hand and stepped into a waiting boat, which at once carried her away from the shore.

Reader, I won't bore you with gory details of the battles and other trials that Gawan endured before he next saw Orgeluse. Suffice to say that he managed to retrieve Gringuljete. After that, he had a marvellous and utterly terrifying adventure in a place called the Castle of Wonders. There he was locked up in a chamber with a bewitched bed that slithered around a glass floor, assailed by a barrage of stones and arrows shot from invisible slings and bows. This was immediately followed by a hand-to-hand fight with a ferocious lion. Though this ordeal left him sorely wounded, he triumphed like a true hero, and thus liberated the castle from the evil which had possessed it.

Afterwards, the castle's grateful and very kindly aged queen nursed him back to health. When he was recovered enough to rise from his bed, he found the Castle of Wonders transformed; thanks to his battle it was now completely peaceful, safe and calm. In the centre of the great hall, he soon discovered its greatest wonder of all: a huge pillar constructed from precious stones. The top was hidden up in the watchtower, but the base constantly revolved round and round, shimmering with extraordinary images. It showed all kinds of people in a variety of landscapes, riding, walking or running – actually *moving* before his eyes.

As he stared at it in amazement, the old queen came in and greeted him warmly. 'I see you're admiring my magic pillar,' she said. 'I confess that I had it stolen from a rival queen. It's such a marvel that I simply couldn't resist it.'

'How does it work?' asked Gawan. 'Who are all those people?'

'It shows everything that happens within six miles of its beam,' she replied. 'Birds, beasts, friends, foes and strangers. Oh, but do look: it's showing a knight and lady riding towards the castle at this very moment. I know that knight; it's Turkoyt, one of the fiercest and most dangerous warriors in my realm. But I don't recognise the lady, do you?'

'I do indeed,' he whispered. 'It's the joy and sorrow of my own heart, fair Orgeluse! But what's she doing with such a brute? I must go out and force him to relinquish her.'

'No, don't even try!' exclaimed the old queen. 'For Turkoyt is as dangerous as he is invulnerable; and you are still weakened by your recent trauma. He's bound to kill you.'

Gawan shrugged off her protests, armed himself hastily and went straight out. He nodded to Orgeluse, then challenged Turkoyt to fight. Within moments he had his opponent sprawling on the ground, offering total surrender and begging for mercy.

However, Orgeluse scorned his victory, saying, 'You've got a nerve, you feeble toad, calling yourself a knight with all those dents and cracks in your shield. And why are you swathed in bandages? You look like the inmate of a hospital.'

'Insult me as much you like, my lady,' Gawan replied, 'so long as you permit me to ride with you and serve you.'

'I'm not stopping you,' Orgeluse retorted with an exaggerated sigh.

So Gawan joyfully went to bid farewell to the old queen. 'I'm very upset to see you go,' she said. 'Especially with that disagreeable duchess, who's sure to pierce your heart with thorns.'

As usual, Gawan brushed this warning aside and hastened back to his lady.

'Well, wretch,' she said, 'since you're so desperate to win my love, follow me to the shimmering forest to pluck a garland from the forbidden tree.'

'Willingly,' he replied. 'But why is the tree forbidden?'

'It was planted by the man who made me cruel,' she said, 'by destroying me with grief.'

'Show me the way at once,' said Gawan. 'I'll do whatever you ask of me.'

So they rode off together, until they reached a forest of tamarisk and nut trees. There was no one else around. Some men would have exploited such remoteness by seizing the object of their desire and forcing her to yield. But Gawan was far above such sin. He followed Orgeluse quietly to the edge of a deep ravine. She pointed across it, saying, 'Look. There, growing on the far side, is the forbidden tree I spoke of. You must find your own way to cross to it and bring me a garland from its branches.'

She left him there and rode away.

Gawan sat on Gringuljete, gazing at the ravine. Far below, a deep, dark river was rushing past, fed by a torrential waterfall. One missed step would be the end for both of them. He twitched the reins and, at once, noble Gringuljete leaped. His front hooves landed on the opposite crag; but then the horse lost his balance and went plunging down. Fast as a hawk, Gawan grabbed an overhanging branch and hauled himself up to safety. Then he looked for his steed, and saw Gringuljete floundering in the water, struggling desperately against the current. Gawan leaned down, dangling his lance. He managed somehow to hook it under the bridle, draw his faithful friend to the bank, and then help him up the steep cliff.

The forbidden tree towered over the path ahead, lighting the sky with perfumed blossom. While Gringuljete shook himself dry, Gawan hastened towards it, reached up and plucked a fine garland of flowers. But when he turned back, he found his way blocked by a brawny knight, carrying a falcon on his wrist.

'Stop there, sir!' the knight yelled. 'I saw you, stealing a garland from my tree. I suppose Duchess Orgeluse sent you to fetch it, eh? Well, she and I are long-standing enemies, and you can't take it to her unless you kill me first.'

'What is your name, sir?' Gawan replied. 'What have you done to offend my lady?'

'*Your* lady?' The other roared with mocking laughter. 'They all call her that! My name is Gramoflanz and I am a king. Duchess Orgeluse hates me because I killed her husband.'

'That's as good a reason as any,' said Gawan.

'I tried to make amends to her,' Gramoflanz continued, 'by offering to marry her. But she refused. Nothing I could say or do would change her mind – even though I promised to serve her unflinchingly; even though I offered her complete control of my kingdom; even though I promised that all my land would pass into her own fair hands. None of this could persuade her to stop loathing me.'

'I'm not surprised,' said Gawan. 'She's not the kind of lady to be forgiving.'

'That's true,' said Gramoflanz. 'So in the end, I gave up on her. But I continue to punish her rejection by preventing any other man from having her. Not that I actually care any more, because now I'm in love with another lady.'

'Who is she?' asked Gawan.

King Gramoflanz's features suddenly softened. 'She's much younger and more innocent than Orgeluse and I know she's interested in me, because she sent me this hawk that I'm carrying. Her name is Itonje, daughter of King Lot. However, even this new love must overcome a great obstacle; for King Lot killed my father in an act of shameful treachery, and I can't declare myself to Itonje until I've punished him for it. Because of that, I fear that she too will reject me.'

'Well,' cried Gawan, 'this is an unexpected twist of fate. For King Lot – who is now sadly dead – was my own father, and Itonje is my sister! You can easily avenge your father's murder by fighting *me* – at the same time as *I* fight *you* for the garland.'

'How extraordinary that we should meet like this,' said Gramoflanz. 'Now, my friend and my enemy, after our disputes are resolved, will you persuade your sister not to nurture hard feelings against me?'

'I'll do my best,' said Gawan.

'Thank you,' said Gramoflanz. 'When you next see Itonje, please be so kind as to give her this.' He pulled a ring from his finger.

Gawan took it from him. Then the two men shook hands and agreed to meet again for their duel in sixteen days time, back at the Castle of Wonders.

Meanwhile, to Gawan's great delight, Gramoflanz let him carry the garland away. Gringuljete sensed his master's change of mood, and this time carried him easily over the ravine. Orgeluse was already on her way to meet them. When she saw Gawan bringing the garland, she jumped from her horse, crying, 'You've done it! You have defeated the hateful king across the ravine! For accomplishing this deed, my lord Gawan, you have won the prize of my love!'

Gawan stared at her, astonished by this change of heart.

'I must ask you to forgive my previous harsh words,' said she. 'It was imperative that I severely tested your supposed declaration of love – for all my former dealings with men have only brought me suffering. But now at last, you have come along and shown yourself to be a true man, as strong as gold purified in fire! Will you listen while I explain my longstanding sorrow? It has been even deeper than that ravine that I recklessly sent you across.'

'Speak on,' Sir Gawan said.

Orgeluse continued, 'Long ago, I was married to a truly outstanding man. He was handsome, faithful and valiant – perfect in every way. We loved each other completely. But my dear husband was slain by that monster, King Gramoflanz – who then proceeded to harass me with duplicitous advances. I finally managed to escape him, and spent many years in mourning.

'Eventually, a good king offered to avenge my husband's death. His name was Anfortas, and he too was a very worthy man. After much hesitation, I accepted his service and agreed to give him my love. But shortly after that, he fought a battle on my behalf that left him severely and permanently injured. My remorse over his wounds almost equalled my grief when my late husband was slain.

'Some time after that, a wealthy sorcerer sought me out and placed me under his spell. To avoid his persecution, I struck a bargain with him. I placed all my earthly possessions into his care, on the following conditions: if ever a knight managed to obtain the garland from King Gramoflanz's forbidden tree, the sorcerer would return all my wealth, and allow me to marry the successful knight. Many attempted the challenge, and at last one succeeded. But though I thus retrieved my wealth, the knight refused to marry me, for it turned out that he already had a wife. Now you understand why I tested you so harshly, for I cannot bear my heart to be broken yet again.'

'I understand, and forgive you freely,' said Gawan.

'Then let me return with you to the Castle of Wonders,' said Orgeluse.

Gawan said, 'Nothing would make me happier.'

By the time they reached the Castle of Wonders, many knights and ladies were already gathered there; for news had quickly spread about the coming battle between Gawan and an unnamed foe. Many damsels were also present, including Gawan's young sister, Itonje.

Gawan was honour-bound to keep his promise to his enemy, Gramoflanz, so he went to Itonje and asked, 'Tell me sister, do you consider yourself old enough for love?'

'Is someone asking for me?' she said carefully. 'It all depends who he is.'

'Your suitor is King Gramoflanz,' said Gawan,

'I did not realise Gramoflanz was a king!' she cried. 'I know him and like him well.'

'I'm glad to hear of your affection for him,' said Gawan. 'But, dear sister, I'm afraid a problem stands between him and you. For Gramoflanz is a long-standing enemy of our late father – and thus my own enemy as well. He is the one I must fight in the coming battle.'

Itonje gasped and tears welled in her eyes. 'Then one of you may die! Oh my brother, if only I had not fallen in love with such a man!'

'If he wins the battle, nothing can stop him proposing to you,' said Gawan. 'And if *I* win, I shall be mindful of you in deciding his fate. Meanwhile, he asked me to give you this ring as a token of his feelings.'

Itonje took the ring from her brother, colouring deeply. 'This ring was originally mine,' she said. 'I gave it to him at our last meeting; by returning it, he shows that he also returns my feelings. But I am distraught that my suitor must fight my beloved brother.'

'Let us hope we both survive the contest,' said Gawan.

Later in the evening, the old queen who ruled the Castle of Wonders threw a great feast. When it was over, fiddlers came in to play, filling the hall with merriment and dancing. Amidst heavy perfume and soft whispers, one couple after another slipped off to be alone. Thus Gawan and Orgeluse found themselves in a fine chamber, furnished with a splendid bed; and there at last they overcame their past discord, and spent a night in joyous love.

Meanwhile, Itonje was left to herself, brooding on the forthcoming battle, dismayed at the prospect of losing either her brother or her suitor.

Now, amongst the guests who had come to watch this battle, was none other than Itonje and Gawan's uncle, good King Arthur himself. Not knowing what else to do, the damsel approached him privately, saying, 'My uncle, will you permit me to ask for a boon? Would you be willing to put a stop to my brother fighting King Gramoflanz?' She began to weep until, with gentle coaxing, Arthur persuaded her to reveal her secret romance.

He was greatly touched by this. 'My niece,' said he, 'if you can prove that Gramoflanz genuinely loves you, I will willingly intervene.'

So messages were exchanged, followed by a letter from Gramoflanz, delivered to King Arthur's own hands, confirming his love for his opponent's sister.

Arthur sent for Gramoflanz and asked why the coming battle against his nephew should take place.

'For two reasons,' said Gramoflanz. 'Firstly, because Gawan's father killed mine, so I am obliged to take revenge against him. Secondly, because I killed the husband of his lover, Duchess Orgeluse, and Gawan has promised revenge on her behalf against *me*.'

'Since there are two counts of revenge, each one way against the other,' said King Arthur sagely, 'you are permitted by law to cancel them out and make peace.'

Gramoflanz, who by now was desperate to marry Itonje, said that he was willing. King Arthur summoned Gawan, who said he was willing too; but that he must defer to his lady, Orgeluse, since Gramoflanz's violence had caused her such enduring sorrow. So now King Arthur summoned Orgeluse and asked her to make peace with the man who wished to marry her own lover's sister. She was reluctant. But with gentle persistence, Gawan persuaded her of the joy of putting old hostilities to rest, and in the end she agreed.

King Arthur oversaw their reconciliation. Orgeluse declared that Gawan's devotion and valour had won her love many times over. Thus she gave all her lands into his care, and also gave herself. At the same time, King Arthur gave Itonje in marriage to King Gramoflanz.

The two couples enjoyed a joint wedding with splendid celebrations.

Parzival, the book from which this story comes, has as its central theme the eponymous hero's quest to obtain the 'Holy Grail'. This is an esoteric and only vaguely described object, possibly a dish, defined in the book as 'the perfection of paradise...earth's perfection's transcendence'. The Grail appears as part of a ritual during a meal or feast and is in the care of the maimed 'Fisher King' – Anfortas, who is mentioned by Orgeluse in the explanation of her long-standing grief. In some texts inspired by the 12th to 13th century French poet Robert de Boron, the Grail is said to be Jesus' drinking cup from the Last Supper, later used to collect his blood at the crucifixion. It is associated with Joseph of Arimathea (who in the Gospels arranges for the burial of Jesus) and, according to some writers, was eventually brought to Britain. The 'Quest for the Holy Grail' became an important constituent of later Arthurian legends. In Malory's *Le Morte d'Arthur (see p. 400)*, it ends in disaster, with many knights dying on their unfulfilled adventures, contributing to the downfall of King Arthur.

There are several other subsidiary tales of love and lust within *Parzival*. The book opens with the story of Parzival's father, Gahmuret, and three different queens who love him. The first is a Moorish queen who he loves deeply, and with whom he fathers a valiant mixed-race son. However, he abandons her since he feels restricted by their relationship and is eager to return to the freedom of being a knight errant – a recurrent theme in Arthurian legend (see *The Lady of the Well*, p.213). He then serves a second queen, but is forced by law to marry a third queen as his prize for winning a series of tournaments. He persuades this wife to allow him to return to a life of adventure, and is eventually killed in battle; soon afterwards, she gives birth to Parzival.

As a youth, Parzival rapes a young woman whose husband then falsely accuses of her infidelity, causing her double distress. Later he seizes the opportunity to make amends to her. When Parzival reaches maturity, he marries Queen Condwiramur; but he too abandons his wife in search of adventure.

Sir Gawan – or Gawain – is one of King Arthur's greatest knights, playing a major role in many Arthurian stories from at least the 12th century. Handsome and golden haired, he is the paragon of knightly courtesy, virtue and courage, often depicted as immensely attractive to women. He is the son of Arthur's half-sister, Anna (Morcadés, Morgause), and Lot (Loth) – described in later tales as King of Lothian and Orkney. He is a major player in *Le Morte d'Arthur*; and is also the hero of the English poems *Sir Gawain and the Green Knight* (14th century) and *The Weddyng of Sir Gawen and Dame Ragnell* (15th century).

THE ROMANCE OF THE ROSE

Guillaume de Loris: *The Romance of the Rose* (first part)
France, c.1225–30

The story retold here, from a translation of the Old French verse original, is actually part of a much longer work by two different authors. The two parts are usually presented together as a single composition. However, it would be more accurate to describe the complete *Romance of the Rose* book as a story and its sequel, since some forty years passed between Guillaume writing his four-thousand-line account of a fantastical romantic dream, and Jean de Meun completing it with a much longer narrative poem (nearly eighteen thousand lines) in c.1269–78.

Nothing is known of Guillaume's life, except that he died c.1278.

A little more information has survived about the sequel writer, Jeun de Meun: he apparently had the nickname 'Clopinel' because he was lame (from the French *clopiner*, to limp), and he spent much of his time in Paris where he died in 1305. He is believed to have written at least two other poems as well as several translations, including the letters of *Abelard and Heloise* (see p.16).

The *Romance of the Rose* is believed to have been a medieval 'bestseller'. At least two hundred manuscripts survive from the Middle Ages, and it was apparently widely read and popular until at least the 17th century.

Some say that dreams are merely lies and fairy tales, and that only fools believe they come true. However, in my experience, dreams often portend events, both good and bad, that later actually happen in real life.

Let me tell you about a wondrous dream that I had in my twentieth year. I call it *The Romance of the Rose*. It taught me everything I know about love. I originally wrote it down for a particular young lady who, just like the rose in this story, is utterly precious and deserving of love.

I hope that you too will find it entertaining.

In my dream, I rose from my bed on a fine May morning to take a walk through the countryside. My path followed the course of a shining stream, through a meadow, to a high, crenelated wall. I could tell that this wall surrounded a fine garden, for hanging over the top were the branches of numerous trees, heavy with flowers and fruit; and the air was full of birdsong.

I could see no way to enter it, so I walked slowly round the wall, studying it curiously. It was painted in strange gold and azure figures that brought to mind gloomy matters such as hatred, cruelty, greed, envy, sorrow and old age.

As I puzzled over these, I suddenly noticed a little door, cunningly concealed under a mass of creepers. It did not yield when I pushed against it. But after I had knocked upon it for some time, it was suddenly opened – by the fairest maiden I had ever seen. Her flesh was more tender than a young chick's, her forehead radiant and her eyes as bright as a falcon's. Her complexion was completely free of spots and sores, her throat as white as freshly fallen snow, her body slender yet well formed and her breath sweetly scented like flowers. She was dressed in fine green garments, richly decorated with gold embroidery. In one hand she carried a mirror, which she was using to arrange her long, burnished hair, as if carrying out an important piece of work. With her other hand, she beckoned me, saying, 'Do come in! My name is Idleness.'

'Is this your garden, Idleness?' said I.

'Oh no,' she replied, 'it was made by my dear friend, Pleasure. Don't you think the trees are lovely? He brought them here from Alexander the Great's distant lands.'

I expressed admiration, then asked, 'Why is the outer wall painted with such miserable pictures?'

'They reflect the horrors of the world beyond,' said she. 'All of us inside the garden do our best to avoid it. We spend most of our time here as Pleasure's companions, enjoying the garden's shady places and sweet birdsong. It's the best place in all the world – don't you agree?'

I gazed around, and had to admit that it was, indeed, just as one would imagine Paradise. A great feeling of happiness washed over me.

Idleness led me down a path to a clearing. Here she pointed out the comrade she had spoken of, Pleasure, who was sitting with a group of young men and women, all as beautiful as angels. In front of them, musicians were playing flutes, tambourines and castanets, to accompany a lady singing. Some of these angelic people were dancing; others were clapping their hands at a group of jugglers. I watched them quietly for a while, until a lady approached me, introduced herself as Courtesy, and led me into the dance.

I became so engrossed in it, that I did not realise I was being watched. The one observing me was no mortal – but the god of Love himself. If only I had looked up, I would also have seen his assistant, who was holding two of his master's bows and ten arrows. Half the arrows were tipped with good qualities, and the other half with evil.

After a while, I stepped out of the dance. Idleness came and stood by me, whispering the various names of the other merrymakers in my ear: 'Look, that lady dancing is called Beauty. There's Courtesy, dancing beside Generosity, and that one's called Youth...Oh, do see how passionately she's kissing her lover!'

When the dance was over, the couples strolled hand in hand into the trees to continue their lovemaking undisturbed. I was left alone but totally content, wandering amongst the flowerbeds and green copses. All the while I remained oblivious to the god of Love – who, like a hunter, was tracking me down as his unwary prey.

I explored for some time, thinking I must surely have seen every delight in the whole garden. But the next moment, I found myself standing underneath an immensely tall, cool green pine tree that I had not come across before. By its roots stood a marble stone, with some writing inscribed around the upper edge. I squatted down to see it properly and read: *Here died Narcissus*. From under the marble, a spring was gushing out to form a pool as clear and still as a mirror. Do you remember the ancient tale of how hard-hearted Narcissus was condemned to fall in love with his own reflection? He admired it for so long that he finally wasted away. This was the very place where it happened! I could see my own face reflected in the pool's depths, and shivered.

I walked on, feeling increasingly apprehensive. Soon I was overcome by an entirely new sensation: neither sight nor sound, but a fragrance so powerfully sweet that I could scarcely breathe. I had stumbled upon yet another new place: a thicket of marvellous roses, redder than I had ever seen in my life. Some were in bud, some fully open. They were all a delight to see; but right in the centre grew one whose beauty made me grow seriously weak: a fully ripe bud on a perfectly formed straight stem, above neat pairs of leaves. It was bursting with promised colour and scent as if longing for a touch to make it spring open. How I yearned to perform the desired task for this perfect flower! But it was surrounded by a thick hedge of sharp thorns, and I dared not reach out to it.

As I was gazing at this rose, I felt a sudden stab of pain in my heart. A great chill rushed through my blood and the next moment, I fainted. When I came round, I felt extraordinarily weak, but was otherwise unharmed. That was when I finally noticed the god of Love.

He had shot an arrow at me! The shaft was sticking out of my chest. I managed to pull that part out, but its point was embedded in my heart. I clutched myself as he attacked me further, shooting a long stream of arrows that sent me into swoon after swoon.

Before he loosed the final arrow, he dipped it into a pot of ointment. This must have contained healing powers, for as it struck me, I suddenly revived. The god stepped forward, crying, 'There! I have captured you completely. You are now my slave, with no chance of escape.' He wielded a golden key, held it to my heart and turned it, saying, 'You are locked into my power. Yield to me!'

What could I do, helpless as I was, except submit? I fell to my knees before him. He hauled me back to my feet and kissed me firmly on the mouth. 'You must serve me faithfully,' he ordered. 'Have no doubt: this will be a burden that will cause you unspeakable pain. Yet if you have enough courage to endure my torments, in the end you will receive a reward beyond imagination.'

'Tell me, sir,' I said tremulously, 'what do you command me to do?'

'Firstly,' he said, 'heed these rules. You must avoid all malice, slander and vulgar language. Be courteous and friendly to everyone you meet, whether highborn or low. In particular, treat all women with honour, do all you can to please them and punish anyone who defames them. Shun arrogance and greed; be generous to all. Bear yourself elegantly, dress well and practise good personal hygiene so that you are always pleasant to be near. Seek out happiness and pleasure; develop your skills of music and singing, ride your horse well and bear arms bravely.'

'Sir,' I answered humbly, 'I will do my best to obey your will.'

'That is good,' he said, 'but at some stage, you may be tempted to give up. To prevent this, I order you to carry out the following penance: you must think of nothing except love, all day and every day, all night and every night. Do you think that sounds easy? Well, it certainly is not. For such thoughts will quickly afflict you with torment. You will constantly sigh and lament, and find yourself withdrawing from company. As you suffer in solitude, an inner fire will burn and inflame the core of your being, threatening to consume you.

'As for your beloved: she will always seem impossible to reach. When you do manage to draw a little closer, this will only worsen your distress. For you will be too bashful to speak to her, and each lost opportunity will wrack you with regret. Perhaps at last you will manage to speak up in her presence; but then you will be mortified by stammering and ill-chosen words, totally unable to voice what you had been planning for months to tell her.

'Every night you will lie awake, constantly haunted by her, hallucinating that she is already lying naked in your bed; but as soon as you reach out to touch her, the vision will melt away to nothing. You will cry out to me, offering to surrender the rest of your life if only you could really experience such joy at least once. Don't expect me to answer that prayer: instead I will ensure the torture continues.

'Perhaps you may find slight relief by waiting outside your beloved's house under cover of darkness, kissing her door, begging her for mercy. But she will never permit you to enter her high sanctuary.

'All these trials will eat away at your health. You will have no appetite for food or drink. You will waste away and lose all your colour. Despite this, you must remember to always behave with utter decorum and magnanimity to all your beloved's acquaintances, even her most lowly maid. For good reputation is your only tool if you have any hope of winning her.'

At last, the god's long speech came to an end. It left me petrified with dismay. 'Sir,' I said, 'I must confess at the outset that I may not be strong enough to endure all these trials. I fear that I may die at some early point along the terrifying road you describe.'

'Let me reassure you,' the god answered. 'Nothing good is obtained without payment; and the more we pay for something, the better we appreciate the purchase. The pangs of love can no more be described than the sea can be drained dry; yet all lovers somehow find a way to live, for life is vital to their cause. Here, I'll give you some things to comfort you and help you along the way.' And into my heart he pressed the following: Hope, Happy Thoughts, Good Conversation and Pleasant Expressions.

The next moment, the god of Love vanished.

As a result of all the wounds he had inflicted, I was filled with insufferable pain from head to toe. I now realised two things. Firstly, that there was only one cure: to somehow obtain my heart's desire. Secondly, that the object of my desire was the exquisite rosebud I had already fallen in love with. But it was impossible to reach her through the thick hedge of thorns that protected her. Besides, if I tried to take her, I would be accused of theft.

As I stood there in despair, I was approached by a young man I had not seen before. 'Greetings,' he said. 'My name is Warm Welcome. You look as if you need some help, so follow me.'

I went after him eagerly. We rounded the thorn hedge and soon came to a narrow gap in it. He led me through this, and beckoned me so close to the roses that I could smell them without hindrance. We moved around them to the bush where the rosebud I yearned for grew. Seeing my agitation, he plucked one of its leaves and gave it to me.

I held it eagerly, casting endless glances towards my beloved. However, the next moment, someone roared: 'Oi, you! Don't you dare touch that – get out of here!' and a rough, villainous-looking man leaped out at us.

'Oh no, we must flee!' Warm Welcome hissed at me. 'That fellow is Rebuff, the guardian of all the roses here. I can see his nasty cronies, Evil Tongue and Fear, lurking just behind him. They must have been hiding in the long grass all this time, spying on us.'

Instead of taking the easy way out by returning to the gap, he jumped hastily right over the hedge. I leaped after him, but by the time I landed safely on the other side, he had already fled.

What should I do now? Where should I go?

At that moment, I saw a grey-haired dame walking briskly towards me, gesturing that I should wait. 'Hello, hello!' she said. 'I don't think we've met before? My name is Lady Reason. I spotted you from my tower and, seeing how miserable you look, I thought I'd better come and give you some guidance. You've been a fool, letting that good-for-nothing damsel Idleness entice you into this garden. I hope it's not too late for you to realise that this thing they call "love" isn't real; it's just an absurd mental disorder. Pull yourself together and fight it.'

'But how?' I said.

'I can see you won't take any notice of me,' said Reason curtly, 'so you'd better go and find the one called Friend. He'll be able to help you.' With these words, she turned away and hurried back to her tower.

I wandered on, feeling more wretched than ever. Every time I met someone, I asked if they knew where Friend could be found, but no one could tell me. Then, by good fortune I stumbled upon him myself. I could tell at once that he was the kind of man who would never let a companion down, so I was greatly relieved. He invited me to sit down with him and listened attentively while I told him everything that had happened. When I had finished, he said, 'I know exactly what to do. It's pointless arguing against Rebuff. Instead, go and apologise profusely for offending him, and solemnly promise not to anger him again. If you butter him up, he'll have no excuse to stop you approaching your beloved.'

Following his advice, I went back to the hedge where I had last seen Rebuff, grovelled before him and said how sorry I was for approaching the roses without his permission. I explained that I'd only done this under the influence of the god of Love's arrows. While I was pleading my cause, two ladies called Pity and Generosity of Spirit came up and spoke in support of me. With their help, I managed to satisfy Rebuff that my remorse was genuine, and he agreed to let Warm Welcome take me back to the roses.

Warm Welcome reappeared at once, and led me straight into the forbidden enclosure. There I quickly espied my favourite Rose. She had grown a little more since I first set eyes on her, and had opened a little, but not enough to reveal her hidden seed. I thought her more beautiful than ever, and was totally overcome by wonder and love.

'Am I allowed to kiss her?' I asked Warm Welcome. 'Surely a single gentle kiss will do no harm?'

'Ah,' he replied, 'if it were for me to decide I would certainly say yes. But I'm afraid that old mother Chastity has forbidden me to allow any lover to snatch even a single kiss. That's because, as she says, "After such a taste, it is always difficult for a man to stop". Who am I to go against her wisdom?'

I was tempted to argue, but realised that this would only make him angry. Just then, another woman came hurrying towards us, splendidly dressed in the most elegant clothes.

'Aha,' Warm Welcome whispered, 'you're in luck, because here comes the god of Love's mother, Venus. She's always criticising Chastity and totally disagrees with her teaching; with any luck she'll help you get what you want. Look, she's brought her special torch.'

'What's it for?' I whispered back.

Warm Welcome smiled at me mischievously. 'She uses its flame to warm up reluctant ladies' desire. Let's hear what she has to say.'

'Now, now, Warm Welcome,' Venus greeted my companion, 'what's going on here? I hope you're not trying to stop this young lover from enjoying a harmless kiss? Shame on you! Why shouldn't he? He's good-looking, gentle and charming, his breath is sweet, his lips are rosy and his teeth are perfectly clean. He could certainly please any lady he fancies!'

She waved her torch at him. Lit by its glow, Warm Welcome said to me, 'Oh, go on then, why not?'

So I leaned forward tremulously and placed my lips against the precious rosebud.

Oh, what joy! How soft was the touch of her petals! Her intoxicating perfume infused my body, soothing away the pain...

But I scarcely had time to relish it, before I was assailed by a torrent of furious shouts. I let go of her reluctantly, spun round – and found myself face to face with the venomous Evil Tongue.

'What's going on here, eh?' he yelled. 'Oh, it's you two again, is it? So, Warm Welcome, you've put the idea of kissing into that other fellow's head, eh? Well, I know exactly what's behind it: once he tires of the flower, you'll be asking him to kiss *you* next!'

His noise awoke a lady called Jealousy. 'My own Warm Welcome,' she shrieked, 'how dare you talk to that man? You're my friend, not his!'

She in turn was assailed by another lady, called Shame, who started scolding her loudly; and then Fear ambled up to join their bitter argument. The end of it was that Fear and Shame both accused Rebuff, saying, 'You wicked man, you've allowed lechery to flourish!'

'I'm sorry, I'm sorry,' muttered Rebuff. 'I'll make amends for this at once. I'll block up the entrance to the rose thicket, and build a brand new fortress right round it. In the middle, I'll erect a high tower – and imprison that troublemaker Warm Welcome inside it. Heh, heh, heh! That'll keep him out of mischief!'

Warm Welcome was seized and bound, then a team of workmen was summoned. They set to work at once, digging a deep ditch right round the roses, then building a thick, circular stone wall inside it, topped by formidable-looking towers and battlements. This was all completed quick as a wink. Next, they carried up many catapults, engines and other weapons to defend it. My opponents Rebuff, Shame, Fear and Evil Tongue took guard of the four castle gates, with a vicious portcullis installed at each one. Meanwhile, other workmen were building the central tower. As soon as it was ready, Warm Welcome was dragged into it...

And there my dream suddenly ended.

I awoke wracked with grief and torment, obsessed with my beloved Rose. Ah, what despair to think of her confined within that impenetrable wall, with all hope of happiness lost!

After the section retold here, Jean de Meun continues the poem in a rather different style, with less story and more protracted philosophical debate. Much of it comprises discussion on different aspects of love, particularly the male/female balance within relationships. This is expressed through the same allegorical characters who appear in the first part, but also quotes examples from the classics and the Bible to back up the opposing arguments. In the final chapter, the god of Love's mother, Venus, destroys the castle built at the end of Guillaume's section, and the narrator is permitted to receive the gift of the rose, since he has proved his love to be true. It concludes with a triumphant erotic scene, symbolising a man's completion of the coital act with a virginal sex object. The poem ends with the narrator awakening from his dream.

The *Romance of the Rose* is usually described as an example of courtly love literature (see p.46). It does indeed describe the male protagonist's physical and emotional despair, an intrinsic part of that convention, as described in the book by the god of Love. However, most courtly love stories (see for example, *Fergus & Galiene*, p.124, and *Guinevere & Lancelot*, p.141) have an equally well-developed female protagonist. In contrast, here the 'beloved' rose is depicted as merely a passive object, the prize for an amorous man who can prove his courage and obedience; she is given neither personality nor the right to refuse his advances.

The ethos of the book was the subject of scathing criticism by the 15th century feminist writer, Christine de Pizan (see pp. 380 and 391)

A close reading of the poem reveals fascinating glimpses of the preoccupations of 13th century French people. For example, in the first section, good hygiene and a healthy skin condition are both praised, suggesting that these were rare and highly valued attributes of the time. A passage in the second part considers whether the correct words should be used for the male genitals rather than the commonplace euphemisms. But the most significant debates take place around the romantic and other qualities of women. It is often derogatory about the female sex, for example:

> There is not a woman who does not laugh when she hears talk of loose living; one is immoral, another paints her face, and yet another gives you come-hither looks.

> Fair lords, be on your guard against women... If you abandon yourself so far as to give them too much power, you will repent too late when you feel their malice.

However, elsewhere in the text, women are strongly defended, with criticisms of the perverse balance of power in both courtly love and conventional marriage, and arguing for equality on both sides. For example, the benevolent character Friend declares:

> She ought not to be his lady but his equal and his companion as the law joins them together, and he for his part should be her companion, without making himself lord and master... No man who wants to be called 'lord' will be loved by his wife, for love must die when lovers assume authority... Anyone who wants to enjoy a woman's favour should always give her freedom... He should never reproach her for her vices, nor should he beat or touch her.

He even advises men to accept punishment from their wives willingly and without complaint. Another character, Old Woman, states:

> Women are born free; the law has bound them by taking away their freedoms... All women, whether maidens or ladies and whatever their origin, are naturally disposed to search willingly for ways and paths by which they might achieve freedom, for they would always like to have it.

THE PRINCE OF BEAUTY

Jacob Ben El'azar: 'The Story of Maskil and Peninah'
from *Book of Fables*
Spain, c.1233

Jacob was a Jewish author who wrote in Hebrew. He lived in Toledo, central Spain in the late 12th to early 13th century. His *Book of Fables* contained ten narratives, and survives in a single manuscript which was copied in 1268. It is written in a mixture of highly stylised 'rhymed prose' and short poems, a technique also used by contemporary Arabic writers.

Medieval Spain was a multicultural country, variously ruled by Moors (Arabic-speaking Muslims from north-west Africa) and their European Christian opponents who spoke Latinate languages. There had been a Jewish community there since at least the Roman Empire, and possibly since biblical times. During the predominately Moorish era (8th to late 15th centuries), the Jews experienced mixed fortunes, sometimes flourishing, sometimes suffering persecution. At the time when he wrote his *Book of Fables*, Jacob's home town of Toledo was ruled by Christians, but had large Jewish and Moorish populations, thus providing a wide range of cultural influences for his work.

Jacob seems to have been bilingual, for as well as his fables and Hebrew works of popular philosophy, he also wrote a Hebrew grammar in Arabic, and translated Arabic stories into Hebrew.

In the realm of the King of Beauty, there once lived many young people. They were all so fair that the king called them his gazelles. But alas, when they grew up, the youths flew away like eagles from their homeland. The girls they left behind spent so much time lazing around and admiring themselves in mirrors that their comeliness faded away like sunlight at dusk.

Because of this, the king feared that no more children would ever be born in his realm, and was overwhelmed with dismay. He reproached his courtiers for allowing this catastrophe to happen. Then he sent them out to seek far and wide for new gazelles, both male and female, ordering that they should be brought to his palace to replace the defectors and idlers. In this way, he hoped to ensure the continuity of his kingdom. The courtiers, recognising the seriousness of the situation, set out to fulfil his command at once.

Before long, some of them returned with a male gazelle – a radiant, unblemished youth of only thirteen summers, graced with plentiful charm. His name was Maskil. The king had never seen such a handsome young man. He nominated Maskil to be his crown prince, to rule the realm of Beauty in the days that were yet to come. Then he ordered his poets to compose a special song in Maskil's honour. They sang:

What joy to behold this fair gazelle!
The children of Love and Beauty are his slaves.
They bow and bend to him,
His allure nailed to their hearts.

Soon after this, more courtiers returned to the king, saying, 'Sire, we have discovered that in the Land of Arabs there are many beautiful gazelle maidens who are ripe and ready for love.'

The king ordered Maskil, the new Prince of Beauty, to harness his horse and ride at the head of the royal battalions to seek them out. When they arrived in Arabia, they found themselves in the midst of a Festival of Love. The streets were crowded with numerous young she-gazelles of the very kind they were seeking, all bright as the sun, kindled with passion's flame. The she-gazelles dallied, kissed and embraced; they danced and strutted in their jewels and trinkets; they played tambourines, singing of ardour and yearning...

Swift as lightning, Maskil's army put an end to these maidens' games. The soldiers captured them all, then took them as prisoners to the Land of Beauty.

Now, amongst these captive maidens was an exquisite princess called Peninah. Maskil had no sooner seen her than he was besotted. Fearing he might lose her, he shut her away in a hiding place, which he forbade her to leave. Peninah did not resent this, for she had fallen in love with him too. She used her solitude to compose this song for him:

> My beloved's face is ruddy as roses
> Scented with aromatic oils.
> Enemies approach him in the shadow of death –
> But I draw near him for the sweetness of life.

Her words and the tune in which she sang them pleased Maskil greatly; he composed a song for her in return:

> My soul's desire is
> Brightest amongst all the stars.
> Roses bloom in her cheeks
> Far and wide glows her light.

In this way, they became soulmates; she was his spouse and his sister, his spirit and his sunlight. She fed him with her own hands and lulled him to sleep between her breasts. They loved each other innocently and purely.

One day, Peninah said to her beloved, 'It is too long since you let me breathe fresh air. So take me out to the River of Love, for I have heard it is the custom for nobles like us to amuse themselves there.'

Maskil concurred and they wandered to the river side by side. The waters lapped gravel that gleamed like sapphires, surrounded by scented balsam beds and spreading trees, where brightly coloured birds were chirping. They sat down to rest in the tranquil shade and amused themselves by composing more love songs.

But suddenly, a wind blew up and quickly became a howling storm. It swirled with dust and bellowed like trumpet blasts. The valleys quivered and the hills trembled, as if shaken in a sieve. Peninah clung to her lover fearfully; but he pushed her away, rose to his feet, shaded his eyes and gazed down the banks of the river.

A terrifying horseman was riding towards them – a giant! His body was so wide – six cubits and a span – that it entirely blocked out the hills behind. His face was charred like wood pulled from a fire, and his eyes glowed like embers. He had six toes on each foot, and six fingers on each mighty hand. His horse came galloping towards them, swifter than a stag. The wind they had felt came directly from his throat – for he was not merely a giant, but also an evil spirit.

'Beware, Maskil!' this being roared. 'I am Cushan of the Cushites and I have come to seize your gazelle. If you wish to escape with your life, hand her over to me now.'

But Maskil, the perfect he-gazelle, the Prince of Beauty, was not daunted by evil. 'Ho, Cushan!' he called back. 'He who made Peninah beautiful made *you* equally hideous. You will never manage to seize her, for I shall kill you first.' And he backed up these insults with a song:

> Arrogant one with sins as vast as your size,
> Kinsman of demons, I shall hack your horns
> And dazzle the wild beasts with your disgrace!
> Your pride leads only to your grave.

This made Cushan even angrier. He roared a torrent of abuse and slander at Maskil, until his tongue broke from the force of it and dribbled down his beard. 'Come then, coward,' he went on, 'fight me for the female – if you really think she's worth it.'

Peninah ran to Maskil, crying, 'Do not be daunted by his haughty tongue, my princely lover. Brace yourself, and fight him!'

Maskil was as yet unpractised in conflict, but he yearned to prove his worth. So he armed himself and ran at his opponent. Peninah, confident of his might, stood close by to watch.

Cushan approached them, his face burning like a furnace, smoke coiling from his nostrils. He roared out a verse deriding Maskil. The youth used a verse of his own to insult the giant in return.

'So,' said Cushan, 'no one can accuse me of rushing to fight you. I gave you a chance to escape; all you had to do was let me take her. I spoke softly on account of your tender years. But instead of accepting my peace offering, you chose to goad me.'

The giant's horse snorted. Maskil saw that its mane was like a nest of serpents; its hooves were like rocks, its spit like flint. Cushan raised his bow and spear and pointed them at the Prince of Beauty. Maskil tasted alarm and recoiled from the giant in fear.

But Peninah cried in her sweet voice, 'My love, do not tremble before this evil one!' Maskil turned and was bathed in the radiance of her eyes. He braced his heart and summoned up the courage of a lion.

The prince and the giant charged at each other. The battle was fierce and angry; clouds of dust rose from the ground amidst their shrieks and bellows. They fought with lances. They fought with bows and arrows. They wrestled with bare arms until both were heavily bleeding. Still they did not tire. It was impossible to see which one fell and which rose up; it seemed that neither would ever win. They paused: Cushan went up the hill; Maskil stayed with Peninah in the valley. The warriors each took fresh weapons, then stepped forward to resume the fight.

Boldly, Maskil called out a new song:

> I am young with a heart full of guile;
> My sword harvests men
> Like a sickle reaping corn
> But Cushan, for all his roaring,
> Is not even worth the dust
> Trodden by my beloved,
> Whose beauty is of the stars.

Then finally, Maskil slew the giant, spilling out his bowels, tumbling his head onto his thighs.

Peninah rose and filled the air with song, summoning all the other she-gazelles, who came running to congratulate her and sing of her deliverance.

Maskil and Peninah went back to the riverbank, and there they quenched their long thirst by consummating their love. Afterwards, both declared they could never have enough of it. So they married and lived together ever after; and each day their lives overflowed with happiness and peace.

The metaphor 'gazelle' for a graceful youth or girl as an object of erotic desire comes from the biblical *Song of Songs* and is also a convention of Arabic love poetry. The story seems to have been composed to entertain a male readership; as in *The Romance of the Rose* (p. 170) the female protagonist is depicted as a characterless, passive object, devoid of any agency.

The poetry of the original text contains many Old Testament references. According to the Bible, the Cushites were descended from Noah; their kingdom was part of ancient Nubia (modern southern Egypt and northern Sudan).

The use of insults as part of battle technique extended to many parts of medieval Europe; there are a number of examples in literature extending as far back as the Viking Age.

The width of Cushan's body is described as six cubits and a span. A cubit was roughly equal to the length of a forearm, typically about eighteen inches (forty-four centimetres). A span was the distance between the tips of the thumb and the little finger.

Image from *Maastricht Book of Hours*
Netherlands, early 14th century

14th
CENTURY

A cooling climate brought harsher winters, reduced harvests and widespread famine. The Black Death plague of 1347-51 decimated Europe's population. Ongoing conflicts, closed frontiers, civil wars and popular uprisings caused further difficulties and pessimism.

Yet against these existential crises, romantic literature flourished and reached new, innovative heights. The century produced a number of highly original world-class authors in the genre, including Dante, Boccaccio and Chaucer.

DANTE & BEATRICE

Dante Alighieri, Italy:
La Vita Nuova (The New Life), written during the 1290s
Divina Commedia (Divine Comedy), written c.1308–20

Dante Alighieri is one of Italy's most celebrated poets.

He was born in Florence c.1265, growing up during a period of great political unrest within and between the numerous Italian city-states. He had an arranged marriage to a woman called Gemma di Manetto Donati and they had at least three children together. He joined the trade guild of physicians and apothecaries, then entered politics in 1293, becoming a member of Florence's council. In 1300 he was elected prior, the highest office in the city, and two years later became ambassador to Rome. Subsequently, due to political intrigue and jealousy, he was found guilty of a bogus charge and sentenced to death if he ever returned to Florence. Thus he spent the final twenty years of his life as an exile from his home city. He died of malaria in 1321, just a year after completing *Divine Comedy*.

The New Life was Dante's autobiographical account of his idealistic youthful love for a young woman called Beatrice, written in his late twenties. His spiritual passion for her was a major inspiration behind the later *Divine Comedy* – which is widely considered to be one of the seminal literary works of the Middle Ages. He was one of the first Italians to write in the vernacular, rather than in Latin.

The New Life

The main purpose of *The New Life* was to present a set of poems which Dante had composed for Beatrice, explaining and analysing each one in some detail. Beatrice has been identified as Beatrice Portinari, apparently the daughter of a banker. The emotional suffering Dante describes here is an extreme expression of the 12th century rituals of courtly love (see p.46 and pp.175-6).

When Dante was a mere boy, almost at the end of his ninth year, his father took him to a May feast held by a leading citizen of Florence. There he first set eyes on his host's radiant young daughter. Her name was Beatrice.

She was slightly younger than Dante, yet already imbued with unearthly beauty and self-possession. He was enthralled by her. Thus, at this tender age, he made Beatrice mistress of his heart and vowed she would rule him forever. From then on, he constantly sought her out, but always inconspicuously. His feelings were like a priceless hidden treasure that he shared with no one.

Nine years passed. Dante and Beatrice both reached the full flush of youth.

One day, on the ninth hour, he happened to see her passing along the street with two older ladies accompanying her. She was dressed in pure white. For the first time, she noticed him too, gracing him with a warm smile and a courteous greeting. He was too intoxicated to reply, but simply gazed at her speechlessly. Then he fled home, locked himself in his chamber, threw himself on his bed – and began to dream.

In this dream, the god of Love appeared, emerging from a mist the colour of fire. In his arms he carried Beatrice, wrapped in a blood-red cloth and sleeping peacefully. He placed her gently down, then brandished something small and smouldering. With a shock, Dante recognised his own heart. The god roused Beatrice, held out the heart to her and ordered her to eat it. She did so tremulously. When she was finished, the god gathered her up again, and together they rose towards the heavens.

As soon as Dante awoke, he went to his desk and composed a sonnet on the subject of love.

This was his first published poem. Many people read it. Some mocked it, others admired it; and because of it, the whole world now knew Dante was in love. He began to display behaviour typical of a besotted lover, almost too enfeebled to function.

No one knew who was the object of his desire. It was imperative to keep this secret. This became easier after he saw Beatrice in church. For another young lady beside her kept turning round to stare at him, as if convinced that *she* was the subject of his poem. He was grateful for this cover, and neither confirmed nor denied it.

However, this other lady later left the city. Dante dreamed again of the god of Love, and obeyed his orders by choosing someone to replace her. But this time he was indiscreet, and found himself the subject of malicious rumours. These spread like wildfire and reached the ears of Beatrice herself. By now, she knew Dante well by sight and always smiled when she saw him. But when she heard the gossip about his incautious affair, she cut him off and totally ignored him.

He was devastated.

The god of Love appeared to him yet again, this time speaking in riddles. 'Dante,' he declared, 'I am the centre of the circle. Everyone on the circumference is equal – except for you. Ask no more, but go and compose a new poem. Dedicate it to Beatrice and confess your love for her. However, write it in the third person; for it is unseemly to address her directly.'

Dante composed this sonnet without delay. Yet it gave him no ease, for he was consumed by contradictions. One moment, he told himself that love was pure virtue, for it distracted the mind from evil; but then he changed his view and decided that love itself was evil because of the dreadful torment it caused. He pondered long over the nature of his beloved, wondering why he could not attract her. He concluded that unlike other ladies, her heart could not be moved; and that he must simply accept this and serve her from a distance. He was like one who cannot choose which path to follow, and thus finds himself going nowhere.

He continued to see Beatrice here and there. On one occasion, his friend took him to a wedding party attended by many merry ladies. Beatrice was amongst them, and the mere sight of her sent Dante into a humiliating swoon. Afterwards, he considered whether to cease trying to seek her out. However, he concluded that, although he suffered terribly every time he saw her, he would die if he did not see her at all.

A number of ladies at this party saw him swoon, and finally realised that Beatrice was the object of his desire. Some time later, he happened upon a group of them, who called him over. Seeing that Beatrice was not amongst them, he accepted their invitation – only to be mortified by their frank questioning. 'We all know who you're in love with,' they said, unable to hide their laughter. 'But why do you always behave like an idiot in her presence? What's the point of such pathetic infatuation?'

'All I desire from her is a single friendly word,' he replied. 'Apart from that, I am happy to just write poems about her.' He beat a hasty retreat before they could interrogate him further.

His distress increased day by day, as did his output of love sonnets.

Meanwhile, Beatrice had become widely renowned for her exceptional virtue: she was gentle, modest and perfectly serene. Wherever she went, people gathered round to admire her exclaiming, 'This is surely no woman – but an angel sent down to us from heaven!'

Beatrice's father died. He had been a leading citizen and the whole of Florence admired him; thus many joined in her bitter mourning. Dante wept too, not for her father, but because of his beloved's grief.

Shortly afterwards, he himself fell seriously ill. On the ninth day of his malady, he dreamed that the sun went out, birds dropped from the sky, the earth quaked and the stars lost all their colour. In the midst of this catastrophe, he saw Beatrice's sweet body carried upward by a cloud of singing angels, as a voice cried: 'Your excellent lady is dead!' He awoke abruptly, unable to stop sobbing.

Just as he feared, this dream was an omen. For shortly afterwards, on the ninth day of the ninth month, Beatrice passed away. Dante was not the only one who lamented her: it was as if the entire city had been widowed by her demise.

On the first anniversary of Beatrice's death, Dante was sitting alone with his memories of her, drawing a picture of an angel on a tablet. Suddenly he felt someone watching him. Looking up, he saw a very attractive young woman gazing at him through the window. It was as if she knew his grief and pitied him for it. He was very touched and did not forget her. Indeed, he addressed his next poem to her, confessing everything he had suffered in the name of love.

After that, they met regularly and became good friends. Her company both comforted and cheered him. At first, he felt guilty, cursing himself for being unfaithful to the memory of Beatrice, who he still regularly saw in visions.

However, perhaps the god of Love had deliberately put this new lady into his path to bring him peace. For some time he struggled: at one moment accusing himself of betrayal, and at the next justifying his relief from years of romantic misery. In the end, he gave in to his desires and married her.

But he did not forget Beatrice and wrote poem after poem about her.

One day, he experienced a vision so moving that he vowed to cease writing about Beatrice until he could do so in a way that had never been used before for any other woman.

He had found his ultimate goal in life.

Divine Comedy

Many years later, when Dante was living in exile, memories of Beatrice were still prominent in his thoughts. He finally began to write the masterpiece he had long been planning for her.

Divine Comedy is an epic poem, over fourteen thousand lines long and divided into three books, each containing thirty-three or thirty-four cantos. It is a celebration of mystical, spiritual love over carnal desire. Its original title was simply 'Comedy'; 'Divine' was added to the title by later admirers. No original manuscripts have survived, but within a few years of his death, numerous copies had been produced. Today there are almost eight hundred medieval manuscripts of Divine Comedy still in existence – second only to the Bible – but since there is considerable variation between them, it is impossible to be certain which is the closest to Dante's original.

What follows is the essence of his extraordinary visionary poem, describing a mystical journey from spiritual wilderness to Paradise.

Rise then, oh reader,
to the lofty wheels with me!
– Divina Commedia, Paradiso, canto 10

Inferno

I was completely lost, deep in a wild and gloomy forest full of dangerous savage beasts.

Suddenly, I heard someone calling me, in the faint voice of one who has not spoken for a long time: 'My friend, do not despair, I have come to help you.'

The next moment, an elderly man appeared out of nowhere. My astonishment was all the greater when he introduced himself as my great literary hero – Virgil himself, author of *The Aeneid*, master poet of ancient Rome!

'I must warn you,' said Virgil, 'that the path I am going to take you on is not an easy one; for it leads right through eternity, via the realm of tormented spirits. Only the best and bravest souls may escape from there, and if you wish to reach the blessed region at journey's end, you will need to find a worthier guide for the final part. For I was once a rebel, and the Almighty has punished me for that by banning me from his Holy City.'

'I much appreciate your proposal,' I replied, 'but it sounds like sheer recklessness. I think I had best decline it.'

'Ah, my friend, do not be so hasty,' said Virgil. 'For I have not yet told you who sent me here to assist you. It was that divine woman – Beatrice.'

'*Beatrice*?' I cried in astonishment.

'Yes indeed. She told me that she had been looking down on you, her old friend, and saw you totally lost on the wilderness road, too afraid to move forward. Remembering your great love for her, she wished to help you. She herself cannot descend from the joyful place beyond mortal reach where she now resides, so she sought me out and exhorted me to approach you on her behalf.' He chuckled. 'She trusted that my elegant tongue would persuade you to accept me as your guide.'

'You have persuaded me indeed!' I said. 'If Beatrice herself has sent you, I have no excuse to hesitate. Lead on!'

And I followed Virgil even deeper into the wood.

After we had walked some way, we found ourselves standing before a high, arched doorway. Virgil pointed to some eerie words inscribed above it:

Abandon all hope, you who enter here.

'Prepare yourself for horror,' he said; then he took my hand and drew me in.

We were immediately assailed by a tumult of pitiful sighs and moans. At first, the darkness seemed to be solid. But as my eyes adjusted to it, I made out ghastly shapes: weeping faces and emaciated, bloody, naked bodies covered in stinging wasps, hornets and worms.

Virgil said, 'This is the abode of wretched souls who were neither good nor bad, but lived only to please themselves. They are not pure enough for Heaven, yet not wicked enough for Hell. Hurry past them, for we must make our way to the river.'

We reached the bank just as a boat came drifting up. From it, a hoary old man called out, 'Woe to you, wicked spirits! Jump aboard for the fire and ice of eternal suffering!' Suddenly, his sunken eye fell upon me. 'But not you, living wretch. This boat only carries the dead.'

'Let him come, Charon,' Virgil hissed.

The boatman shrugged and let us board the ferry alongside his cargo of doomed spirits. He pulled away and soon the river widened to a murky lake surrounded by wheeling flames. On the far side the spirits hurled themselves ashore, as the earth shook with a mighty blast of red lightning and a crash of thunder.

'Welcome to Limbo,' said Virgil. 'The souls here are of my own kind – worthy enough people who are unable to progress because we were not baptised. In my case, it was not out of choice, for I lived before the Gospel was even declared; but that does not absolve me.

'Nevertheless, some of my fellows here receive honour and favour to reflect their achievements in the living world. That shining mountain peak up there beyond the wood is where Homer of ancient Greece now dwells, alongside many fellow great poets of old. And that walled castle surrounded by a meadow is for the war heroes of antiquity.'

Just ahead lay a series of abysses, each surrounded by a circle of rock. As we picked our way through them, we were assailed by a hubbub of ear-splitting wails and bellows from damned spirits enduring their punishments. Men and women were being dashed against rocks for their incontinent earthly lusts. Gluttons, perverts, spendthrifts and thugs were wrestling, biting and striking each other, toppling into seething mud pools where they thrashed about helplessly, gasping for breath.

Reaching another stretch of filthy water, we were rowed across by a reluctant, cantankerous spectre. On the far side, Virgil briefly abandoned me while he went to negotiate entry to an iron city with flaming minarets. By the time he returned, I was shivering with fear, for three bloodstained, snake-haired female furies had suddenly appeared on its tower, clawing and tearing at their own flesh. My guide scolded them and covered my eyes. A whirlwind passed over us, driving thousands of condemned spirits before it. Virgil led me to the city gate and struck it open with his wand.

We entered a place of burning tombs with gaping lids from which came heart-wrenching cries of pain. 'This is the abode of the arch-heretics of every sect,' said Virgil. He drew me down a secret path between the towering walls, where ghostly voices screeched out their tragic stories from every side. Below, amidst choking fetid fumes, we found the tortured spirits of frauds and murderers, plunderers and robbers, suicides and blasphemers, witches and seducers, usurers and pretenders, hawkers of church pardons and other scum. Our next stop was at a ford flooded with blood, where the spirits of once eminent men were desperately struggling not to drown. A centaur carried us across it on his back. Our path went on through a forest, where sinners had been transformed into trees, doomed to be torn to shreds by vicious mastiffs.

Thus one horror after another beset us. Sometimes we heard the sufferers' names; they included well known clerks, politicians, scholars and benefactors, who had all polluted their good works with immorality. A hideous, fork-tailed monster carried us on his back through wind and fire to the base of a rocky chasm. There he tipped us off, then shot away like an arrow.

We continued through a fortress where horned demons were whipping a groaning crowd of naked rapists, philanderers and harlots. Other wretches were stretched across chasms, with feet immersed in fire and heads swivelled backwards by winged devils. This was their punishment for simony, sorcery and swindling; parsimony, embezzlement and the persecution of Jews. Beyond them were stealers of church treasures who had framed others with the crime. They were bound with living snakes and bitten by adders until their bodies were dust – only to rise again for another cycle of torture. Nearby, God's minister,

Justice, was busy stacking up forgers all higgledy-piggledy, alongside disfigured alchemists and false accusers.

We saw so many miscreants from every time and place suffering such ghastly punishments, that I felt broken myself as we grappled our way up a concealed, vertiginous stairway between a mountain and jagged ice. But when we finally emerged from it into a cave, we beheld the most uplifting sight above: the beautiful lights of heaven – the stars!

Purgatorio

We now entered that marvellous region where the blemishes of sin are purged from the human spirit, to prepare for the ascent to Heaven.

The air here was sapphire-blue and totally pure. As I gulped in deep breaths of it, I realised we were being watched by a venerable old man with long white hair and beard. 'What are you doing here?' he exclaimed. 'Who dared to break the ancient divine laws to let a condemned soul approach my caves?'

Virgil pressed me to kneel before him submissively, then said, 'Sir, this traveller is not yet condemned. A woman of Heaven sent me down to rescue him from his existential anguish, and lead him up here from the lower reaches. I implore you, hallowed spirit, let us pass.'

'If a woman of Heaven directs you,' he answered, 'that is enough. Go yonder, wash the sordid stains from his face and use the reeds growing there to clothe him. After that, follow the rising sun to find the easiest way up.'

We did as instructed, crossing a deserted plain to a seashore suffused with tender dew. Virgil used this to bathe me, then helped me fashion a reed garment to wear. By the time we were done, the sun was setting. We stayed there until the first light of dawn revealed an angel, whose wings were steering a small boat towards us. In it were hundreds of loudly singing spirits. The angel blessed them, dropped them on the shore then sped off. They all gazed at me in wonder, and one greeted me excitedly – for he was a long lost friend of mine! But the venerable elder shooed them away and ordered us to proceed.

We scrambled up a steep mountain in blinding sunlight, climbing a set of steps to a high ridge where we were surrounded by throngs of ghosts. These were people who had died violently but repented during their last moments, thus earning the hope of redemption.

As I stared at them, Virgil suddenly startled me by announcing, 'Happiness lies ahead. For Beatrice is waiting for you on the next peak.'

'Beatrice?' I cried. 'Oh master, then let us hurry! I am no longer tired.'

Darkness fell too quickly. To avoid the mischievous night spirits, we rested in a hollow adorned with precious stones and flowers. The next morning, I woke in great confusion, for we were in a totally different place.

'While you slept,' said Virgil, 'an angel carried us up to this summit. The way leads on through that gate across there.'

I jumped up and followed him to it, past a gatekeeper with a dazzling face, and down three coloured steps. Here we met an angel in ashen robes sitting upon a diamond rock by a seemingly impenetrable door. On Virgil's advice, I prostrated myself at his feet. The angel drew out a gold and silver key, turned it in a lock and thus thrust the door open.

'Enter,' he bellowed. 'But be warned: do not look behind, or you will be cast out.'

As we crossed the threshold, we were greeted by a chorus of holy singing – so different from the shrieks of Hell! The door clanged shut behind us. We started up a towering cliff, passing a troop of wailing spirits bent under huge boulders. 'They are purging themselves for succumbing to the Devil's temptations,' Virgil explained. He said a prayer for them and, in return, they pointed out an easier route to the top.

'Master,' I said to Virgil as we climbed, 'I seem to have suddenly lost weight.'

'That is because this mountain heals those who climb it, so you are gradually shedding your sin,' he replied. 'Eventually, you will be completely clean and thus weightless. Here, let me wipe away some more of your sin.' Smiling, he brushed his hand against my brow.

On the summit, we passed dark crouching shadows, and a line of wretched ghosts in sackcloth, weeping through wire threads sewn in their eyes to blind them. Virgil said, 'These are jealous people who must be whipped by Charity until they are pardoned.'

My head was swirling with questions about faith, virtue and joy. I put them to Virgil, but his answers were bewildering. 'You are still obsessed with earthly matters which conceal the true light,' he said. 'But don't worry: Beatrice, will explain everything.'

We passed some spirits praying to loosen the bonds of anger, then started up a ladder. Night fell again, but this time we did not stop to rest. I dozed off into a disturbing dream of Virgil bewitched and led astray by a siren. In the morning he laughed when I told him about it, saying, 'Just concentrate on your goal.'

The next spirits we saw were lying prone on the ground around a pope, who was paying the price for his worldly greed. Then we saw a tree laden with luscious fruit, where a voice called out, 'Reject feasting! Consume only simple food and drink.' A line of ghostly, hollow-eyed gluttons passed by, amongst whom I recognised a number of old acquaintances. Disembodied voices intoned sorry tales of braggarts and narcissists.

Now we came to a flaming void and trod gingerly along the scorching edge. Twisted spirits kept leaping out, trying to snatch illicit kisses from me, then scuttled away screeching, 'See how we suffer for our bestial lusts!'

An angel appeared and ordered: 'Enter the fire!'

I was terrified. But Virgil said, 'My son, remember the ordeals I have already safely guided you through. Even a thousand years in these flames would not harm a single hair on your head. And this is the last barrier that divides you from Beatrice.'

Trembling, I followed him into unbearable heat. Somehow, I made it through to the far side.

When night engulfed us, we huddled to sleep beneath some rocks.

In the morning, Virgil said, 'My son, this is the day you have been hungering for. I cannot accompany you any further, but the most difficult paths are far behind you now. From now on, pleasure shall be your guide. Enjoy this sunny land of trees and flowers. Here you are free to make your own decisions.'

Then he was gone.

I did not allow myself to regret our parting, but strode forward eagerly, relishing the soft breezes and cheerful birdsong. Soon I met a lady picking flowers. She explained this was the celestial garden of peace, originally created for everyone on earth, then taken away to punish human weakness.

An extraordinary procession came thundering up in a brilliance of white flames, trailing seven colours behind them. In it were marvellous winged animals crowned with leaves, and a triumphal chariot drawn by a griffin, surrounded by golden birds with silver veins. Nymphs in red, emerald, white and purple danced at the wheels; at the rear walked a line of wise old men.

As I stared at it in wonder, on the far side of the stream – Beatrice suddenly appeared!

'So, you have come,' said she.

'I have,' I whispered. 'But tell me, why have I been brought here?'

As if in reply, the procession set up a loud chant and the nymphs scattered cascades of perfumed flowers. Out of these stepped a beautiful young temptress in scarlet robes. At once my blood began to quiver with the old, familiar desire. Mortified, I turned to Virgil for help – then remembered my protector was no longer with me.

'Ah, Dante, do not weep,' said Beatrice. 'In your youth I inspired you to walk upright and behave well. But when I passed away you soon forgot me and were overwhelmed by bad seed. Without good husbandry your plant ran wild. You became deceitful, worshipped false images and gave yourself to others.'

'But I did not forget you,' I cried. 'I dreamed of you constantly.'

'Yes,' she said, 'I tried to call you back. But you had fallen so low, I realised the only way to save you was to reveal what it means to suffer divine punishment. That is why I sought out your hero Virgil from amongst the dead souls and asked him to guide you here. Now you must learn how to repent.'

'It's true,' I groaned. 'I gave in to unsavoury pleasures.'

'You succumbed to temptation because you knew you could never find my equal,' she said. 'Would it not have been better to follow me quickly to this realm?'

I stood silently, like an ashamed child, eyes cast down.

'Look at me,' said Beatrice.

Across the wide stream and through her veil, I saw she was even more beautiful than on earth. I was overcome with remorse for all the lovers I had succumbed to since her death; how loathsome they all seemed now!

I swooned; and came round to find the lady of the garden immersing me in the stream up to my neck. She helped me back onto dry land, where four nymphs beckoned me saying, 'We are Beatrice's handmaids, come to take you to her.'

Beatrice was waiting by the griffin. The nymphs danced up to her singing, 'Beatrice, we beg you to reward this faithful traveller for his arduous journey: let him see your inner beauty.'

She turned to me and lifted her veil. Ah, to see her at last, after all the long years of thirst! She was more dazzling than sun reflected off a mirror, yet I could not stop staring at her.

I managed to look away as the procession started up again. It circled a completely bare, lifeless tree. A shout went up: 'Here is the tree which feeds evil. And here is the one who resisted its temptation.' Beatrice sat down at its roots and, at once, the tree sprouted a mass of green leaves and shoots.

She called to me: 'Watch!'

Singers chorused, 'The heathens have come!'

An eagle dived down and a fox ran out of the forest. Together they struck the chariot hard. The earth split open. A dragon leaped out and thrust its forked tail through the chariot floor. A three-headed monster emerged from the remains, where a brazen whore and a giant were mingling kisses. The whore's eyes met mine, at which the giant began to whip her. Then they all scuttled away exultantly into the forest.

Beatrice rose and called to me, 'Come with me, brother. I know what is in your heart. Cast away your shame and fear.'

'But I do not understand why you say I forgot you,' I said. 'I do not remember being guilty of that.'

She replied, 'The very fact that you do not understand indicates your guilt.'

The sun had reached its zenith. We paused by a fountain, fed by a sacred river. Here she let me drink, and at once I felt rejuvenated.

Paradiso

That evening, we began to rise through the splendours of Heaven's different realms. Beatrice spoke of many things that I scarcely understood: of the primal source, the sea of being, predestination, righteousness and God's love. She described my various sins and their rightful punishments, promising my redemption. When I begged her to answer doubts that troubled me, she simply said, 'The eternal light is already shining in your mind and kindling love.'

Heavenly choruses rang out and joyous spirits surrounded us. I entered the sun itself. Beatrice cried out, 'Thank God for raising you to this height!' Then I understood that my desire to surrender to God was stronger even than my love for her. She read my thoughts and smiled in delight. I had earned the right to be received as an honoured guest of Heaven.

And so we floated up, still higher and higher, through hymns, whirling stars, voices of revelation, twinkling lights...and always Beatrice's infinite sweetness. At one point, I found myself face to face with the spirit of my own great-great-grandfather, who revealed that my future on earth would be troubled; but Beatrice comforted me, pointing out that God makes amends for every wrong. An eagle with open wings and eyes like rubies called to me, 'Divine justice is beyond human comprehension, but hope and fervent love can conquer Heaven.' Like sweet medicine, his words cleared my mind.

For an ecstatic moment I found myself alone with my lady's smile; at the rapturous love in her eyes, my soul was totally contented.

Before us stood a golden ladder rising beyond sight, hung with unimaginable splendours. I ascended it and looked down through the seven spheres of Heaven. Below, I saw the earth that I had once loved so much – and realised how pitiful it really is.

There came a burst of heavenly music. St Peter stepped out of a flame and questioned me carefully on my faith; I answered him well, by declaring that God is love. Other saints followed him with more questions; I satisfied them too. I met old father Adam, who told how his brief earthly life was soiled by transgression. Hymns rose and fell. I gazed down at the swirling vapours below and realised how far I had travelled.

Beatrice saw this and said, 'The mortal lusts of earth do not even rise above the waves before they are drowned. But *you* have glimpsed divine love and goodness, the motionless centre of Heaven that all life revolves around.'

She had truly drawn the veil from my eyes and shown me the wretchedness of mortal life. Oh, the day-star of my eyes!

I cannot find adequate words to describe her beauty. It surpasses everything except her Maker.

Finally, she led me, marvelling and speechless, into the supreme radiance of Heaven. I gazed at it in awe then turned back to thank her – but she had vanished.

In her place was an old man, his eyes glowing with friendly joy. 'Beatrice asked me to help you achieve your greatest wish,' he said softly. 'See, there she is in her full glory.'

He pointed upwards. I saw Beatrice sitting on a throne, her brow wreathed in the sunbeams of eternity. Humbled, I knelt and prayed to her: 'My beloved lady in whom rest all my hopes! Everything I have seen, I owe to your power, goodness and grace. I beg you, do not forsake me. You have made my spirit whole. When it is freed from my body, I pray that you will favour it.'

Beatrice looked down on me and smiled.

I found myself carried into the supreme light, reaching for that place where all wishes are fulfilled…

And then I wakened from my dream.

I remember it perfectly and its sweetness still trickles through my heart.

It revealed to me what *true love* is. Reader, it has nothing to do with lust. It is the universal light from which the whole universe unfolds.

The extraordinary cosmos portrayed in *Divina Commedia* has been described as both strikingly original and coherent in structure.

As Dante travels through Hell to Paradise, he encounters the spirits of many famous people from antiquity and myth alongside political, religious or creative celebrities of his own time. They represent all points of the moral compass, including Helen of Troy and Paris, Cleopatra, Tristram and Achilles; Thomas Aquinas, St Bede and St Peter.

Beatrice is an unusual and remarkable literary character in many ways, a blend of real-life and 'ideal' woman. Dante admires her not simply for her physical beauty – which in medieval literature typically symbolises spiritual perfection – but mostly for her powers of intellectual discourse, explanation and debate; and ultimately for her spiritual purity. Such qualities were not normally associated with the female sex in medieval literature.

Dante's guide through Inferno and Purgatorio, Virgil (c.70 to 19 BC), is regarded as as one of ancient Rome's greatest narrative poets. His most famous work today is *Aeneid*, a twelve-book epic about the travels and experiences of the hero Aeneas after the fall of Troy.

THE LADY OF THE WELL

Anonymous: 'Owain' or 'The Lady of the Fountain',
from *The White Book of Rhydderch*
Wales, 14th century.

The anonymous author of this tale based it on the 12th century French story *Yvain (The Knight with the Lion)* by Chrétien de Troyes (see p.46). It may also have existed in old Welsh storytelling traditions, either derived from Chrétien's book, or from much older oral sources. With its Arthurian context, it is appropriate that a Celtic author reclaimed it from France, since some of the oldest references to, and stories about, King Arthur and his knights come from Wales. The Welsh version is much simpler and more down to earth than Chrétien's narrative.

The *White Book of Rhydderch* is the oldest surviving collection of Welsh prose texts, and also contains some poems. The hands of five different scribes have been identified in the manuscript. It is believed to have been made for Rhydderch ab Ieuan Llwyd (c.1325–1400) from Ceredigion, whose family had a tradition of literary patronage. Alongside the slightly later *Red Book of Hergest*, it was first translated into English by Charlotte Guest in the 19th century, in a collection which she called *Mabinogion*.

Arthur, high king of Britain, had his court at Caerllion ar Wysg, and from there his knights often went out hither and thither on quests and to seek adventure.

Rumours came to Caerllion that, somewhere beyond the forest, there lay a marvellous, secret country. It was said to be out of bounds to all outsiders and accessible only via an uncanny supernatural well.

The valiant knight Sir Owain was eager to find this land. So he rode off through the forest, on and on, until at last he reached a clearing. There he was assailed by an unwashed, one-eyed giant.

Owain bid him a courteous 'good morning'.

In response the giant growled, 'What are you doing round here, you squirming maggot?' He seized a colossal iron club and waved it menacingly at Owain's head.

'I'm just wondering if you happen to know the way to the supernatural well?' said Owain.

'Yah, I know the way all right,' the giant smirked. 'But why do you want to go there? It'll only bring you trouble.'

'Nevertheless,' said Owen, 'I'd be glad of your directions.'

The giant snorted and pointed into the distance saying, 'See that hill? Go right up to the top and down the other side to the river valley. The well's underneath a great fir tree there.'

'And how do I get from there to the forbidden country?' said Owain.

The giant said, 'Next to the well is a marble slab with a silver bowl hanging from it by a silver chain. Fill the bowl in the well, throw the water over the slab – then watch out!'

Owain thanked him and made his way to the well, where he did everything the giant had told him. As soon as he threw water onto the marble slab, he was assailed by a deafening noise. It was twice as loud as thunder, as if the whole world was being shaken violently to the core. This was followed by a torrent of lashing hailstones. But the storm passed as quickly as it had come. Then the sun came out and the tree filled with exquisite bird song.

The next moment, a knight in black armour appeared from nowhere, galloping furiously on a jet-black charger. He brandished his sword and challenged Owain to battle. They began to fight. For a while they seemed evenly matched; but then Owain struck his blade right through the black knight's helmet and mail cap – through his hood, down through his skin, his flesh and his skull – right into his brain.

'You bastard,' the black knight screamed, 'you've killed me!'

He turned his horse and fled. Owain galloped after him, eager to finish him off; but the other managed to keep well ahead. They reached a castle where the gates stood wide open. The ailing black knight rode straight through them and vanished. Owain made to follow; but as he entered the porch, two portcullises crashed down, one immediately in front of him and the other behind. He was trapped!

Through the inner portcullis he could see a row of houses. Suddenly a well-dressed damsel appeared at the far end and came running down the street towards him.

'Just look at you!' she cried. 'God knows, I've never seen such a fine knight! I can tell from your face that you're a trustworthy friend of women, and a chivalrous lover too – just the kind of man who deserves to be helped. So take this.' She thrust a ring through the bars. 'Slip it on your finger so the stone is in your palm, and close your fist around it; it'll make you completely invisible. Now listen, my friend. That black knight you just mortally wounded is the lord of this castle. His men know you've followed him, which is why they've trapped you here. But so long as you wear this magic ring, they'll never find you. Soon they'll open the portcullis; run through it to that mounting block over there, where I'll be waiting for you. You'll be invisible to me too, so put your hand on my shoulder to signal you're there. As soon as I feel it, I'll lead you somewhere safe.'

She ran off as Owain put on the magic ring. Some guards marched up, opened the inner portcullis and started rooting around for him. The invisible Owain slipped past them and dashed across to the mounting block. From there the damsel led him into a wing of the castle, up some steps and through a door into a large and very well-appointed chamber.

'Welcome, my friend,' she said, and turned to light the fire. 'Now listen. Between me and God, my name is Luned, and it's time to take off the ring.'

He did so. The damsel set the table with all kinds of food and drink in golden vessels, and they feasted together all afternoon. Neither was in the least bit inhibited when it came to conversation; but suddenly their revels were interrupted by a terrible wailing outside.

'Ah, that must be for the lord of the castle, who you mortally wounded,' said she. 'They'll be giving him the last rites. Well, my friend, you've had an eventful day, and if I were you, I'd go to sleep.'

She showed him a splendid bed with silken sheets and ermine coverlets. No sooner had Owain's head touched the pillow than he was snoring, while Luned sat chastely in a chair beside him. At midnight he was startled into wakefulness by more wailing outside; but Luned said, 'Don't worry, it's only because the lord of the castle has now died. Go back to sleep.'

At dawn Luned shook him awake, crying, 'Get up, oh do get up! They're taking the lord's body to church for his funeral. Come and look out through the window. I promise you won't be disappointed.'

So Owain got up and surreptitiously peered outside. He saw a bier carried by barons, followed by trumpeters and a crowd of chanting mourners; but what really caught his eye was the lady who walked behind them. She was surely the most beautiful person who ever lived in all the world. But her yellow hair was hanging loose, all stained with blood from her late husband's wounds; her silken dress was torn to tatters and she was wringing her hands, shrieking twice as loud as all the rest of the mourners put together.

'That's my mistress,' said Luned proudly, 'the Lady of the Well herself – who *you* have just widowed. She's the wisest, most generous and noble lady the world has ever known.'

'God knows, I've fallen in love just at the sight of her!' Owain cried.

'And God also knows that your case is hopeless,' said the damsel. 'Having slaughtered her beloved husband, surely you don't expect she could ever return your love?'

'Then my heart is lost, and so am I!' cried Owain.

Luned tut-tutted. 'By God, I don't like to see you looking downcast, my friend. Didn't I promise to help you? Well I haven't finished with you yet, and I'll see what I can do. Just come back inside and wait here; I'll go courting on your behalf.'

Luned hurried off through the castle to the private chamber of her mistress, the Lady of the Well. She found her sitting there all alone, tearing her hair and weeping copiously.

'Good morning, madam,' Luned said.

The lady was too distraught to answer.

'Good morning, madam,' said Luned again, more loudly; again she got no reply. 'By God!' she cried. 'What's wrong with you, my lady? Nothing's to be gained by wallowing in grief. Weeping won't bring your husband back, so what's the point of it? You'd do better to think about finding someone to take his place.'

'Impossible!' the lady wept. 'My husband is irreplaceable.'

'If I might say so, madam, that's nonsense,' Luned said. 'He was good, but you can surely find someone even better.'

'How dare you speak so treacherously?' the lady cried. 'If I wasn't so fond of you, I'd have you executed!'

'I'm not being treacherous,' said Luned. 'I'm trying to point out what's in your best interests. You need to find a new man, powerful enough to take your husband's place and protect your kingdom at the Well. And I know exactly where to find such a warrior.'

'Where?' said the lady wretchedly.

'At the court of King Arthur, of course,' said Luned. I tell you what, I'll go there myself, right now, and bring back a suitable candidate by tomorrow at the latest.'

'Oh, very well, do whatever you think best,' said the lady, who was too upset to argue any further.

So Luned hurried out. But don't think she went anywhere in the direction of Caerllion. Oh no, instead she returned straight to Owain. 'My mistress is willing to see you tomorrow,' she said. 'I'll help you wash and shave and dress in some fine new clothes, to make a good impression.'

The next day, Luned returned to the lady, with Owain at her side, splendidly attired in a tunic, surcoat, cloak of rich brocade and boots fastened with a golden buckle. The lady looked him carefully up and down, then said, 'This knight doesn't look as if he's just made the long journey from Caerllion.'

'I swear he's one of King Arthur's knights,' Luned retorted.

'In fact,' said the lady, her face turning angry, 'he exactly fits the description they've given me of the rogue who killed my husband!'

'So what if he is?' said Luned. 'What he did in the past is over and done with. And the fact is, madam, by killing your husband, this knight proved himself to be even stronger than him. Isn't a strong man exactly what you need right now?'

The lady said she must take advice. So she summoned all her noblemen, explained the dire situation that they were now in and asked, 'Do you think I should marry a new warrior to defend the realm?'

All her noblemen said that she should.

So without further delay, she summoned her bishops and got them to conduct her wedding to Owain – who, of course, was more than willing to go along with it.

Well, how do you think Owain felt now, being married to the beautiful lady of his dreams? He was ecstatic, of course!

He didn't let her down, but defended her kingdom valiantly. Whenever any knight tried to invade it via the Well, not only did Owain defeat him, but he also ransomed him at high value, and shared the takings from this equitably with the local barons and knights – which, of course, made him very popular.

In this way, things went on very pleasantly for everyone concerned, for three whole years.

By that time, the friends who Owain had left behind at Caerllion ar Wysg were missing him badly.

Remembering he had gone off to find the way into the secret realm, a group of knights followed in his footsteps, led by King Arthur himself. They too were directed by the giant in the forest, found the marble slab and threw water on it. This called up the hailstorm and then the black knight – who, of course, was now none other than Owain. After a fierce battle, Owain revealed himself, to his opponents' astonishment. A truce was called and their long-neglected friendship was renewed. Naturally, they all wanted Owain to return to Caerllion, at least for a while.

So Owain went to the castle and asked his beloved lady's permission to go.

'I'm not at all happy about that,' she said. 'When do you plan to come back?'

'I'll be gone for no more than three months,' said Owain. He begged and cajoled her with much flattery and many empty promises until, very reluctantly, the lady agreed.

But you know how it is when a man's enjoying himself: a promise made to his lady is easily forgotten. Owain was so busy drinking with his old companions and taking part in jousts and adventures, that he scarcely noticed the passing of time. The Lady of the Well and her realm gradually faded from his memory like a dream. His three-month deadline to return passed unnoticed. A year went by, then two years, then three.

One evening, Owain was sitting at the Round Table, feasting and making merry with his companions. Suddenly, the door burst open to reveal a well-dressed damsel mounted on a horse with golden trappings, heading straight for Owain. 'Shame on your beard, you treacherous cheat!' she cried. Then she leaned down, snatched the ring from his finger, turned the horse and rode out as quickly as she had come.

Owain stared after her in bewilderment. Where had he seen her before? Ah, by God, it was Luned!

Suddenly, the memories of his beloved wife came flooding back. How could he have abandoned her at all, let alone for so long? He rose from the table abruptly and rushed to his chamber; but he could not sleep for remorse and shame. The next morning he rose at dawn, slipped out barefoot from the castle and made his way into the wilderness.

He walked through it for days, for weeks, for months, living on wild seeds and fruits, sleeping rough, mixing only with wild animals. His clothes grew torn and tattered, he wasted away and his hair and beard grew into a long tangle. His mind became as chaotic as his body.

You'll not want to hear too much about this degradation. Suffice to say that eventually he was found and healed by the lady of a castle. After that, with a new horse, he resumed his knightly demeanour. Nevertheless, still full of remorse, he continued to wander in the wilderness.

And he maintained his solitude; his only friend now was a pure white lion which he had rescued as it was about to be bitten to death by a venomous snake.

One evening, as Owain and this lion were sharing a meal of freshly caught venison, they heard a desperate groaning nearby. Owain jumped to his feet. 'Who or what is there?' he called. 'Are you beast or human? Where are you?'

'Human,' a damsel's voice answered plaintively. 'Turn round and you'll see a huge, hollow stone. I am imprisoned inside it.'

Owain looked around. Sure enough, through the dusk, he saw an enormous stone with a slit cut roughly into the top. Behind the slit, a pair of eyes was watching him.

'Who are you?' he said. 'Why are you shut up in there?'

'Between me and God,' the damsel answered, 'my name is Luned. 'I was shut up because…'

'Luned,' said Owain softly. He felt a stirring in his heart.

'You speak like a friend,' she said, 'and though I don't know your name, sir, I sincerely hope that you are. For I badly need some help. Until recently, I served the Lady of the Well. She used to treat me very kindly, in gratitude for me arranging her marriage to the valiant Sir Owain, who she loved with all her heart. However, after only three years, he abandoned her, promising shortly to come back; but he never did. Thus my lady's heart was broken. She blames me

221

for introducing her to this heartless man and thus causing her unbearable suffering. As punishment, she has had me incarcerated in this stone vessel, waiting to be killed.'

'That is truly an unjust punishment for something beyond your control,' said Owain; and the remorse that had troubled him for so long, now utterly overwhelmed him. 'Is there no way you can be saved?'

'The only way,' said Luned, 'is for someone to defend me on the actual day I am condemned to die. That is the day after tomorrow. I once had a dear friend who I believed would help me in my time of need, just as I once helped him. But that was Owain himself, my lady's absent husband – and he has abandoned me as well as her. So my death is surely inevitable.'

Owain was too ashamed to tell Luned who he was. However, to comfort her, he stayed beside the stone vessel and talked with her all night. At dawn he said, 'Now I shall go out to find the saviour you mentioned.'

'Oh, please go in all haste,' she begged. 'For there is only one more day until my execution.'

He mounted his horse and called the lion to follow. His plan was to make a short circuit, then return early next morning, in time to reveal himself and save Luned. But fate delayed him, as it often does to the most worthy of knights. He found himself diverted to a castle, where he had to rescue the lord's daughter from a monstrous giant, and then waste time refusing the reward of her hand in marriage. But at last he was able to ride back at full speed to the stone vessel where Luned awaited either deliverance by Owain, or her death.

He arrived not a moment too soon. For the stone vessel was now empty and his friend was already bound to a stake above a stack of firewood before a gawping, jeering crowd.

Even as he drew near, two squires were approaching the bonfire, carrying lighted tapers.

Owain galloped towards them, leaped to the ground and wrested the tapers from their hands. The squires fought back fiercely. But the white lion that had followed him faithfully for so long sprang to his aid to defeat them. In this way, Luned was saved.

Hastily, Owain untied her bonds. When the intrepid damsel was standing unencumbered before him she exclaimed, 'By God, Owain, so that fellow I met last night kept his word. He managed to find you, just in the nick of time!'

Owain did not admit that he was one and the same man. But he knew that his long-standing debt to his dear friend Luned had now more than adequately been repaid.

All that remained was for Owain to make peace with his Lady; but that was not so easy.

'My friend,' said Luned, 'I must warn you: she doesn't want you back.'

'Then I shall die and so will she,' said Owain. 'For I'll go to the Well, and call up a storm violent enough to destroy her entire realm and all her people.'

He did not hesitate to carry out this threat. Soon the Lady of the Well's castle and town and the fields beyond were all being ravaged by a barrage of rain and gales. Luned hurried through this deluge to her lady's chamber.

'How did you get back here, causer of my heartbreak?' cried the lady in astonishment. 'Why have you not been executed?'

'I'm sorry you're not pleased to see me,' said Luned, 'even though I always served you both diligently and loyally. Well, despite your recent cruelty to me, madam, I have come to offer a solution to this crisis.'

'Hmm,' said the lady. 'If you can calm this storm, perhaps I may even forgive you.'

Luned lowered her voice. 'Between me and God, madam,' she said, 'there's someone else you must calm and forgive; for he is the one who called up this storm, and the only one who can vanquish it. I mean...your own husband, Sir Owain.'

The Lady of the Well turned pale.

'Owain has returned to our land,' said Luned. 'It was he who just saved my life. If you would find it in your heart to pardon him for his great wrong in abandoning you, he promises to make amends. Not only will he end this storm, but he will also return to serve you faithfully for the rest of his days.'

The Lady of the Well sat in silent thought for a long while. Finally she said, 'I suppose I have no choice. Go at once to Owain, Luned, and beg him for mercy.'

Luned did not hurry to obey. First she went to a chest, brought from it a holy saint's relic and thrust it into her lady's hands. 'Madam,' she said, 'to ensure that all is done as it should be, you must first swear an oath not to change your mind.'

The lady listened to the storm battering the walls and dripping through the roof; she saw through the broken windows that the town outside was rapidly flooding. She clutched the relic to her heart and whispered, 'If Owain ends this storm for ever, I swear to restore him to the fullness of my love.'

As soon as this was done, Luned rushed back to Owain and told him of her lady's oath. Then she led him through the tempest to the lady's chamber.

'Come now, madam,' Luned said, 'forgive your husband in fulfilment of your vow.'

'Ach, this is a trap you've caught me in,' the lady protested. 'You are trying to force me to love a man who has proved by desertion that *he* does not love *me*.'

Owain did not wait to hear any more. He threw himself to his knees before her and wept profusely, holding up his hands in supplication, crying, 'Have mercy on this sinner! I fully admit my guilt, and if you knew the sickness of mind and body that I suffered in consequence of my behaviour, you would know that I paid dearly for it. I beg you to accept me back, my lady. If you do, I solemnly promise never to wrong you again.'

'I swore an oath and I cannot be guilty of perjury,' the lady sighed. 'So I must forgive you, my husband.'

Owain was overjoyed.

As for Luned, she was very happy too; for now there was to be enduring peace between the two people in the world that she cared for most; and she was at the core of it.

This time, Owain took great care to keep his word. He took the Lady of the Well to King Arthur's court to celebrate; and from that time on, they enjoyed each others' company every day, for as long as they both lived.

Thus ends the tale of the Lady of the Well.

The ending of the Welsh version of the story tails off rather unsatisfactorily, so in this retelling the final paragraphs about Owain's reconciliation with his lady is taken from Chrétien's account.

The idea of a go-between facilitating a romance, whilst also being a stalwart friend of both parties, was similarly used by Chaucer in *Troilus and Criseyde* (see p.289). It is interesting that here the role is played by a very confident woman, and that she maintains a strong platonic friendship with the hero.

Stories from
DECAMERON

Giovanni Boccaccio: *Decameron*
Italy, c.1353

Giovanni Boccaccio (1313–75) was born in a small Italian town to an unknown single woman who had an affair with his married father, Boccaccio di Chellino, a prominent banker. He was raised by his father's wife and spent his childhood in Florence, a major financial and trading centre. When he was fourteen, the family moved to the teeming city of Naples, where he resisted his father's advice to become a lawyer, preferring to pursue scholarship and literature. He was a great enthusiast of the work of Dante (see p. 192), who died while Boccaccio was still a child, and in later life became a friend of his eminent contemporary, the poet Petrarch. He began to write in the 1330s, publishing many works in both prose and verse. He returned to Florence in 1341, and by the 1350s had become one of the city's leading citizens and writers.

He began work on *Decameron* around 1349, shortly after Florence had been devastated by the plague, also known as the Black Death, which killed over half the city's population. Written in prose, it comprises a hundred short stories, many of them drawn from folklore and legend, set within a 'frame story'.

The book opens with a description of how the plague has overwhelmed Florence, and introduces seven young unattached noblewomen sitting in a corner of a church, discussing the alarming situation. One suggests that they all protect themselves from the epidemic by leaving the city with their staff, and moving around between their various country houses. At that moment, three young men enter the church, each having some family or romantic connection to at least one of the ladies. The ladies ask the young men for their brotherly support and protection in this project, which is immediately given. The following week, the ten friends and their retinues meet at a hilltop palace surrounded by gardens, two miles outside the city, to begin their adventure.

They settle into their temporary home, planning to enjoy themselves with food, music, dancing and games, with each taking turns to be a leader ('queen' or 'king') for a day. The first leader is chosen by a vote, then appoints the following day's leader, and so on. On the first day, after their siesta, they sit in a shady meadow to escape the heat, and start telling stories. They continue to do this each day, taking breaks on Fridays and Saturdays, with regular moves to different accommodation. After fifteen days, everyone has had a turn as 'queen' or 'king', and each has told ten stories. Fearing that staying together any longer might lead to discord or intrusion, they return to Florence.

Decameron is written in prose with elegance, vividness and warmth, with charming poems bringing each day's storytelling to an end. Most of its stories are about normal people: gentry, merchants, townsfolk, clergy and so on, including some real life characters. They are full of humour, but often with a malicious slant, taking delight in mocking underdogs and naive characters. Although female characters are often proactive, some stories are blatantly misogynous, with domestic violence portrayed as normal and acceptable.

Around a third of the stories have a theme of lust, just under a fifth have a theme of love, and a handful combine both. There is a wide range of plots within these categories. Although some condone and even laugh at the sexual abuse of girls and women, others celebrate women who exploit men for their own enjoyment, or who outwit a disappointing (usually elderly) husband in order to take a younger husband of their own choice.

Hundreds of early manuscripts of *Decameron* have survived, some believed to be in Boccaccio's own handwriting.

The Gardener and the Nuns

'The Third Day, the First Story'

Many people believe that once a white veil is bound around a girl's head and a black cowl placed on her back, she is no longer a woman and no longer subject to feminine appetites – as if becoming a nun had changed her into stone. This story shows the error of such beliefs.

There was once a convent famed for its exceptional piety. It housed only eight nuns and their abbess, all of whom were very young.

The convent was surrounded by a pleasant garden in which vegetables were grown for the nuns' table. However, the crusty old gardener who tended it resented the young nuns ordering him about, and also considered himself to be grossly underpaid; so he walked out of the job and returned to the village where he had grown up.

Amongst his fellow villagers, there was a strapping and handsome young labourer called Masetto. When he heard that the job of convent gardener was vacant, he thought to himself, 'What an opportunity for getting hold of some girls! Whoever's in charge will quickly see that I'm more than strong enough to do all the heavy digging. Hmm… The only problem is that the abbess might consider me too good-looking to be allowed near the nuns.' He mulled this over for a bit, then came up with a brilliant idea: 'Ha! I'll pretend that I'm a halfwit. And totally deaf for good measure, and that I can't speak. That way, she'll think I'm not capable of doing them any harm.'

Once he had settled on this plan, he changed into beggar's rags, hoisted an axe over his shoulder and, without telling anyone where he was going, walked the long road to the convent. As he arrived, the steward happened to come round the corner. Masetto composed his face into a vacant and humble expression. Then he approached the steward and used sign language to beg for food, indicating that he could chop some wood in lieu of payment. The steward, being a good Christian man, brought him some victuals, and also a pile of logs that needed cutting up. Masetto performed this task so quickly and skilfully, that the steward asked him to stay there for a few days, offering to pay him to do a number of similar tasks.

A couple of days later, the abbess saw Masetto at work. 'Who's this?' she asked the steward.

'Madam,' he replied, 'he is a simpleton, a deaf beggar who's helping me out.'

'Really?' said the abbess. 'Would he be suitable to replace that old fellow who recently left? Does he know anything about gardening?'

'I don't know,' said the steward. 'But such work doesn't need much intelligence, and I'm sure he could easily be taught to dig the soil, plant seeds and nurture them. He's certainly a strong, willing fellow; and too stupid to cause any trouble with the nuns.'

'I can see you're right on that score!' said the abbess, looking Masetto up and down with a very critical eye. 'See if you can teach him what he needs to know, and treat him kindly. Give him a pair of shoes and an old hood, and make sure he has plenty to eat.'

As they spoke, Masetto was busy sweeping up some leaves. Of course, neither of them realised he could hear what they were saying – and he kept his face completely deadpan. But he thought to himself, 'Just what I wanted! Once they let me into the garden, I'll till that vegetable patch like it's never been tilled before!'

After the abbess had gone, the steward used sign language to ask if Masetto would like to work for the convent permanently, and learn a new skill. Masetto indicated that he would be very happy to do so. So the steward instructed him in what was required.

Masetto soon settled into his new job, and worked hard. However, the young nuns did not give him the respect he deserved. For when they learned that he was deaf, they forgot all their Christian charity and took to mocking and goading him whenever they walked past the vegetable patch, calling him all kinds of derogatory names. Masetto just chuckled to himself, thinking how this was all to the advantage of his plan. The abbess tut-tutted over their rudeness, but decided to say nothing, assuming the gardener was too stupid to understand them.

One day, after a hard morning's labour in the hot sun, Masetto lay down to take a quick nap before resuming his labours. As he dozed, two young nuns wandered out of the flower garden and along the path to where he lay. One of them giggled and said, 'Can you keep a secret? Because I've got a brilliant idea.'

'Speak up,' said her friend eagerly. 'Whatever it is, you can be sure I won't tell anyone.'

'Well,' said the first nun, 'you know how men are forbidden to come inside these walls, except for the only two we ever see: the steward – who's old enough to be our great-grandfather – and this handsome but idiotic lump of meat? And you know how when ladies visit from outside, they gossip amongst themselves about how wonderful it is to go with a man?'

'Oh yes,' said her friend. 'I've heard such talk. They say nothing can beat it.'

'Exactly,' said the first nun. 'I don't know about you, but I keep wondering whether this is really true. And I've thought of a perfect way to find out – by getting together with this stupid gardener. As he never speaks, there's no danger he'll give us away and get us into trouble. What do you think?'

At first her friend was shocked. 'Surely you don't mean this?' she cried. 'But we've all promised our virginity to God!'

'So what?' said the first nun. 'Think of all the other promises we make to God all day long; none of us keep even half of them. Anyway, what's so special about *our* virginity? There are plenty of other nuns who can give theirs to God if we don't!'

'But if we do this, we might get pregnant,' her friend wailed.

'There's no point in worrying about problems unless they arise,' said the first nun. 'If the worst happens, there's bound to be a way to get round it. But listen: we must keep this totally secret.'

Her friend was silent for a long moment, considering the idea. Just thinking about it gave her a great itch to find out what sort of animal a man really was. 'All right then,' she said at last. 'How do we get started?'

'We need to check that no one else is around,' the first nun said. 'Because obviously, we mustn't be discovered. We should be fine at the moment, because the others are all having their siesta. Once we're sure the coast is clear, we'll simply shake the gardener awake, take his hand and lead him into the toolshed over there. He's so simple, he's bound to do exactly as we want. We'll take it in turns: one inside with him and the other outside keeping watch. Then we'll swap.'

They didn't realise that Masetto had heard everything they said. Oh, he was excited! He lay totally still, waiting for them to claim him.

The pair looked around the garden very carefully. There was no one in sight, and the gate was closed. So the first nun walked up to Masetto and nudged him gently with her foot. He opened his eyes slowly, as if he had been fast asleep, sat up and pretended to gaze around in bewilderment. She took his hand, helped him to his feet and led him to the toolshed. He followed her meekly as a lamb. She pulled him inside, closed the door firmly and then... Well, it didn't take much persuasion to make Masetto do exactly what she wanted!

As soon as she had finished enjoying him, the first nun went out, signalling Masetto to stay exactly where he was, and let her friend go in. Masetto was very pleased to satisfy her too.

Was that enough for the two nuns? Not at all! Before they left him, each had to test his riding abilities again – and he was very willing to oblige. At last, after her second session, the second nun emerged and left the door open for Masetto to leave when he wished.

'What did you think of that, then?' said the first nun as they walked away with big grins on their faces.

'Just as wonderful as I've heard,' said her friend.

'Or even better?'

'Yes, yes!'

After that, whenever they had an opportunity, the two nuns would take their pleasure with the gardener. He certainly didn't complain – for that was exactly what he'd hoped for when he'd sought work at the convent.

Thus things continued for some time... Until, one day, some of the other nuns saw the gardener being led to the shed, and the two friends taking turns to go in there with him. At first they were shocked and decided to report the incident to the abbess. But when they saw the two very satisfied sisters coming out of the shed with huge smiles on their faces, they thought that maybe they were missing out; so they asked if they could join in. Before long all eight nuns were making full use of Masetto's excellent services.

One hot day, the abbess herself went for a walk in the garden, seeking relief in its shady places from the blazing sun. There she came upon Masetto stretched out, fast asleep, under a spreading almond tree – literally exhausted from his endless equestrian activities. He looked so handsome there, and it was such a hot day and... Well, no need for explanations. The sight of him fired the same appetite in her that her nuns had experienced. So she gently roused the gardener and without further ado, led him up to her chamber. There she kept him for several days, constantly tasting new varieties of his endless forbidden delights, to her great enjoyment. She did not let him out even for his gardening duties. This caused much annoyance amongst the nuns, who could be heard complaining loudly about their neglected vegetables, and how the soil urgently needed watering.

Eventually, the abbess let Masetto return to his own lodgings, on condition that he answered her every summons without delay. However, what with her, and the even greater demands of the eight amorous young nuns, the gardener eventually found himself flagging and urgently in need of respite. So, one night, as he lay beside the satisfied abbess, he decided to loosen his tongue and speak to her.

'Madam,' he said, 'I've heard that one cock is sufficient for numerous hens, but I am only a man, and servicing nine of you so regularly has worn me out. I simply can't keep it up any more, so you ladies will either have to let me go, or find some other way of settling the matter.'

The abbess was astonished both to hear his voice, and to discover that she was not the only one in the convent who was making use of his services.

'But... I thought you could not speak!' she cried.

'Yes, er, well, I couldn't for a while,' stammered Masetto. 'It was...um...the result of an illness. But I'm better now, and I can hear everything and speak normally.'

'I can tell you're not as stupid as I originally thought,' said the abbess. 'Well, Masetto, I certainly don't want to let you leave! And it sounds as if all the young sisters will agree with me. Now that everything's out in the open, I think the best course is to discuss the matter with them, and work out how to preserve your talents and wellbeing. Obviously, it's vital that we keep this matter from the outside world, to preserve the convent's pious reputation.'

The abbess left Masetto to rest for a while, summoned all the nuns and ordered them to confess what they had been up to with him. At first they were all very nervous; but when the abbess revealed her own illicit activity, they laughed in relief. They agreed to spread a story outside the convent walls that Masetto's longstanding disability had been healed by their joint earnest prayers on his behalf. As their old steward had recently died, the abbess appointed Masetto to take his place, securing his position in the convent. Then they drew up a rota to share his services, and thus protect him from the strain of any unreasonable and excessive demands.

True to say, he sired a number of miniature monks and nuns during the course of his work; but this was all managed with such discretion that nobody outside the convent had any idea what was going on.

As the years went by, and Masetto grew old, he began to tire of horsemanship, so he asked permission to retire. Since the abbess and her nuns were all rapidly ageing too, this was agreed without any fuss.

Thus he returned to his home village in great contentment, having fulfilled his duty of fathering plenty of children – without any of the trouble or expense in rearing them.

An overriding ethos of *Decameron* is that men and women of all classes have strong sexual appetites, which both genders have the right to enjoy. In the world of stories, this extends right inside the walls of monasteries and convents; apparently a reflection of real medieval life, judging by ecclesiastical records of misdemeanours in holy orders from several countries, and the letters of *Abelard and Heloise* (see p.16).

Decameron contains another amusing tale about nuns' deviant behaviour ('The Ninth Day, The Second Story'). Here a nun has an illicit relationship with a young man, who she first sees through the convent grate when he accompanies a relative on a scheduled visit. He sneaks in to her regularly, but is eventually spotted by some other nuns, who rush to the abbess to report her. The abbess, however, is at that very moment in flagrante with her favourite priest, who was smuggled inside the convent concealed in a linen chest. In her haste to dress in the dark and rush to deal with this disciplinary matter, she inadvertently puts on the priest's underpants instead of her wimple. When the original culprit notices this and points it out to the sisters watching as her punishment is meted out, the abbess's own guilt is revealed to all. She concludes the matter with some heartfelt advice for the nuns: to always seize opportunities for pleasure, so long as they are discrete.

Decameron also contains some lighthearted but very callous stories about monks seizing opportunities to satisfy their illicit lusts.

The Donkey Kicks Back

It might be an inherent defect in human nature, or something we learn through perverse customs, but the fact is that we all find scandal far more entertaining than virtue. The intention of this story is to make you laugh; so although it's rather risqué, why should that stop me sharing it with you? Simply do as you would in a garden: stretch out your hands to pick the roses – and leave the thorns well alone!

In Perugia there once lived a rich man called Pietro di Vinciolo who was endlessly subjected to malicious gossip about his unconventional romantic tastes. To deflect this, he found himself a wife. It was a most unlikely match. For she was a buxom, positively glowing young woman who could happily have entertained two husbands or more at once; whereas he was not attracted to women at all.

It didn't take her long to realise that he had no interest whatsoever in her numerous charms. At first, she expressed her disappointment by constantly grumbling and arguing with him. However, eventually she realised that all this achieved was to make her exhausted. She said to herself, 'Huh! I brought a big dowry to this marriage, but I would never have accepted his proposal if I'd known then that he's not a proper man. If I'd wanted to renounce pleasure, I would have become a nun. Since he insists on trotting his clogs through sandy deserts, why shouldn't *I* find myself another passenger to ride me through the swamps? I'll still be waiting for him to act like a proper husband when I die! He's set the example of enjoying things to his own tastes, so I shall do likewise.'

Before going ahead with this, the young woman decided to consult an old crone who was highly regarded for her shrewdness and and piety. She explained her situation to the crone, and asked for advice on her proposed solution.

'Daughter,' said the crone, 'I'm sure that in God's eyes you have chosen the right path. The only alternative is to completely waste your youth. From my own experience, the worst grief in the world is to lose an opportunity. Look at me: all I'm good for these days is watching the ashes round the fire-pot and brooding on all the chances I let slip away; it's far too late for anyone to spark my fire now. It's different for men, of course: they're born to do thousands of things, as well as what we're discussing – and on that subject, most of them improve as they get older. But we women are only good for love and bearing children; and we only have limited years for doing even that. I'm sure you'll have no regrets if you pay your husband back with the same coins that he uses. We all get from life whatever we put into it.

'Moreover, my dear, I know exactly how to get round men. So just tell me which one you fancy, and I'll set you up with him. All I ask in return is that you bear in mind my poverty, and support me in my devotional processions.'

The young woman thanked her profusely and described in detail a particular young man she was very attracted to, giving the crone a good portion of salted meat as a gift. The crone sent her away with her blessing.

A few days later, when the young woman was alone at home, the crone came to visit her, bringing the very young man she had mentioned. The young woman hastily secreted him away to the bedchamber and took her enjoyment of him – which he was very willing to give. Some days later, she met the old crone again and mentioned another handsome young fellow that she had spotted; and he was soon brought to her too. Thus it went on, week by week. The young woman now felt much more content; though she lived in mortal fear of her husband discovering what she was up to.

One evening, Pietro went out to dine with his friend Ercolano. As soon as the coast was clear, the crone visited the young woman, bringing with her the very handsomest and most amiable youth in all Perugia. The young woman was thrilled! Before their sporting began, she invited the youth to sit down and eat with her. However, before they could taste a single mouthful, there came a raucous knocking at the door, followed by her husband's voice yelling, 'Open up, wife!'

The young woman feared that everything was lost. Hastily, she bustled the young man outside into the yard and shooed him into the chicken coop, which she then covered up with a pile of sacking. Then she rushed to let Pietro in, saying, 'That was a quick dinner you went to.'

'That's because I never had a single bite of it,' he replied. 'We'd just sat down to start – that's me, Ercolano and his wife – when we suddenly heard someone sneezing loudly close by, over and over again. Ercolano was already in a temper with his wife because she'd kept us waiting for our meal, so he said to her, "Who's that sneezing?" When she didn't answer, he jumped up, marched out to the storage cupboard under the stairs and opened the door. A great stink of sulphur came wafting out of it, followed by billows of smoke. "What's this about?" Ercolano demanded. "Oh, it's nothing," his wife answered. "I was just bleaching my veils in sulphur fumes before Pietro arrived, and I put the pan in the cupboard to cool down." But that didn't explain the sneezing. So when the smoke died down, Ercolano peered right into the cupboard – and saw a strange man squatting inside! If the door hadn't been opened right then, the fumes would have ensured that he never sneezed again.

'Now Ercolano understood why our dinner was delayed. You can imagine his fury: he roared at his wife with a stream of really terrible threats. When she fled, Ercolano yelled at the stranger to come out; but he couldn't move, being half-suffocated from smoke. So Ercolano hauled him out with his own hands and grabbed a knife, ready to stab the poor fellow to death. I rushed in to separate them, because I didn't want to be present at a murder. Some neighbours heard the commotion, came charging round and carried the stranger away before Ercolano could actually harm him.

'That's why I'm back so early.'

The young woman was intrigued to learn that she wasn't the only wife with a secret lover; but she also shuddered to think of the danger that such an affair could bring. She realised that, if she tried to defend Ercolano's wife, Pietro would become suspicious of *her*. So she said hastily, 'Doesn't it go to show: you can think a woman's really upright, and all the while she's cheating behind her husband's back. Shame on her! In my view, she deserves to be hurled into a fire and burned alive!'

Then she suddenly remembered her own lover, hiding in the chicken coop. She yawned pointedly and said, 'Well, after all that to-do, I'd have an early night if I were you, Pietro.'

'No,' he replied. 'I'll never be able to sleep; besides, I'm too hungry. Rustle up some dinner for me, will you?'

'Dinner?' she cried. 'Oh, I never have dinner when you're out – not like that Ercolano's wife, entertaining strangers on the sly. No, I just nibble a bit of this and that. I really think you should go to bed.'

While they were talking, some labourers who worked for Pietro had arrived to discuss business matters with him. They took their donkeys round to the yard and tethered them but did not give them any refreshment. One of the donkeys was very thirsty, and managed to break free. It wandered round the yard, looking for water. As it snuffled here and there, it stumbled against the chicken coop where the young woman's secret lover was cowering on all fours. His fingers were sticking out beyond the frame, and by a stroke of bad luck, the donkey trod on them hard. The lover gave a shriek of pain.

'What's that?' Pietro cried at once, for he was still on edge from the recent trauma at Ercolano's house. He dashed out to investigate – and quickly spotted the donkey with the lover's fingers under its hooves.

'Sir,' the youth groaned, 'I beg you: get this beast off me!'

Now, it so happened that the young man was no stranger to Pietro. In fact, he had recently been trying to get hold of him for his own amorous purposes, and thus was more than delighted to find him on his property. So he immediately pulled the donkey away and said in a very pleasant voice, 'Ho, young fellow, don't worry, you can get up now. But whatever are you doing here?'

The youth wriggled out of the coop in relief. He was in such a state of shock that he confessed exactly why he was there. Pietro was so pleased to have the desired youth in his power, that he only half listened, not caring at all about his wife's shenanigans. He took the young man by the hand and dragged him straight up to his chamber – where they found the young woman, trembling with trepidation because her secret life had been discovered.

'Well, well, well,' said Pietro, smiling at her cruelly, 'what a tirade you made against Ercolano's wife for having a secret lover – but you never mentioned that *you* are equally bad.

Women! Ugh, you're all liars who try to cover up your own faults by criticising the sins of others. May you all burn up in hellfire!'

The young woman was relieved that these malicious words were the only beating her husband saw fit to give her. She realised that he didn't care a jot about her – because his own secret life was about to get a big spur! All he had to do was persuade the handsome youth to accommodate his wishes.

So she retorted, 'Obviously, you want to see all us women burned up, since you have no use for us at all; but by God, you'll never get your wish. Meanwhile, I'd like a little chat with you. Don't you go comparing me to Ercolano's wife. She's a craw-thumping hypocrite who gets everything she wants from *her* husband – which is more than I can say for our marriage. All right, I admit you keep me in shoes and fine clothes; but I get nothing at all in the other, more important department. I can't even remember when you last lay with me – that's if you ever did at all. To be frank, I'd rather go barefoot and in rags, if it meant I could get what I wanted in bed. Listen and try to understand this, Pietro: I'm a woman and I need what other women get. If you won't give it to me, then don't complain if I go out and find it for myself. And you should…'

Pietro guessed that she would go on at him all night if he didn't distract her. Besides, he had more interesting things on his mind. So he said, 'All right, wife, that's enough. I'll give you full satisfaction on this matter in due course. But meanwhile, I beg you to bring us some food; because I'm starving and, by the looks of it, this young man is too.'

'You're right there,' said the wife, 'he hasn't eaten yet either. We were just about to dine together when you came barging in.'

'Well then,' said Pietro, 'if you fix the food, I'll fix the other matter in a way that gives you no cause for complaint.'

The young woman, glad beyond measure that her husband was so calm, immediately went and relaid the table, brought in the dinner she had prepared earlier, and shared it with her husband and the youth.

As for the after-dinner arrangements... Well, you can be sure that Pietro organised matters for the satisfaction of all three of them. Unfortunately, the exact details have completely slipped my mind! But I do remember this: the following morning, when the youth was escorted back to the public piazza, he was grinning *very* broadly.

It's certainly true what they say: any donkey that kicks the wall will get his own kicks right back.

In the late Middle Ages, the Church taught that sexual behaviour was purely for procreation, and that any acts that did not promote this were sinful, with homosexuality being regarded as one of the worst sins against this 'natural law'. Punishments for male homosexuality ranged from castration, through dismemberment to burning.

On the other hand, the beating that both wives in this story feared was considered acceptable punishment for disobedience to one's husband. However, if the woman miscarried, or was permanently maimed or died as a result of her actions, it might be regarded as criminal.

There are several stories in *Decameron* which feature domestic violence; the ethos of the book was not so much to condone it, as to portray it as an inevitable consequence of certain behaviours. Sometimes, Boccaccio even treats it as humorous; and he takes the liberty of making one of his female storytellers declare that 'the stick' is a necessary way to ensure that women behave correctly.

Surplus Love

It's always a useful skill to be a good public speaker –
especially useful in a time of dire need, as this story
will amply demonstrate.

The city of Prato used to have a very cruel law that
condemned prostitutes to death by burning; and also
ordained that any married woman caught committing an act
of adultery should be punished in the same way.

In the city there lived a very beautiful married woman
called Madonna Filippa. One night her husband, Rinaldo,
found her – in their own bedroom! – in the arms of her secret
lover, a handsome and noble youth called Lazzarino de'
Guazzagliotri. Rinaldo was so outraged that he almost
slaughtered them both on the spot. It was only his fear of
being executed for double murder that prevented him from
doing so.

Instead, first thing the next morning, he took steps to have
his wife legally killed by lodging an accusation against her
with the chief magistrate.

Madonna Filippa was immediately summonsed to appear
before the court. Her friends were horrified, and urged her
to flee.

However, Lazzarino's deep love for Madonna Filippa had
made her feel so strong that she refused to do so, declaring,
'I'm not afraid to answer the summons, admit my affair and
die bravely. It would be cowardly to run away and live in

exile as an outlaw. It would also be totally unworthy of my beloved, who chose me for my good character.'

Thus she presented herself brazenly before the magistrate, accompanied by a great throng of female and male friends. As well as her personal supporters, almost the entire city came to watch. Everyone was fascinated by this case concerning one of the best known and most admired female citizens.

The magistrate noted Madonna Filippa's dignity and confidence, and could not help but warm to her. He began to dread being obliged to condemn her to death. However, he could not avoid his duty to interrogate her.

Before he could even begin, Madonna Filippa herself opened the proceedings, demanding in a firm voice. 'Why have you summonsed me?'

'Madam,' he said, 'your husband here has lodged a complaint against you. He says that he found you committing an act of gross adultery with another man and asks that you should be executed for this crime. However, I cannot sentence you without your full confession. I thus advise you to be very careful how you answer this charge. Tell me if the crime of which your husband accuses you is true.'

Madonna Filippa was not in the least dismayed. 'Indeed sir,' she replied, 'that's my husband standing beside you, and it is absolutely true that he found me in the arms of Lazzarino – where I have often been many times before. I love Lazzarino with all my heart and I won't deny it. However, as you know, by natural justice, laws should apply to *everyone* in the same way. Well, that's certainly not the case with the law being used in this instance – for in Prato it only applies to half the population: us unfortunate women. Why should women be sentenced to death for adultery whilst men are allowed to get away with it? Not only is it unfair, but it's ludicrous! After all, women are much better physically equipped than men to keep a number of partners satisfied.'

The magistrate found himself nodding, and hastily composed his features.

Madonna Filippa spoke on: 'Besides, laws are supposed to be made with the consent of all those whom they concern, but this law was made by men. No woman was ever given the chance either to accept or decline it. Because of that, you have to agree that it is a totally evil piece of legislation. I realise it's your job to put this law into practice. But I warn you, it will not only harm me; it will also harm *your* soul.

'Before you proceed to pass judgement, I would like to request a favour. Please could you question my husband. Ask him whether or not I have fulfilled my conjugal duty to him. Ask whether I have always given myself to him as often as he wanted, and in every way that he requested.'

'Well, Rinaldo,' said the magistrate, 'what is your answer?'

'I suppose that's true, your honour,' he admitted. 'Every time I've asked for it, she's willingly let me take my pleasure of her.'

'There we are, my lord!' Madonna Filippa cried. 'He gets everything he wants and needs from me – so after fulfilling my husband's requirements, what am I supposed to do with what is left over? Should I throw it to the dogs in the street? Surely it's better to use my surplus love to gratify a gentleman who loves me more than himself – rather than just letting it spoil or waste away?'

The people gathered there to observe the trial all burst out laughing. As if with one voice, they all cried out:

'She's right!'

'She's made some very valid points!'

'You can't condemn her now!'

So the chief magistrate dismissed the case. And before the crowd dispersed, he also announced that he would change the cruel law she had challenged. From that day, it only applied to women who betrayed their husbands by whoring themselves in return for money.

Thus Rinaldo gained nothing from this legal action except embarrassment and shame. He slunk out of the court very quietly.

Madonna Filippa, on the other hand, returned in triumph to the house that she shared with him – joyful, free and, as one might say, raised from the fire to a new life.

A number of prominent women are known to have been executed for adultery in medieval Europe; and a wife's adultery was also one of the few reasons that permitted a man to divorce her.

According to ecclesiastical law, adulterous wives and husbands should be treated in exactly the same way: both were forbidden to indulge in extramarital sex. But, in reality, unfaithful husbands were often allowed to get away with their affairs, whilst wives had to either suffer in silence, or see their complaints ignored by the courts. Although murder of an unfaithful wife was not officially condoned, a husband who did so might get away with it.

Madonna Filippa's assertion that all should be equal before the law was based on a principle of Roman law still current in 14th century Italy: 'What effects everyone must be approved by everyone.'

The Price of Lust

'The Eighth Day, the Tenth Story'

In Palermo, as in other maritime cities, merchants usually unload their cargo into a customs warehouse maintained by the local lord or government. They give the officer in charge a written inventory of all their goods, stating their value. The officer then allocates a storeroom in which the merchandise is deposited under lock and key. Later, as the goods are sold, the officer collects the appropriate fees. Brokers can see from the register all the goods held in bond there, what they are worth and who they belong to, thus facilitating trade deals.

There used to be some very beautiful Palermo women who posed as honourable and virtuous to strangers, when in reality they were the exact opposite. In their dealings with men, to put it bluntly, they delighted in completely flaying them. Whenever new merchants arrived in Palermo, these ladies would hurry to examine the customs register. If the value of their goods was high enough, they would use charming wiles and honeyed words to lure the newcomers into their snares. These snares were baited with lust and supposed love, with the sole purpose of extracting as much wealth from their victims as possible. So sweetly did these she-barbers ply their razors, that many merchants lost everything to them: their goods, their ships – and sometimes their very flesh and bones.

One day, a young merchant of Florence called Salabaetto arrived in Palermo. His master had entrusted him with a large consignment of fine woollen cloth to sell, worth some five hundred gold florins. He filled in the customs papers, put the goods in the allocated storeroom, then went out to explore the city.

Salabaetto was fair complexioned, blond haired and handsome, very spirited and personable; but also rather naive. He was quickly spotted by one of the she-barbers, a lady who called herself Madam Biancofiore. She found out his name, then hurried to check the customs register for the value of his goods. She was well satisfied by what she read, and began following him down the street.

Salabaetto noticed this, and was both flattered and excited, for her fine clothes and confidence indicated that she was a very great lady. How wonderful it would be to have a love affair with someone like her! He watched her ostentatiously turn into her house, and the next day he made sure to walk past it again. He was rewarded by the sight of her looking out for him. For several days, he strolled past the house and she either gazed out from her window or followed him at a distance, always kindling him with her eyes.

Madam Biancofiore's maids were well schooled in the arts of allurement and other tricks of her trade. When she was certain she had Salabaetto under her spell, she sent one of these maids to tell him frankly that her mistress was besotted with him.

'She asks if you might agree to a private meeting,' the maid said. Without waiting for an answer, she pulled a ring from her purse and gave it to Salabaetto saying, 'She asked me to give you this, as a token of her feelings.'

Salabaetto could scarcely believe his luck. He snatched the ring, kissed it ardently, then set it firmly upon his finger. 'Please hurry back to Madam Biancofiore,' he cried breathlessly. 'Tell her that I reciprocate her love – and will be delighted to meet her wherever she wishes, at whatever time she names.'

'Wait here,' said the maid. She scurried off and soon returned, telling Salabaetto to meet her mistress at a bathing house away from the main part of town, immediately after vespers the following day.

Salabaetto told no one about this liaison. The next evening he arrived excitedly at the said bathing house, and found that Madam Biancofiore had reserved the entire building for her sole use. She was not yet there, but as he hovered in the outer lobby, two slave girls arrived, bearing piles of equipment on their heads. They were shown to an inner room. Through an open door he saw them lay out a fine, wide mattress filled with fluffy cotton wool. They spread this with a pair of silken sheets trimmed with exquisite lace, a snow-white counterpane and two beautifully embroidered pillows. Then, ignoring Salabaetto's stare, they stripped off their clothes and stepped through an archway to the bath, which they carefully swept, washed clean and filled with water.

Soon after that, Madam Biancofiore herself bustled in, flanked by two other slave girls. She greeted Salabaetto warmly, embracing and kissing him with heavy sighs. 'You gorgeous man,' she exclaimed, 'you've set me on fire!'

She told him to undress, and did likewise. Then she led him into the bath, accompanied by two of the slave girls. She did not let them touch Salabaetto, but with her own hands washed him carefully and lovingly from top to toe, with musk and clove-scented soap. Then she let the slave girls wash her. As soon as they were finished, the other slaves came to the edge of the bath, each holding out an enormous white linen towel smelling of roses. They wrapped

Salabaetto in one towel and the lady in the other. Then they carried them both to the bed, released them from the towels, laid them between the silken sheets and sprinkled them with rose, jasmine, orange and citron-flower perfume from gleaming silver bottles.

Next, they produced a basket containing flasks of wine and many delicious titbits. Madam Biancofiore ate these with relish. However, Salabaetto was too excited to swallow anything – for he felt as if he had somehow arrived in Paradise! He could not stop gazing at Madam Biancofiore; every moment that he waited to be alone with her seemed to him like a hundred years.

At long last, the lady signalled the slave girls to go, leaving one torch to softly light the chamber. As soon as they were alone, she turned to Salabaetto with a seductive smile and embraced him. Thus they spent the night together, with Salabaetto enjoying pleasures far beyond anything he had ever known, or even imagined, before.

When dawn broke outside, Madam Biancofiore said it was time to rise. She summoned the slave girls, who helped them both dress, and offered more refreshments. This time, Salabaetto ate and drank hungrily. All too soon, it was time to depart. With a heavy heart, he gave his lover a farewell kiss. But as he turned away, she put her hand on his arm and murmured, 'Dearest, may I ask you a favour? Might you be willing to come to my own house this evening to share a meal, then spend another night with me?'

He took these words, and the look in her dark eyes, as a sign that his own feelings were more than reciprocated. 'Madam,' he cried, 'it gives me great joy to meet your every desire. Both tonight and at all times, I will gladly do whatever you command.'

Thus they parted.

The lady returned to her house, where she had her maids and slaves decorate her bedchamber and prepare a mouthwatering meal. At sunset, Salabaetto hurried there, and Madam Biancofiore welcomed him with open arms. They shared the meal as if it were a celebration, and afterwards withdrew into the bedchamber together.

For a brief, disconcerting moment, a memory flashed in Salabaetto's mind of a warning he had once heard in the city taverns, about apparently glamorous ladies who exploited gullible men. However, the sight of her rich furnishings reassured him beyond doubt that she was far too wealthy to ever stoop to such sharp practice. 'Thank goodness Madam Biancofiore took me in before any of those unsavoury types could sink their claws into me!' he thought happily. That evening, their shared pleasures reached new, indescribable heights.

The next morning, she buckled a silver belt around his waist, with a fine purse attached. 'Salabaetto,' she said, 'everything I have, is now yours as well. As for myself...' she smiled lasciviously, 'I am totally at your service.'

He kissed her once more, then reluctantly bid her goodbye – though only for a very short while.

For after that, he saw her almost every night. Not only did she give him everything that he wanted, and more, in terms of her body, but she also shared her possessions, so that Salabaetto spent none of his own meagre resources. No wonder he felt himself the happiest man alive! He was totally entangled with his lady and could not now imagine life without her.

In due course, Salabaetto sold the woollen cloth he had brought to Palermo for an excellent profit. He did not mention this to Madam Biancofiore, wishing to avoid anything changing between them. Nevertheless, she soon heard about it, for the city streets were always abuzz with gossip.

One night, when Salabaetto came to stay with her, she started chattering and teasing him until he felt he would go mad with delight. Then she offered to give him a pair of beautiful silver goblets as a gift, but he declined them, saying, 'No, my love, it is too much! You have already given me so much – and these must be worth at least thirty florins! I can't accept another groat's worth from you.' She laughed and began caressing him again working him up into a state of ecstasy even greater than before.

Just at that moment, they were interrupted by a knock at the door. From behind it one of the maids called out, 'Madam, forgive me for disturbing you, but you must come quickly!'

Now, unbeknown to Salabaetto, Madam Biancofiore had instructed the maid to do this before he had arrived that evening. She dressed quickly and rushed out, closing the door behind her. She came back shortly afterwards, her lovely face stained with tears. She threw herself onto the bed and fell to sobbing and lamenting grievously. Salabaetto took her gently in his arms and cried, 'Whatever is the matter, my love, my soul? Tell me what it is, and I will do whatever is needed to help you.'

She sobbed for a while longer, then sat up, delicately dabbing her eyes. 'Thank you, my darling, but I do not think you can help me. For I have just received a letter from my brother in Messina, begging me to send him a thousand florins within eight days. If I don't, he will be beheaded! Eight days is not nearly long enough: I will need at least double that time to call in some outstanding debts and sell off one of the farms I own. And then it would take the same time again to collect the money and send it to him. It's impossible! Oh, I would rather die myself than see my beloved brother face such a sorry end!'

Consumed as he was by the flames of love and lust, burnt by them almost to a cinder, Salabaetto was no longer in possession of any common sense or caution. He dried her eyes with his own shirt and said gently, 'My dear, I am so sorry; I cannot raise a thousand florins within the time needed. But it so happens that only yesterday I sold my consignment of cloth for five hundred florins, so I can easily lend you that much to save your brother. You can repay me once you've called in your debts and sold the assets that you just mentioned. I urge you to accept.'

Her answer was not at all what he expected. 'Dear me!' she exclaimed. 'I had no idea that you were short of money until you made your sale yesterday. You should have mentioned it to me: I would gladly have lent you a few florins whenever you needed them. Since you were too proud to seek any help from me, I certainly can't accept your help now.'

'But that's ridiculous,' Salabaetto retorted. 'I was never in need as much as your brother is. You *must* accept my offer.'

'Oh, Salabaetto,' she said, 'your generosity shows how deeply you love me. Even before this, I was entirely yours – but now I shall be so even more! I'll never forget that I owe my brother's life to you. But I'm taking your money very unwillingly, especially as you depend on it for your business transactions. I'll only accept it because of this dire situation, and also because I can guarantee to repay you very soon. For the rest of what's needed to save my brother, I'll pawn some of my possessions.'

She fell weeping on his neck. Naturally, he did his best to comfort her; and naturally, this comfort soon took another form, so that for a while they forgot the crisis in the sweet mists of unbridled pleasure. After he left her the next morning, he very soon hurried back, pressing into her hands his entire earnings from the sale of his cloth – the full five hundred florins. He insisted that he did not need to write out a bill stating what she owed him, for in his naive passion, he trusted her completely.

Madam Biancofiore accepted the money tearfully; but in her heart – oh, how she laughed!

After that fateful day, things began to change between them. Previously, he had been able to see her whenever and as often as he wanted; but now there were suddenly all kinds of unforeseen circumstances that kept getting in the way. At first, each excuse seemed genuine. But, after a while, he realised that he was only able to make love to her on perhaps one out of every seven occasions that he proposed. And even when they did lie together, her manner had become cold and distant.

The deadline for her repayment passed. She did not offer it, and he did not like to ask for it. A month passed, then two months. He plucked up courage to request the outstanding money, but received only excuses. Even worse, it was plain that her love for him had died.

Now at last, his eyes were opened and he saw Madam Biancofiore for what she really was: a callous trickster. 'What a total fool I've been!' he thought. 'And I have no legal means to obtain repayment, for there's nothing in writing: just my word that I lent the money to her, and her word that she would pay it back; and she is bound to deny both.' If only he had heeded those tavern warnings! He was too ashamed to confide in anyone about his folly, realising it would only bring him mockery.

In the midst of his despondency, he now received a letter from his master, asking him to forward the money from the sale of the cloth entrusted to him. Unless he sent it forthwith, he would surely be indicted for misappropriation. So, instead of returning to Florence, where his company was based, Salabaetto fled on a small ship bound for Naples.

In that city there dwelt a man called Pietro dello Canigiano, who was not only a long-standing close friend of Salabaetto's family, but also a former treasurer to the Empress of Constantinople. He was a wise and compassionate man. Salabaetto went to him in despair and confessed the full extent of his reckless behaviour, asking for advice. He was too afraid to return to Florence, but wondered if he might be able to start afresh by finding work in Naples.

Pietro scolded him severely, which was what Salabaetto knew he deserved. But then the older man said shrewdly, 'What's done is done; the important thing is to move forward.'

He lent Salabaetto a little money. With this, Salabaetto loaded a ship with sealed oil casks and locked crates, and sailed back to Palermo. There he took them to the customs house and completed the required documents, showing the value of the goods they contained as two thousand florins. After he had stored them in his allocated store, he announced that he would leave them there until another consignment arrived for him, which would be worth *three* thousand florins. Then he went into the city, talking freely about his latest dealings.

News of this soon reached Madam Biancofiore. 'Hmm,' she thought, 'I would never have been satisfied with a mere five hundred florins from him if I'd realised he'd soon be dealing in much larger fish! I'd best pay back what I already owe him, so I can work him for a share of this five thousand that he's now controlling.'

She sent her maid to Salabaetto with the following message: 'Madam Biancofiore asks me to say how much she's missed you. She apologises with all her heart for her recent coolness towards you, and begs your forgiveness.'

Salabaetto was now her equal in cunning. He pretended to accept her apology and hurried to her house, making out that he was still as naive as ever.

She fell into his arms, sighing with pleasure. 'Can you forgive me?' she asked, smirking to herself as she buried her face in his chest. 'I only avoided you out of shame, because I found myself unable to repay your generous loan. I was too agitated to tell you or even to see you. You can't imagine how hard it is for a woman to get hold of money: people made empty promises to me, then let me down one after another. But...'

'Hush, hush,' he soothed her. 'I would tear out my own heart for you and not ask for it back, just to please you. Now listen. I have sold most of my possessions and used the money to buy some very costly goods, with more on the way – they're worth five thousand gold florins altogether! I'm going to move permanently here to Palermo to sell them – so I shall always be near you.'

'How wonderful!' exclaimed Madam Biancofiore. 'Now we can look forward to endless happy nights together. But you didn't let me finish. Shortly after you vanished, I *did* manage to get hold of what I owed you, thanks to a particular moneylender. But since you left no message saying where you had gone, I couldn't send it to you. However, it's not too late, my darling. Just wait a moment.'

She sent her maid to fetch the purse in which she had hoarded away the original five hundred florins that he had lent her, and thrust it into Salabaetto's hands. 'Count it,' she said. 'Check it contains the full amount I owe you. Then take it back, for this money is yours.'

Salabaetto made a big show of counting the coins, then put the purse away on his belt. 'Madam,' he said, 'thank you for telling me the truth. I wish to make a promise to you. Once I am properly established here in Palermo, if ever again you find yourself in need, what I have is yours.'

Thus both had now deceived the other, each secretly relishing their own planned swindle. Soon they were again enjoying their old sport together, finding their pleasure sharpened to even greater intensity by the whetstone of treachery.

They arranged their next liaison for a few days' time. This gave Salabaetto plenty of leisure to plot his tactics. On the agreed day, he arrived at his lover's house in great distress. She kissed him deeply and, when he did not respond in kind, she stood back and asked, 'Whatever's wrong?'

'I'm ruined,' he groaned. 'The ship I was expecting has been seized by pirates off the coast of Monaco! They're holding it to ransom for the full three thousand florins that its cargo is worth. I've got nothing to pay them with at all.'

'What about the five hundred florins I returned to you the other day?' asked Madam Biancofiore.

'I've just sent the entire amount to Naples,' he replied, 'as part payment for the very goods that the pirates have now seized. And it's no use trying to raise funds from what I've already got stored in the customs house, because now is a terrible time for selling: I wouldn't get even half their true value. I can't think of any solution; if I don't pay the ransom by tomorrow, I'll lose the entire cargo!'

'Oh dear, oh dear,' said Madam Biancofiore. 'How I wish I could help you... Let me think... There's the money lender I use of course, but he demands a solid pledge as security... Well, because I love you, I'm willing to pledge *myself* and all my possessions to him; but he also demands thirty per cent interest on any loans, and that's too much for either of us.'

Salabaetto knew full well that she was only offering to help because she feared losing the fortune that she hoped to milk from him. He also realised that the greedy money lender she spoke of did not really exist, for she had simply kept the five hundred she had just repaid him hidden in her own coffers. Working hard to maintain his air of worry, he said, 'Thank you, my dear. My goods in the customs house can be used as security for this loan. Tell me who the money lender is, and I'll get them all transferred into his name at once. But I need to keep the storeroom key myself, to display the goods to potential buyers in the meantime, and to ensure that no one tampers with them.'

'That sounds an excellent way forward,' said Madam Biancofiore. 'Go back to your lodgings to rest, my darling, while I arrange it all.'

As soon as Salabaetto left her, Madam Biancofiore summoned a broker who was as devious as she was. Handing over three thousand gold florins from her own coffers, she told him to pretend they were *his* funds, and gave him the address of Salabaetto's lodgings. There the broker conducted dubiously brief negotiations with Salabaetto, who transferred all his goods at the customs house into the broker's name. After they had both signed the relevant documents, the broker gave Salabaetto the lady's three thousand florins, to pay off the Monaco pirates – who of course did not really exist.

Thus, Salabaetto was now in possession of three thousand, five hundred florins in all. With this, he immediately boarded a ship to Florence. When he arrived, he went at once to the office of the master who had sent him to Palermo with the original consignment, and confessed everything that had happened. He repaid his master the full amount that he owed him – which still left him with three thousand gold florins to keep.

You can imagine how he made merry with it, and what entertainment he provided in the city taverns, recounting how he had outwitted the lady trickster who had tried to bleed him dry.

Meanwhile, back in Palermo, Madam Biancofiore was annoyed to discover that Salabaetto had absconded again. She waited patiently, constantly anticipating his return; but he never came back. At last, she decided to seize the items he had transferred to the broker as security. Since Salabaetto had taken the key, she had to get some men to force the door. Once she was inside, she ran to the shelves to gloat over the expensive goods, which were now hers to sell. First she went to the casks, which he had confided were full of the finest-quality olive oil. But when she broke them open, she found to her dismay that they were all filled to the brim with only seawater! As for the crates that were supposedly full of cloth, they actually contained mouldering straw.

So it was that, in this venture, the cunning she-barber gained nothing for her efforts except loss and widespread scorn.

In the 14th century, the city of Palermo was part of the Kingdom of Sicily.

Florins were gold coins, originally from Florence, which in the 14th century was one of Europe's main financial centres. They were minted from the mid-13th to early 16th centuries. Similar coins were also used in numerous other European states, and florins were used in international trade as far away as the Middle East and North Africa. The medieval purchasing power of a florin is difficult to establish; one rough estimate claims that in today's terms a single florin might be worth anything between £100 – £750.

A Muddle of Beds

Praiseworthy friends, I would like to tell you a story of how a good woman's ready wit prevented a terrible scandal before it even began.

In the plain of Mugnone, there once lived a man who hosted a small café for passing travellers. Sometimes he would also provide overnight lodgings, but only for people he already knew; for his house was rather small. His wife was a goodly woman. They had a very pretty sixteen-year-old daughter called Niccolosa, and also a baby son.

A young gentleman from Florence called Pinuccio often passed their house, and was very taken with Niccolosa. In fact, he had already made a declaration to the girl, who was most flattered to have caught the attention of such a sophisticated and pleasant youth. The attraction was mutual, so whenever he was around they would spend as much time as they could talking together. In truth, both were very eager to fulfil their desire; but there was never a suitable opportunity.

Pinuccio, being a lusty young man in his prime, grew ever more desperate to find some way of being alone with the girl. After endless thought, he decided the solution was somehow to contrive a way of spending a night in her house. He was aware that her father's café only contained two rooms. 'But surely if I spend the night there,' he thought, 'I should be able to make love to her while her parents are fast asleep.' He asked his trusted friend Adriano to help him put this plan into action.

Late one afternoon, the pair hired horses, filled the saddlebags with worthless straw, and set out on the road from Florence to Mugnone. When no one else was around to see them, they diverted, went in circles and switched directions, until it appeared that they were now on their way back from Romagna. As darkness fell, they knocked loudly on the café door until the host opened up.

'Good evening, sir,' said Pinuccio very politely. 'We're sorry to trouble you at such a late hour. We're on our way home to Florence, but we've been delayed on the way. With all the armed robbers around these days, we think it's unwise to travel on through the night. We were wondering if it might be possible to sleep on your floor, just until dawn.'

'Well, hello Pinuccio,' beamed the host, 'it's always good to see you and your friends. Hmm, let me see… You know I'm a very humble man, so I can't offer you luxurious lodgings suitable to your breeding. But you're very welcome to stay here, and you don't need to sleep on the floor. Put your horses in the yard round the back, then come in, come in!'

The youths settled their horses and took up the invitation. They had brought a picnic, which they ate discretely at the host's table, so as not to deprive the family of their own simple meal. When they had all finished, the wife showed them the cramped family bedroom.

There were three beds in the room, with scarcely any space to pass between them. The wife bustled in and made up the largest bed, telling the two youths that was the best she could offer, if they wouldn't mind sharing it. They both lay down on it, and with many nudges and muffled guffaws, soon started to snore – although in fact, they were both wide awake.

Hearing their snores, the host said to his daughter, 'Now you must turn in, my girl. Take one of the empty beds; your mother and will I share the third one.' Soon they were all snug and settled, with the baby's cradle squashed in beside the mother.

Pinuccio lay very still, listening intently, until it seemed to him that all the family was fast asleep. Very softly, he rose, tiptoed across to Niccolosa's bed and snuggled into it beside her. Was she alarmed, or delighted? Well, when he silently initiated the pleasure that both had so long yearned for, she certainly didn't resist!

Afterwards, as they lay entangled in each others' arms, a cat stalked into the other room and knocked over a pot with a loud crash. The wife, being a light sleeper on account of the baby, woke up with a start at the noise. 'What's that?' she wondered. 'I'd better go and investigate.' Even though she always slept stark naked, she wasn't worried about their young visitors seeing her, because it was pitch dark; besides, she was sure they were both lost to the world after their long journey.

Just after that, Adriano also awoke, in his case to an urgent call of nature, so he also got up. Feeling his way to the door in the unfamiliar room, he knocked against the cradle. As it stood right next to the wife's side of her bed, there was no space to pass it, so he moved it to his own bedside, intending to replace it when he returned. But by the time he had relieved himself, he had forgotten all about it, so he got sleepily back under the covers – leaving the cradle exactly where it was.

Meanwhile, the wife shooed the cat outside and went back into the bedroom, groping her way to the bed where her husband lay. She got in and reached out to check the baby; but since it had been moved, her fingers met empty air. 'Wooh, that was a close thing!' she thought to herself. 'This must be the bed where the two youths are sleeping – and to think that I almost got into it!'

She turned, felt her way through the dark and soon located the cradle beside the bed where Adriano was lying – with the other side vacant, on account of Pinuccio having moved to Niccolosa's bed. 'Here's the right one,' she thought. And she got under the covers beside Adriano – assuming he was her husband. Adriano was wide awake and grinned to himself. He gave her a big welcome and soon hoisted his topsail! – to the great satisfaction of the unwitting wife.

Now that Pinuccio had satisfied his desire, he began to worry that he would be caught out by his girlfriend's parents. So he hastily crept back to the bed he had been sharing with Adriano. But he couldn't get into it, for the cradle was now blocking the way. 'Whoops,' he thought, 'this is the wife's place.' He backed away, and groped through the dark to a bed that was loud with masculine snores. 'Ah, here's Adriano,' he thought, and got under the covers – not realising that he was now in bed with the host.

This disturbance made the host wake up and turn over.

'Ah, so you're awake, are you?' whispered Pinuccio. 'Guess what? I've done it! I've had my way with her! I can tell you for sure, Niccolosa is the sweetest girl who ever lived, and I've had the rarest sport that any man could ever hope for. I've been into the countryside more than six times with her tonight!'

The host was shocked to hear such lewd talk about his own daughter. 'What the hell's this lad been up to?' he wondered. 'And what's he doing in *my* bed?' He was so furious, that he didn't stop to consider what would be the wisest way to deal with this outrageous situation. Instead, he hissed at him: 'Pinuccio, how dare you abuse my hospitality by violating my daughter! By Christ's body, I'll get my revenge!'

Pinuccio was cockier than ever after his triumph. Even though he now realised his error, he did not attempt to retrieve the situation. Instead, he retorted, 'Oh yes? And how will you do that?'

Across the room, the wife – in bed with Adriano, who she believed to be her husband – heard their raised voices. She nudged Adriano and whispered, 'Listen to our guests across there. They've got a cheek, squabbling so loudly – they've woken me up.'

Adriano had more wit than his friend, and played along with her. 'No doubt they're just drunk,' he laughed. 'I'd leave them to get on with it.'

The wife realised that the voice of the man lying beside her was not her husband's – and recalled with horror what she had recently done with this young man! But she was a very wise woman.

Without a word, she got up, carried the cradle through the dark to the side of the bed where her daughter lay, put it down there and got into bed beside the girl. Then she called out across the room: 'Husband, you disturbed me so much with your snoring that I had to move to Niccolosa's bed – and now you've started shouting. Whatever's going on? What are you and Pinuccio arguing about?'

'It's because he says he's had his way with Niccolosa tonight!' the host roared.

'Oh, I heard him twittering away at some nonsense of that kind,' said the wife. 'You old fool, you know what young men are like, bragging about imaginary conquests. He's lying through his teeth! He couldn't possibly have been in Niccolosa's bed – because *I've* been lying in it next to her all night; and I haven't been able to sleep a wink. You men are all as bad as each other: you drink all evening, then spend the night disturbed by crazy dreams, and sleepwalking, and imagining impossible things. It's a shame you don't break your necks in the process! Anyway, why is Pinuccio lying next to you?'

Meanwhile, Adriano was full of admiration for how cunningly the wife had covered up not only her own shame with him, but also her daughter's with Pinuccio. To join in the fun, he yelled, 'Pinuccio, I've told you a thousand times or more: stop talking about your stupid dreams as if they really happened. I warned you that you'd end up in trouble. Come back here at once!'

When the host heard not only what his wife said, but Adriano too, he became convinced that Pinuccio had indeed been talking unconsciously about a fantasy he'd enjoyed in his sleep, rather than something that had really happened. So he gave the young man a hard shake and bellowed into his ear, 'Go back to your own bed!'

Of course, Pinuccio had heard the whole conversation and realised how both his friend and the good woman had saved his skin. To play along with it, he started raving aloud, as if he were now having a nightmare. This made the host laugh heartily as he continued to shake the young gentleman. At last, Pinuccio pretended that he had finally been woken; he sat up, looking bewildered, and said thickly, 'Did you call me, Adriano?'

'Yes I did,' said Adriano. 'Come over here.'

Pinuccio rubbed his eyes sleepily, slowly swung his legs onto the floor and stumbled over to his friend's bed. There the two young men lay quietly side by side until the new day dawned, then they dressed and went outside to fetch their horses. As they came round to the door to say goodbye to the host and his wife, the host burst out laughing and slapped his knees with merriment. 'Oh, Pinuccio,' he chuckled, 'you should have heard yourself babbling in your dreams last night, you young fool! It was so... No, I'm certainly not repeating what you said to me, I don't want to embarrass you.'

Pinuccio simply shook his head and grinned. The two young gentlemen rode back to Florence, both feeling very satisfied with how they had spent the night, and how the good woman had saved them both from trouble. Niccolosa was able to assure her mother that, from her point of view, nothing untoward had happened. Her mother, who very clearly remembered enjoying Adriano sharing her bed, assumed that she and he were the only two who had actually been awake through the night.

Well then, what of Pinuccio and Niccolosa? I am pleased to tell you that, in the months that followed, they found plenty more occasions to enjoy their love.

A very similar story appears in Chaucer's *Canterbury Tales* (see p.322), under the title of 'The Reeve's Tale', only there it has rather a nasty twist: the two youths take advantage of the shared bedroom situation to avenge themselves against an arrogant and dishonest miller.

The King's Appetite

'The Tenth Day, the Sixth Story'

Illustrious ladies, you must have heard of King Charles the Old? A hundred years have now passed since he overcame the Ghibelline faction and thus briefly restored the Guelphs to rule Florence.

At that time, there lived a Ghibelline gentleman called Messer Neri degli Uberti. Since his side was now considered hostile, he fled the city with his entire household and bought an estate in a quiet part of the countryside, surrounded by olive, walnut and chestnut trees. There he built a fine, comfortable house, and planned to peacefully live out his days there. He also laid out a delightful garden, arranged round a central pond filled with brightly coloured fish.

The garden soon became famed for its flowers, shady paths and, most of all, for its unusual fishpond. Eventually, news of it reached King Charles himself who, being in need of some respite, travelled out into the countryside to visit it. The king was aware that Messer Neri had formerly been on the enemy side and did not wish to alarm or embarrass him, so he made his visit very informal. He waited until he had arrived in the area, then sent Messer Neri a message, asking if he could view the garden later that very day. He said he would arrive incognito, with four companions.

Messer Neri was taken aback by this sudden intrusion. However, he knew it was in his best interest to give King Charles a hearty welcome, and thus immediately set his servants to work in preparation.

On the king's arrival, Messer Neri gave him a grand tour of the garden, then pressed him and his retinue to stay for a meal. The king accepted graciously. Water was brought for them to wash, then they sat at his host's table beside the glimmering fishpond, alongside a choice of expensive wines. The king complimented Messer Neri on his hospitality.

While they were sipping the wine and enjoying the soft breezes, two girls came into the garden. One carried a pair of small fishing nets and a long pole over her shoulder; while her companion brought a frying pan, a faggot of wood, a trivet, a flask of oil and a lighted torch. They were both about fifteen years of age, with angelic faces and hair like threads of gold curled into ringlets. They wore soft flowing robes of snow-white linen, and necklaces of vivid blue periwinkle flowers. The king was bewitched by them. He waited on tenterhooks to find out what they were doing.

When the girls saw the king watching them, they blushed and curtseyed. Then they went to the banks of the fishpond, carefully put down the items they were carrying and waded into the water well above their waists. Meanwhile, a servant lit a fire under the trivet, set the pan on it, filled it with oil and left it to heat up.

In the pond, one girl used her pole to coax the fish from their hiding places, and the other deftly caught them in the nets. The king's eyes were glued to them; he was enthralled. The girls took some of the fish to the servant, who cooked them in the frying pan. Then they began to whisper, giggle, and nudge each other. Mischievously, they tossed the remaining fish ashore, so that they landed on the table, right in front of the king. The fish wriggled about there, gasping for air, their rainbow colours shimmering and sparkling in the dappled sunlight. The king roared with laughter and tried to catch hold of them; but they slithered about deliciously in his bare hands. At last he succeeded in tossing the fish back to the girls – who at once threw them back to the king in a convulsion of merriment.

'Whoah, steady on!' the king exclaimed. 'This is surely the best game I have ever played in my life!' But secretly he thought that the game itself was nothing compared with his two exquisitely charming playmates.

Once the fish were cooked, they were served as an appetiser. Then the servants brought out a stream of far more splendid dishes. While the men were eating, the girls came out of the water, apparently unaware of how their soaking dresses clung revealingly to their delicate bodies. They walked quietly past the table and into the house.

'Goodness,' said the king to his men, 'have you ever in all your lives seen such pretty and graceful young women?'

All agreed that the girls were exceptional, then tucked into their meal. But the king himself was so taken with the girls that he could scarcely eat. If someone had stuck a pin into him at that moment, he would have been too distracted to feel it – for desire had awakened his heart and stirred his body to a fevered frenzy. 'I must possess them,' he thought. 'Not just one of them, but both.'

So he turned to Messer Neri and said, 'Tell me, good sir, who are those angelic beauties who caught the fish?'

'Oh, they're my twin daughters,' the gentleman answered. 'Ginevra the Fair and Isotta of the Golden Hair.'

'You are the luckiest of men!' the king cried. 'No doubt you have already found them both the best husbands in the land?'

'I wish I could,' said Messer Neri with a sigh. 'But since I lost so much in the war, I'm afraid I don't have the resources to give them decent dowries.'

The king picked at the rest of the meal absent-mindedly, unable to stop thinking about his host's twin daughters. How he wished he could see them again!

When everything had been eaten apart from the final course, his wish was granted, for the two girls came back out to the garden, now wearing modest silk gowns. Each carried a large silver platter laden with the best seasonal fruits, which they set down on the table right in front of the king. At last he peeled his eyes away from them and chose some fruit to eat. Then the maidens drew away, stood side by side and shyly began to sing an aria. Their voices were so sweet and melodious that the king put down the remains of his fruit and his mouth dropped open. Not only were they ravishingly beautiful, but their song made him feel as though all the angels in heaven were serenading him.

All too soon for the king, the performance was finished. The girls knelt before him, saying, 'My lord, may we have your permission to leave?'

The king secretly could not bear for them to go, but he kept these thoughts to himself and said with forced cheerfulness, 'Of course, my dears. Good night.'

At their departure, the whole dinner was concluded. The king thanked Messer Neri for his hospitality and rode with his men back to their lodgings for the night. He said nothing to anyone about his feelings for Ginevra the Fair and Isotta of the Golden Hair. That night, he lay awake entangled so tightly in the snares of desire for them both, that it became an all-consuming obsession.

He stayed in the area for much longer than he had planned, regularly revisiting the garden. Every glimpse of the gentleman's daughters only fired his ardour even more. Finally, he could contain himself no more, and confessed his longing to Messer Neri, saying, 'I wish to take both your daughters away with me.'

Messer Neri had long been suspicious of the king's excessive interest in his garden, so he was not surprised. But nor was he was happy, for it would do his daughters no good to become the king's secret concubines. On the other hand, to offend the king would bring trouble to them all.

So he thought for a long moment, then answered carefully, 'My lord, I am amazed at what you tell me. I could well understand how my beautiful girls could inflict a *youth* with such desperate desire – but you are rapidly approaching old age. It is not my place to criticise you, and I beg you to forgive me for even expressing an opinion. But please listen to what I say and consider it.

'Sir, you have only just conquered this realm. Your hold on it is so fragile that I see you still feel obliged to carry arms wherever you go. You are obviously aware that if you alienate the people here, they may turn to resistance and treason. You well know that one reason for your popular support was your promise to end your predecessor's violence towards women. Yet now you have the hypocrisy to try and force your own lecherous desires onto my young daughters! I advise you to forget such thoughts. Instead, go home and concentrate on the matters of state you have neglected during your protracted visits to my garden.'

The king said nothing.

'Besides,' Messer Neri went on, 'I feel grossly insulted by your request. I have gone to efforts far beyond my reduced means to repeatedly host you here; yet in return you intend to snatch away what I love most in all the world. Clearly I misjudged the kind of man you are. I had believed you to be an honourable king; I would never have let my daughters walk before you in such light clothing on that hot day if I had suspected your carnal thoughts.

'Please don't excuse yourself by pointing out that I was formerly on your enemies' side; that's a cowardly way to mete out justice. If you betray those who put faith in you, it is not only a stain on your excellent reputation, it is also a gross sin that may bring you eternal punishment. Instead of lording it over your newly conquered subjects, you would do far better to try and conquer your own lewd appetite.'

These words stung King Charles' conscience to the quick, for he knew that they were true.

'You are right,' he said. 'It is easy for a well-trained warrior to overcome his enemy; but to overcome his own appetites is far more challenging. Your sage words have stirred me to find the strength to do so.'

Then King Charles bid Messer Neri farewell for the last time and returned to his other realm in Naples. The first thing he did there was seek out suitable husbands for Messer Neri's daughters. He forced himself to do this, even though he still ached to take possession of them both for himself. He conducted his quest and his negotiations with as much zeal as if they had been his own daughters, singing their praises far and wide, and offering huge dowries to the best young men he could find. Thus he matched each of them to an exceedingly noble baron-knight.

By the time he had done this, King Charles was in extreme distress. So he went away in solitude and engaged in labours so long, harsh and extreme that they completely mortified the agony of his lust. After that, he remained totally free of unchaste yearnings for the rest of his life.

King Charles the Old, or King Charles I of Anjou in France (c.1226 –1285) briefly ruled a great Mediterranean empire. Despite this story, records show that Charles was faithful to both his wives, with his second marriage taking place after he was widowed

In the 13th century when this story is set, Florence was a flourishing and expanding city with some thirty-thousand inhabitants, but it suffered recurring conflict between its two main political factions. The Guelphs traditionally supported the Pope, whilst the Ghibellines were allies of the Holy Roman Emperor and supporters of the nobility. The Ghibellines ruled the city from 1244, but were deposed in 1250 by the more popular Guelphs; who in turn lost power in 1260.

The Apothecary's Daughter

'The Tenth Day, the Seventh Story'

One day, King Pedro of Aragon held a festival in the city of Palermo. The highlight was a jousting tournament in which the king himself took part. Close to the jousting ground, a young woman named Lisa was sitting by her window to watch. When King Pedro's turn came to enter the lists, she was instantly smitten with love for him.

However, her love was totally hopeless, for the king was already married. Besides, her father was only a humble apothecary – an occupation so low in status that no nobleman, let alone a king, would consider even bestowing a glance on her.

Day by day she brooded alone on her impossible love, confiding in no one, until she had made herself seriously ill. She began to waste away like snow melting in the sun. Her father and mother, having no idea what was wrong, brought doctors to examine her and dosed her with medicines. Their efforts achieved nothing, for Lisa was in such despair that she wanted only to die.

However, she did not wish to do so without first informing the king of her love. She spent long hours trying to devise a way to do this, and came up with the idea of asking a family friend called Minuccio d'Arezzo for help. Minuccio was a professional singer who sometimes performed before King Pedro.

She asked her father to bring Minuccio to their house to sing for her. Her father readily agreed, eager to do anything that might cheer her up. When Minuccio arrived and saw how ill Lisa was, he spoke to her kindly, then entertained her with a selection of songs. Unfortunately, they were all *love* songs, which only increased her distress.

Tearfully, Lisa asked her father's permission to speak to the singer alone. Again, her father did not hesitate to agree. The family all withdrew to another room. Then Lisa said to Minuccio in a low voice, 'Sir, I asked for you to come here not only to hear your beautiful songs, but also to seek your help. In doing so I must share a secret with you. Would you promise to reveal it to no one, except the man it concerns?'

'Speak up,' said Minuccio. 'I promise you can trust me.'

Lisa sighed and went on, 'I believe that my father has told you that I am suffering from a terrible fever of the mind, though he has no idea of its cause. The truth is, that ever since I saw King Pedro jousting at the festival, I have been tormented by love for him. I know that it will never come to anything, but I can't escape my feelings. They cause me such excruciating pain that I have resolved to kill myself. However, first I wish the king to know that *he* is the cause of my misery, and thus of my impending death. I understand that you have access to him – so I beg you to tell him this.'

She began to sob so violently that Minuccio felt tears come to his own eyes. 'Lisa, my dear,' he said, 'you could not love a greater man than the king. Permit me not to waste any time: I will go at once to find a way to help you. Hopefully, you will receive some welcome news in the next few days.'

Lisa thanked him profusely and sent him off with her fervent blessing.

Minuccio hurried to a friend of his, a renowned poet called Mico da Sienna, and told him of his mission – without revealing the identity of the young woman it concerned. The two sat down together and got to work. Mico composed a poem as if written in the voice of a young woman suffering from hopeless unrequited love. Minuccio set it to plaintive music and practised singing it over and over.

Then he hurried to the palace, arriving just as King Pedro and his courtiers were finishing dinner, and offered to entertain the king. He performed his new love song, imbuing the words with the bitter-sweet passion of a heartbroken young woman. It was so moving that all the courtiers were struck dumb – the king most of all.

'Tell me,' he cried, when Minuccio had finished, 'does this song refer to a real girl?'

'It does, my lord,' Minuccio replied. 'And I can tell you who she is, but it must be for your ears only.'

The king was greatly intrigued, and ushered Minuccio into his private chamber. He sealed the door and windows, and ordered the musician to speak. Thus Minuccio told him about Lisa, so young and innocent, and how her obsession with King Pedro had made her mortally ill. The king shook his head in wonder and pity.

'Go to this young woman at once,' he ordered Minuccio. 'Give her my sincere good wishes, and tell her I will visit her this very evening.'

Minuccio, full of avuncular sympathy for Lisa, hastened back to her, gave her King Pedro's message and performed the song that had stirred the king's sympathy. Lisa was greatly comforted that the king was at last aware of her feelings for him, and awaited the evening with impatience.

Meanwhile, King Pedro pondered the matter carefully. He was a humane man and greatly desired to bring some solace to this innocent, vulnerable girl. At sunset, he announced he was going for a solitary ride. Huddled incognito inside his cloak and hood, he made straight for Lisa's house, where he revealed himself to the apothecary – who was overwhelmed by his royal visitor. The apothecary took the king into his garden, since it was more pleasant than his cramped house.

The king chatted to him amiably about this and that. Eventually he said, 'Good fellow, they tell me that you have a very attractive daughter who has come of age. Is she betrothed to anyone?'

'Unfortunately, no,' the apothecary replied, 'for poor Lisa suffers from a mysterious illness, which we fear may be fatal.'

'How terribly sad,' said the king. 'Is there no hope for her?'

'None at all,' sighed the apothecary. He hesitated, then added, 'Though, strangely enough, just today she seems considerably better than she has been for a very long time.'

The king smiled behind his whiskers, guessing that his message must have reached Lisa and had the desired effect. 'It would be a shame if she were to leave this world at such a tender age,' he said. 'Is it possible for me to see her?'

The apothecary had only just got over his shock at the king's unexpected visit, and was even more taken aback by this suggestion. Obviously, he could not refuse it. So he took King Pedro indoors and led him up the narrow stairs to the chamber where Lisa lay in bed as usual, pale and wan, propped up on pillows.

The king strode to her bedside, took her hand and exclaimed, 'Now, now, whatever is the meaning of this? A fine young lady such as you should not be lying abed wallowing in misery! Rise up at once! Go fulfil your duty – which is to comfort your elders who are *genuinely* sick.'

When she heard his firm words, and felt the warm touch of the hands that she long had dreamed of, Lisa was engulfed in waves of both shame and joy. 'My lord,' she managed to whisper, 'I have never been very strong, so when I found myself struck by a terrible burden, I could not help but yield to it. However, your generous visit now gives me hope of a cure.'

The king was the only one who understood what she meant, and was very impressed by her dignity. He thought to himself, 'What a pity she is the daughter of such a common man; a girl like her deserves a rich and noble husband. Still, no one can change what God has ordained.' He spoke with her quietly for a while longer, trying to offer some comfort; then took his leave.

The king's visit pleased Lisa as much as if he had actually reciprocated her love. She began to recover dramatically, and within a few days she was back to her former self. Despite the apothecary's discretion, news somehow got around that her recovery was linked to the honour of a private visit from King Pedro. The king was widely applauded for his compassion.

Now, the king had long been married and greatly cherished his wife, the queen. Naturally, he told her all about his encounter with the apothecary's daughter, and sought her advice on how to reward the girl's naive love for him in an appropriate way that would aid her recovery.

On the queen's suggestion, a few days later, he sent a message telling Lisa and her parents to meet him again in their garden. When they were assembled there, the king and queen arrived with a company of barons and ladies. The queen engaged Lisa in friendly conversation, until the king beckoned the girl before him and addressed her as follows:

'Noble young lady, your exceptional love for me is a great honour, and I wish to reward you for it in the following ways. Firstly, since you are of an age to marry, I intend to find you a suitable husband. Secondly, and regardless of your forthcoming wedding, I wish to call myself your own true knight – forever.'

Lisa gasped, unable to speak.

'In return for becoming your knight,' said the king with a smile, 'I must ask you to grant me a single kiss.'

The poor girl blushed so much that she could scarcely stand. At last she managed to reply in a voice so low that only King Pedro could hear it, 'My lord, I know it is totally preposterous for a humble girl like me to fall in love with an illustrious king like you. But it seems to me that passion is usually determined not by suitability, but by unquenchable yearning and weakness. I have tried so hard to fight against it, to no avail. Be assured that because I love you so deeply, I will obey whatever you demand of me – even if you order me to walk into a fire! Since you wish to give me a husband, although I can never love any other man as I love you, I will gladly marry him and be a good wife to him – because I know it will give *you* pleasure. As for your proposal to become my own knight – oh sir, such a privilege is far beyond my wildest dreams! With my lady the queen's permission, I will happily grant you the kiss that you have asked for. May God bestow you with endless blessings for all your kindness!'

The queen, standing close by, was charmed by Lisa's innocence and integrity. She called over the apothecary and his wife, and the king told them what he had offered the girl. They both eagerly agreed to it.

So the king sent messengers through the town to bring a fine young man he knew of, called Perdicone, to the house. Perdicone was of noble birth, but had fallen into poverty through no fault of his own. When the king asked him to marry Lisa, he was thrilled; and Lisa could tell at once that the king had made a good choice on her behalf.

The king, who had brought rings in his pocket for that very purpose, conducted the wedding on the spot. Afterwards, the queen presented Lisa with a chest filled to the brim with precious jewels; to which the king added two large estates to complete her dowry. Thus the young couple could look forward to a life of more comfort than either had ever known.

Finally, King Pedro turned to Lisa and said, 'Now it is time to pluck the fruit of your love for me, as you have promised.' He took her head gently in his hands, and kissed her on the brow.

When this was done, the king's servants got to work organising a splendid wedding feast with celebrations such as Lisa had never imagined anyone of her status could enjoy.

After that, for as long as he lived, the king kept his covenant with Lisa. He always styled himself as her knight, and never went to any battle or tournament without wearing one of her personal tokens.

Ah, if only all the rulers in the world would act so graciously as him! Then they would truly win their people's hearts and encourage them to live well by following their noble example; and they would die with impeccable reputations. But alas! Most kings nowadays are cruel and tyrannical, and few bend their bows to such wisdom.

The king in this story may have been Peter III of Aragon (c.1239–1285), who was also proclaimed king of Sicily at the city of Palermo in 1282. Perhaps the story of him being stirred to pity by a sad love song was inspired by his patronage of the troubadours; he is known to have composed at least two songs for them, which he also performed himself.

An apothecary prepared and sold medicines both to doctors and directly to patients, and offered medical advice. Their shops also sold wine, spices and herbs. They trained through apprenticeships and established guilds, so their social status was on the same level as traders.

THE NUN AND HER FAITHLESS LOVER

Anonymous: *Beatrijs*
Netherlands, 1374

A single manuscript survives of the original Dutch poem, believed to be a copy of an earlier text. It comprises over a thousand lines, beautifully written out and decorated on high-quality vellum. The anonymous, and apparently impoverished, poet says he retold it from a narrative shared by a man called Brother Ghisbert, who in turn had found it in some books.

The story is based on a legend that goes back to at least the early 13th century. It was clearly widely known across western Europe, since there are prose versions in many languages.

A convent was visited each year by a venerable abbot, who would invite each nun to come to him privately to make her confession. In this way, he ensured that no dishonour or blasphemy could breed within the sacred walls.

One year, he asked all the sisters to assemble before him, for he wished to tell them of a miracle. He was a splendid raconteur, and this is the story he shared with them:

Truthfully now, dear sisters, I will tell you of a nun enticed by the Devil himself to break her vows in the most despicable way.

This nun was young, sweet and much praised for her diligence. Her name was Beatrijs. She worked in the convent as a vergeress, ringing the bell, lighting the lamps and calling the other sisters to prayer.

But deep in her heart she nursed a sordid secret: she was in love with a man.

Her lover was a squire who had cast his spell over her long before she took her vow of chastity. Despite good intentions, self-rebuke and many fervent prayers, she could not shake off the thorns of desire; her head was constantly full of tantalising thoughts about him. The Devil soon spotted this weakness, and exploited it to bend her to his will. Under the influence of the Evil One, and in defiance of the convent rules, she smuggled out a message to the squire, urging him to come to her secretly.

He did so at once. Beatrijs was looking out for him, sitting behind a window; he came and stood below it. The heavy, iron cross-bars kept them chastely apart, but could not prevent their exchange of fervent and sacrilegious words.

'Venus has shot an arrow into my heart,' whispered Beatrijs. 'I beg you to remove it, or I will never know happiness again.'

'I can't, my beloved,' the squire replied. 'That cruel goddess has afflicted me too, ever since we were children; yet she has never even allowed us the relief of sharing a kiss.'

'Is there no way we can overcome this torment?' Beatrijs groaned.

The squire answered, 'I believe there is. If you will name a time when I could safely creep back here undetected, I will bring you some clothes befitting a lady, carry you away from this musty convent and make you my bride.'

The young nun was so much under the Devil's influence, that she forgot she was *already* a bride – of Christ. She did not hesitate to accept this outrageous proposal. 'Return here in eight nights' time,' she whispered. 'There is a briar rose growing in a corner of the orchard: I will meet you there.'

Thus they agreed it and, in an inferno of excitement, bid each other adieu.

Seven days and nights passed. On the eighth night, after matins, when all the other sisters had returned to the dormitory, Beatrijs lingered alone in the chapel. She was in great excitement, but also in great anguish. She knelt before the altar, imploring Mary the Mother of God to understand how the Devil was torturing her, begging to be pardoned one day for the enormous sin which was about to engulf her. She took out the sacristy keys that were entrusted to her keeping and hung them up on Mary's statue, where they would easily be found. Then she pulled off her nun's habit, scapular, hood and veil and laid them neatly across the altar, placing her shoes at its base.

Now she was almost naked, except for her light shift. She tiptoed to a small side door, opened it, peered around into the darkness and stealthily crept through it. The world outside was awash with moon and starlight. She padded softly into the orchard and across to the briar rose. The squire revealed himself there at once, making her blush – for she stood before him wearing nothing but her shift, her head and feet entirely bare.

But he charmed her with soft words, saying, 'Don't be ashamed. How lovely you are! Look, here are the fine clothes I promised you.'

He led her under the sweet-smelling briar and gave her a package. Inside she found a splendid gown, a hooded mantle lined with precious fur, a girdle, silk stockings, sparkling jewellery, soft shoes of cordovan leather and a flowing veil of white silk. When she emerged wearing them, the squire cried, 'Your brightness is like the sun lighting the night!' Then he took her in his arms and kissed her. She did not resist him. She was so happy when he lifted her onto his saddle, mounted close behind her and galloped away with her into the dawn.

As the sky lightened, she began to feel afraid. But the squire hushed her with empty promises. 'Don't worry, my love,' he said. 'I will always stay with you and keep you safe. Only death can part us.'

'But what shall we live on, out in the cruel world?' she asked. 'How will you keep me from poverty?'

'I have brought a thousand marks of silver,' he answered, 'secreted away from my father's coffers.'

If she thought that was unscrupulous, she did not say so; nor did she ask him to turn back. For the unknown country they had now entered seemed so welcoming after the cold gloom of the cloisters; it was full of singing birds and bright flowers. At one point she did wonder if she had made a mistake – for he suddenly stopped in a lonely glade and asked her to learn love's game with him right there out in the open, like a whore; but he hastily accepted her objection to this, soothing her with honeyed words.

And so they rode on and on together, over hills and across plains – who knows where? – for many days. At last they reached a town in a valley. There they settled down to live; but not in holy matrimony. Instead they chose diabolical free cohabitation, enjoying bodily sins without any constraint.

She bore him two sons. He freely squandered the wealth he had stolen from his father. Seven years passed.

Then suddenly everything changed.

For the squire had spent the very last mark of all their money. In order to buy food to keep their family alive, he began selling off all their fine possessions – horses, jewels, even their spare clothes. Finally, they had nothing left at all. Since he was a nobleman's son, raised to a life of leisure, he had no idea how to work to pay his way. As for Beatrijs, she had been closeted away as a novice at a tender age, so she had never even learned the craft of spinning, which might have earned her a small but honest wage.

They grew hungry. They grew miserable and angry. They barely even spoke to each other. Their love died.

'I'll pop along to see my father,' said the squire one day, 'and ask him to help us out. I won't be away for long.'

Ah, sisters, beware the wiles of worldly men! Beatrijs never saw him again.

Now, despite Beatrijs' incessant decadence and daily transgressions, there was one redeeming aspect of her life: she had never forgotten her prayers. Every single night, all through those seven years, she had made sure to beg forgiveness for exchanging her vocation for the foul pit of wickedness. Now she could see no way for her fatherless family to survive, except by her committing the most abhorrent sin of all. But before she embraced it, she followed her usual habit of falling to her knees to pray.

'Mother Mary!' she wailed. 'What I always dreaded most has finally come to pass. My lover has betrayed and abandoned me, leaving our children to starve. I've thought and thought, but there's only one way I can see to save them from dying – I'll have to go out and work as a whore! I beg you, despite this abomination, Holy Mother, please, please, do not forsake me!'

Thus this one-time pious nun, who had so eagerly sold her soul for worldly love, now received her just desserts. She was forced to lower herself to the ultimate degradation – by also selling her body. From then on, every day, she walked the streets and lay in the fields over and over again, letting the lowest men of all men abuse her. Truly, she despised herself as much as she despised them.

My sisters: do you think this meant that the wretched Beatrijs was now irreparably damned, condemned to eternity in Hell?

No, it did not.

For though she spent the *next* seven terrible years struggling in a cesspit of immorality, all her ill-gotten earnings went to sustain her innocent children. Even more importantly, she still kept up her daily prayers.

The Holy Mother heard, and eventually washed Beatrijs's soul completely clean. Now the former nun resolved to degrade herself no more.

Beatrijs took her children from the hovel where they were sheltering, and reformed herself by becoming an honest beggar. Together they wandered from one town to another – until they found themselves near the very convent from which Beatrijs, as a young nun, had fled so long ago.

She sought alms at a nearby cottage, where a kindly old widow offered the ragged family a bed. Beatrijs asked her for news of the convent, and the widow told her it was flourishing.

'Has it got over that scandal many years ago, when the vergeress ran away with a squire?' Beatrijs asked.

'My dear!' the widow exclaimed. 'Wherever did you hear such a nasty rumour? It's certainly all lies. The same vergeress has been there since she joined the convent as a young girl, and she has the reputation of being almost saintly.'

Beatrijs was mystified. How could that possibly be?

Late that evening, she crept out to the convent. The gate into the orchard, where she had first trysted with her treacherous lover, was unlocked. So too was the side door through which she had slipped out to illicit freedom. She passed through one door after another unheeded, and soon found herself in the chapel, standing near the altar, before Mary's statue.

Listen carefully and believe me, sisters, for I tell no lies.

All her garments were still there, exactly as she had left them, twice seven years ago. It was as if she had discarded them only momentarily. She picked them up and put them on. The sacristy key was still hanging exactly where she had left it. She took it, fetched the candles and lit them, just as she always used to do. The clock struck midnight. The prayerbooks were in their usual place; hastily she set them out, then pulled upon the rope to sound the bell for matins. As the nuns came scurrying out of the dormitory, they nodded at her only briefly, as if she had never been away.

Suddenly, Beatrijs understood.

Every single day since she had fled holy orders and abandoned her chastity – even while she was sinning freely with her false lover, even while she was whoring – she had expressed deep remorse in her prayers to the Holy Mother. Mary had heard her. In her grace and mercy, she had assumed Beatrijs' shape and taken her place in the convent, waiting patiently until the time was right for her young protégé to return at last and repent.

But though Mary knew the depth of remorse in Beatrij's heart, there was still one more hurdle to overcome for her total redemption: she must make full confession. I was the one who God sent to hear it; I was the one who absolved her, and gave her back the promise of eternal life in Heaven. I also took her two sons and raised them in my abbey, where they both grew up to be admirable, pious men.

My sisters, you will never meet Beatrijs or know her true identity, for she lives in a community far away. I share her story to show you how the spiritual love of the Holy Mother is far stronger and more constant than any carnal love of mortal man. One day, the Devil may tempt some of you too beyond endurance. If that should ever happen, remember how Beatrijs survived such a fall through ceaseless prayers, and finally found redemption. Praise God and sing her fame!

The original poem ends with an abbot on his annual visit to the convent to check it is free of scandal. Beatrijs, still much troubled by disturbing dreams, begs him to hear her full confession. She reveals every detail of her troubled past, and he fully absolves and pardons her. He then says he will use the example of her life in his sermons, promising to protect her anonymity, in the hope of bringing more people to honour Mary. This inspired the present retelling as if in the abbot's own words.

During the Middle Ages, Mary – the mother of Jesus – was widely revered and worshipped, and is thus the subject of hundreds of miracle stories. She was idealised as womanly perfection, her sexual purity representing freedom from female sin. The image of 'Virgin and Child' was widely displayed in churches and roadside shrines and amulets. Women prayed to her for help in conception, to protect their children and ward off illness. See The City of Ladies, p. 380

The use of seven as a significant number is a common motif in European folk tales and legends.

Stories from
CHAUCER

England, late 14th century

Geoffrey Chaucer was born in the early 1340s. His father was a
prosperous wine merchant who later became a deputy butler to
the king; his mother was the niece of a royal mint official. At the
age of fifteen, Geoffrey became a page to the Countess of Ulster.
This position provided an entrée into court circles, and an
introduction to great men, such as John of Gaunt, first Duke of
Lancaster, who later became Chaucer's patron and protector. He
fought briefly in the Hundred Years War against France; he was
taken prisoner, but freed by a ransom paid partly by King Edward
III. In 1367 he began to work for the king, who sent him on several
missions abroad. Later he became a customs comptroller, a knight
of Kent and a justice of the peace, and also took charge of repairs
to public buildings in London. He married Phillipa de Roet, an
attendant to the queen, and they had at least two sons and two
daughters. He died in 1400 and was buried in Westminster Abbey.

Chaucer was an accomplished linguist, speaking Latin, French,
Anglo-Norman and Italian. He was knowledgeable about
astronomy, physics, medicine and alchemy; and well read in the
classics, the Bible and the works of Dante (see pp. 192) and
Boccaccio (p. 226). His other published writings include a
translation of *The Romance of the Rose* (p. 170), books of
philosophy and science and a number of shorter poems.

The passages quoted below are from the classic 20th century
verse translations by Nevill Coghill

Troilus & Criseyde

Troilus and Criseyde
written c. 1382–87

❦

This long, irresistibly lively and very humorous, epic poem is split into five books, containing over a thousand verses of seven lines each. Though less well known than *The Canterbury Tales*, it is a more complete and satisfying work.

Chaucer makes it plain that he did not invent the plot and characters himself, but based it on an earlier text, thus excusing any imperfections in his narrative:

> For those to whom my story may be soot
> or sugar – I follow what my author put...
> ...in his ancient book ...

> '...I cannot tell it all
> as excellently as my author can
> Yet I have given – and with God's help shall
> the gist and substance of that learned man'

(Book III, verses 171-2 and 201)

The source he used was *Filostrato* (written c.1335–40) by the Italian author Boccaccio (see p. 226). Chaucer used the same plot and dramatis personae but added his own idiosyncratic humour, particularly in the characterisation of Pandarus. Boccaccio had in turn been inspired by a 12th century French poem, *Roman de Troye*, via its 13th century Italian translation, in which the heroine is called Briseida.

It is often told how, in ancient times, Prince Paris of Troy abducted fair Queen Helen from the Greeks; and how, for ten long years, the Greeks besieged Troy in revenge.

Paris had a younger brother called Troilus, who abhorred the trouble this romance had brought to their kingdom. He strutted around, loudly denouncing Paris and urging his fellow knights to abandon all thoughts of women for good.

These preposterous words fell mostly on deaf ears; but there was one who heard him clearly, and he was outraged. This was not a man, but the god of Love himself.

The year turned until it was time for the annual feast of Palladion. All the young people gathered excitedly at the temple to celebrate it; but as usual, the atmosphere was quickly spoiled by the arrival of Troilus, jeering at the knights for ogling the ladies. This time, however, the god of Love took aim at him and shot an arrow straight into his heart.

Troilus felt a brief pain as it struck him. However, he had no time to worry about it – for the very next moment, for the first time in his life, his eyes were irresistibly drawn to a dazzlingly beautiful lady.

Troilus clutched his chest, tried to steady himself and hastened into the temple. But he found it impossible to concentrate on the feast day service. By the time he emerged, he was trembling all over. He rode home to the palace at a gallop and threw himself onto his bed.

Alone in his room, his thoughts were in turmoil: 'How slender she is, how soft and clear her skin! She looks so proud and noble...yet she's very modest too. Those black clothes she wears...she must be in mourning... But her smile is bright as the sun. Oh! Oh! What shall I do? Who can I ask for advice? No one. They'd all sneer at me for caving in to the very thing I've always preached against. What a fool I am! I must stop this nonsense at once and forget her... Ach, but I can't!'

In this fashion, Troilus passed a sleepless night, tossing and turning, suffering desires he had never even dreamed of before. The next night was the same, and the one after that. His days drifted by in a stupor of bewildered, restless yearning.

One morning, as he was wrenching himself wearily out of bed, someone knocked at the door then thrust it open. In walked an older man, his good friend Pandarus.

'Go away,' groaned Troilus.

'But I haven't seen you for ages, my dear fellow,' Pandarus beamed. 'I thought something might be wrong, and I can see at once that it is. What's up? You look pale as death. Are you ill?'

'There's nothing wrong with me, Pandarus...well, not physically, anyway.'

'Not physically, but...?' Pandarus pressed him.

'It's ridiculous, I can't possibly tell you.'

'Of course you can. Whatever it is, I promise not to laugh or scold you. I've known you since you were a young lad: you can trust me.'

'Well...all right then,' said Troilus in a low voice. 'But swear to keep this totally secret; absolutely no one else must know. It's hopeless. I...I think I'm dying, Pandarus...of *love*.'

'Ha ha ha!' Pandarus chuckled. 'I should have guessed. After all your endless prudish pontificating, Troilus, you've got your comeuppance at last! Well, there's no point in dying of it – because then the lady of your dreams will never know that you fancy her. Who is she?'

'I dare not say.'

'Go on, it's for my ears only. If I know who she is, I may be able to help you.'

'Rubbish, Pandarus! Your own love affairs never go anywhere, so what can you possibly do for mine?'

The older man smiled ruefully. 'I can help you learn from my mistakes. Maybe I'll be more successful as a go-between than as a playboy, eh? Who is she?'

'I truly can't tell you, because I don't know her name. But I can tell you what she looks like. The most astoundingly gorgeous...'

'They're all astoundingly gorgeous. Be more specific. Where did you see her? What was she wearing?'

Troilus let out a deep sigh and spoke in a solemn voice, like one describing a sacred vision. 'She was standing in the shadows by the temple door before the Palladion feast, and she was dressed from head to toe in black.'

'Ahah! Oh my! What splendid luck!' Pandarus exclaimed. 'I know exactly who she is, Troilus. Would you believe it? You've fallen for my very own niece!'

Troilus gawped at him in astonishment. 'Then tell me about her, I beg you, tell me *everything*. What's her name? Why does she dress in mourning?'

'Her name's Criseyde,' said Pandarus. 'She's the daughter of priest Calkas.'

'Oh no, not the Calkas who recently defected to the Greeks?' said Troilus. 'The traitor!'

'The very one,' said Pandarus. 'But don't worry, Criseyde is ashamed of her father's treason. She's refused to join him, and will have nothing more to do with him. She's a sweet-natured, friendly soul, and no one holds her responsible for her father's misdeeds. She's adamant that she will stay here in Troy and accept whatever fate the gods bring her. In fact, your own brother, Prince Hector, has put her under his protection...'

'Not a whisper to Hector of my feelings for her!' Troilus cried.

'Of course not,' said Pandarus, patting his young friend's arm. 'I swear not to tell anyone…except for Criseyde herself, of course.'

'Tell me more,' Troilus begged him. 'Does she already have a lover or a husband? Am I too late?'

'Since I'm her uncle,' said Pandarus, 'I know more of her affairs than most. I'm fairly sure she doesn't have a lover. As you've seen, she wears black, and you can easily guess why: she's not a virgin, but a widow. That's great news for you, Troilus, since your own lack of experience will be more than compensated by her prior knowledge. Now then! If you want me to help you, pull yourself together and get back to your princely duties. Your family's conducting a war out there, in case you'd forgotten. Eat a good breakfast, then put your armour on and go help with the fighting. You need to win fame as a peerless warrior, if you want to impress Criseyde.'

Helpless as he was, Troilus resolved to obey his friend.

Meanwhile, Pandarus set to work too. His first task was to visit his niece. He found Criseyde sitting gaily in her parlour with two other ladies, listening to a girl reading to them from a book.

'Hello uncle, do come in,' she cried when she saw him. She shooed her companions into another chamber so they could talk privately.

'Dear niece,' said Pandarus, 'what on earth are you doing indoors on this fine spring day? Let me take you dancing to celebrate May-time.'

'Tut-tut, uncle,' she giggled. 'Dancing? Celebration? Have you forgotten I'm a widow? It would be more fitting for you to take me out to a dark cave and read me the lives of martyrs.'

'Nonsense,' said Pandarus. 'When you hear my news, you'll be desperate to dance and celebrate!'

'What kind of news is that, uncle?'

'We-e-ll,' said Pandarus tantalisingly, 'Once you know it, you'll be the proudest lady in Troy. Hmm, but maybe I shouldn't tell you after all. I don't want to embarrass you, or make you angry...'

'Don't drop hints, uncle, then leave me on tenterhooks. Tell me!'

'Very well,' said Pandarus. 'Sit still and listen carefully. You've heard of Prince Troilus, brother of mighty Hector?'

'I believe I know his name,' said Criseyde cautiously.

'And you've surely also heard about his gallantry?' said Pandarus, laying it on. 'And of his good nature and warmth, of his nobility and fearlessness, of his stamina and generosity, of his...'

'Yes, yes,' said Criseyde, 'but please get to the point.'

'This Troilus is madly in love with you.'

'With *me*? How come?'

'He fears he'll die unless you accept him,' said Pandarus. 'Dear niece, Troilus is a long-standing friend of mine, a really splendid fellow. To be honest, I care for him almost as much as I do for you. Nothing would make me happier than to see you together...'

Criseyde was blushing furiously. 'Uncle, what are you asking of me? It's not appropriate...'

'I ask nothing of you,' said Pandarus quickly. 'Nothing that would compromise you, nothing that would commit you. But only this, Criseyde: next time Troilus rides past you in the street, would you be kind enough to smile at him? Don't look so alarmed. As you well know, it's quite normal in our city for knights and ladies to be friendly towards each other.'

'Hmm,' said Criseyde, 'but where will a smile lead?'

'To love of course, my dear,' said Pandarus.

'Uncle, I'm shocked. Remember, I'm a respectable widow. If *I'd* asked *you* for help with starting a romance, you'd have scolded me harshly.'

'Oh, for goodness' sake,' said Pandarus. 'Let the dead bury the dead: life's for living and haughtiness only leads to regret. My suggestion is completely harmless. But if you were to reject him outright, now that *would* be harmful. Troilus is bound to either kill himself or die of a broken heart...which will make me feel so guilty, I'll have to kill myself too.'

'You're backing me into a corner,' said Criseyde. 'I suppose, if I *pretend* to accept his love, that's the lesser of two evils. But I can't *genuinely* love him in return.'

'Excellent, excellent my dear,' beamed Pandarus. 'What a lucky girl you are to have caught such a fish without even lowering your net.'

'Don't be so crude, uncle.'

'Sorry, my dear. Forget I said that.'

They embraced and parted on good terms.

After her uncle had gone, Criseyde sat alone pondering this strange new situation. Before she could reach any conclusion, she heard a loud commotion outside. The servant girl, who had been reading to her earlier, ran in, saying, 'My lady, everyone's saying there's a hero riding down the street! May I open the window so we can see him?'

Criseyde nodded absent-mindedly. The girl opened the window just as a new shout went up: 'Make way for Troilus!'

'Troilus?' thought Criseyde. 'That's a coincidence. Well, this is a useful chance to take a look at him.'

She concealed herself by standing to one side of the window, and peeped out. A magnificent bay horse came into sight, with a powerful, richly armoured warrior mounted on its back. The warrior carried his helmet in his hand, and Criseyde could see his face quite clearly. 'Hmm,' she thought, 'I have to admit, he's very good-looking. And how gently he's riding that wounded horse of his, not hurrying it; he seems like a caring kind of man.'

The crowd was cheering Troilus loudly, for he had just led a small victory against the Greeks. He acted as if their praise meant nothing to him.

'Although he's clearly regarded as a great hero,' Criseyde thought, 'he seems very unassuming. Fancy him falling for me! I suppose I wouldn't mind being his friend... But I've so enjoyed my freedom since my husband died; I'd be a fool to give that up for another man. Anyway, love affairs only lead to misery, with all the stupid mistrust and conflict they bring... On the other hand, it would be an adventure to have a lover like him. Nothing ventured, nothing gained... But nothing lost either. Dear me, whatever is for the best?'

Thus her thoughts ran on. To distract herself, she spent the rest of the day with her companions. But when she went to bed that night, she had a disturbing dream in which an eagle swapped her heart with Troilus's. When she woke up, she still did not know what to do.

Meanwhile, when Troilus returned home from the battle, Pandarus was waiting for him. 'So, everyone calls you a hero now, eh?' he teased him. 'Perhaps they don't realise how badly wounded you are?'

'Never mind,' said Troilus. 'Tell me at once, Pandarus: should I weep or sing?'

'Sing!' said Pandarus. 'I've fixed it. She's agreed to be your friend.'

'My *friend*? Is that all?'

'It's a work in progress, dear fellow. The next thing is to write her a letter, imploring her to have mercy before you waste away with lovesickness. Make it modest and informal, and blot it with tears. I'll deliver it to her tomorrow. While I'm at her house, you must ride casually past her window in your best armour. I'll make sure she looks out at the right moment; your ears will glow as you pass! I'll bring you back her reply that very same day.'

Though Troilus was sick with apprehension, he did as he was told. The following morning, Pandarus visited his niece again, led her into the garden and gave her the letter.

'I don't want it,' she protested.

'For pity's sake, just take it,' Pandarus insisted. He thrust it into the bosom of her gown. Then he began to distract her with jokes and tall stories, until she could not stop laughing. In this mood they went in to dine together.

Afterwards, she made an excuse and slipped away to a quiet spot where, despite herself, she opened the letter and carefully read it.

'You were a long time,' Pandarus remarked when she returned. 'You've almost missed a procession going past.' He caught her hand and took her to stand directly before the window – just as Troilus and his men came riding into view. This time it was too late to hide: he gazed directly in as he came level, and for a long moment their eyes met. Criseyde blushed deeply; and then he was gone.

'Well?' said Pandarus.

'I read the letter, uncle,' she admitted.

'And?'

'I... I will write him a reply.'

She went to her chamber again, took up parchment and a quill and wrote, in an exquisite flowing script:

> To the noble prince Troilus, I return your greeting.
> Pray accept my thanks for your correspondence
> and your honourable declaration of good intent. I
> regret that I am unable to fulfil the hopes you
> expressed therein. However, if it will comfort you, I
> am willing to offer you a little sisterly friendship.
> I trust that you fare as well as I do,
> Criseyde

Before she could change her mind, she pressed the letter into Pandarus's hand. He snatched it greedily and bid her a hasty goodbye.

Pandarus delivered the letter to Troilus, grinning to see its ambiguous promise stoking the fire of his friend's desire. 'Just keep hacking at her will, like a woodsman chopping down an oak,' he advised. 'She's certain to fall in the end.' Then he hurried off to construct a complex plot of lies and rumour to bring the pair together.

The outcome of it was, that innocent Criseyde found herself threatened with a lawsuit, for some reason that she could not fathom. While she was worrying about it, she received a dinner invitation for the next day from another of Troilus's brothers, Prince Deiphebus. Thinking that one of his guests might be able to help her out of this legal tangle, she accepted.

Meanwhile, Pandarus told Troilus to arrive at Deiphebus's house just before the dinner, then feign sudden illness and go to bed there. Troilus readily agreed, pointing out that there was not even any need for pretence, since he genuinely was too lovesick to enjoy the company.

The dinner-party guests included Troilus's sister-in-law, the famous Queen Helen. When they sat down for the meal, she enquired with some concern about Troilus's mysterious malaise. Everyone was eager to suggest some cure or other. 'It's no use,' said Pandarus, 'he's tried everything but he simply can't rise from his bed.' Criseyde alone offered no opinion, for she secretly guessed that she held the only key that could heal him.

Then Pandarus raised the matter of Criseyde's legal problem. 'She's been threatened by a fellow called Poliphetes,' said Pandarus. 'Does anyone here know him?'

They all shook their heads, except for Helen, who said that she'd heard this Poliphetes was a friend of Troilus's.

'Really?' said Pandarus, as if he did not already know. 'Then, perhaps Troilus can advise Criseyde on how to get him off her back. I'll pop into his bedchamber and ask if he's feeling well enough to have a quick chat with her.'

He soon came back, reporting that Troilus would see Criseyde, as long as she did not stay long enough to tire him. Helen offered to be her chaperone, and they followed Pandarus into his friend's bedroom. There, Pandarus explained how Poliphetes was threatening Criseyde. Troilus offered to speak to Poliphetes on her behalf when he felt better, then sank back onto the pillows. The others withdrew, Helen stepping into the garden to join the other ladies.

Criseyde made to follow her; but Pandarus seized her arm and hissed: 'Now is your chance to ease his pain! No one will notice your absence for a few moments.'

He hauled her back into Troilus's chamber, calling softly, 'Look who's back!'

Troilus was lying with his back to them. 'Who's there?' he said weakly.

Pandarus nudged Criseyde, who said hoarsely, 'Um...it...it's me, Criseyde.'

'My beloved lady!' Troilus cried, struggling to sit up. 'Forgive me, I'm too weak to rise and kneel before you.'

'Don't be ridiculous,' said Criseyde. 'I don't want you kneeling for me. I only came back to...er...' she scowled at Pandarus, '...to thank you again for offering to help with this lawsuit.'

Troilus flushed with emotion, too overcome to reply, and groaned: 'I will do anything to help you, fair lady, *anything*! But unless you have mercy on me, I'll kill myself!'

Pandarus gave Criseyde's elbow another hard jab. 'Answer him.'

Criseyde sighed. 'I'm sorry, I'm...I'm not used to such drama. What exactly do you want of me, Troilus?'

'Only your permission to serve you,' said he.

'Now, my dear,' said Pandarus, 'that's not much to ask, is it? How can you refuse?'

'Well...all right,' said Criseyde. 'I'll accept your service.'

'Then I am the happiest man alive!' he cried.

'But I warn you, Troilus,' Criseyde added hastily, 'you may be a war hero and a king's son, but you don't have any romantic claim on me. If you dare overstep the mark, I'll punish you. But if you behave calmly, I'll consider returning your affection – a *little* bit. Those are my terms; you can choose whether or not to accept them.'

Before Troilus could respond, they heard voices as the other guests went past. Troilus immediately resumed groaning and gasping as if he were experiencing a new attack of his supposed illness. Pandarus ushered Criseyde from the room.

Once she was mingling with the other guests, Pandarus crept back in to Troilus and shut the door behind him. 'There, my friend,' he said. 'I've done as much as I can. I just want to say this: though I've acted as a go-between, remember, I'm not a pimp. Don't you dare do anything to tarnish my niece's reputation, or tell anyone of my role in this affair. I have my own good name to guard as well.'

'I owe you everything!' cried Troilus. 'Be assured, I shall never let you down.'

Thus Troilus was twice warned; but in the end, caution was unnecessary. For Criseyde could not help but be flattered by such passionate declarations from a real prince – especially since she clearly had the upper hand. Pandarus stoked up the fire by regularly bringing her more love letters from Troilus. She agreed to see her admirer again...and then again. Naturally, this was easily arranged with the help of their mutual friend and go-between. Criseyde now found herself looking forward to each tryst as eagerly as Troilus did. Pandarus always ensured they had a chance of a few tantalising private moments together, enabling them to gradually become better acquainted. Criseyde was impressed to discover that Troilus was dependable, discreet and, above all, obedient. At last she admitted to her uncle that she had grown quite fond of him.

Pandarus chuckled and rubbed his hands together.

One morning, he paid a visit to his niece. As they chatted about this and that, Pandarus was on top form with his jokes, and had her rolling around with merry laughter. Then he suddenly turned serious and said, 'My dear, will you come to supper this evening?'

'But uncle,' said she, peeping out of the lattice window, 'look at those dark clouds hanging over the city. It's sure to rain this evening.'

'Then come early,' said Pandarus, 'to be sure you don't get wet.'

'I don't know… Will Troilus be there?'

'Troilus?' said Pandarus. 'Good gracious, no, he's fighting out of town at the moment. Besides, what would it matter if he *were* there? So long as you're discreet, no one will guess about your…er…'

'Our *friendship*, uncle, that's all it is. Well, all right, if the rain holds off, I'll come.'

'Excellent, bring some friends, as many as you like. You know there's always plenty of room at my table, and plenty to eat and drink.'

The rain held off. Criseyde, still in a merry mood from the morning, gathered together a party of ten ladies and a handful of their favourite knights, and they all trooped along to Pandarus's house. He ushered them in with a hearty welcome, and soon they were all enjoying an excellent supper. No sooner were the tables cleared away, than some entertainers arrived. There was music and song, followed by lively games; and when everyone was tired, they settled down to hear some storytelling.

At last, the guests stood up and prepared to leave, with Criseyde in their midst. Pandarus had plied her with plenty of his best wine, and she could not stop yawning. A servant opened the main door, revealing that the expected rain was now bucketing down, spattering in all directions, blown up by a fierce wind. No matter, everyone must make their short journeys through the damp streets if they were to bed down that night. Criseyde prepared to go out amongst them; but Pandarus drew her aside.

'My dear niece,' he said, 'as your nearest kin living in Troy, I feel responsible for you. I beg you, do not go out into this wet, lest you catch a chill, or slip and fall into the flood. I have a small chamber with its own bed where you can sleep tonight in comfort and safety. Your maids can stay here too and guard your chastity by sleeping on pallets nearby.'

'But uncle, I mustn't put your household to any trouble...'

'It's no trouble at all,' said Pandarus. 'And if you sleep well here tonight, well then...' he stifled a grin, '...ahem, you may wish to be my overnight guest more often. Now then, this way, if you please.'

He took her past the parlour, down a long passage leading away from the main part of the house, to a room she had never seen before, next to a row of storage cupboards. It was just big enough to hold a fine bed, which was already made up with crisp white linen. He waited outside while her maids helped her undress and lie between the sheets. When the maids emerged, they started to settle down on the hard floor outside the door. But Pandarus shooed them away and said, sotto voce, 'There's no need to guard your lady, no one can possibly disturb her here. Come, my dears, there are some pallets prepared for you along here.'

The maids made half-hearted protests, not wishing to shirk their duty, but Pandarus assured them that everything would be fine. They had enjoyed a fair share of wine too, and were too tired to argue. Before long, they were comfortably lying down, back in the main part of the house.

Pandarus listened for a long while, until he was certain that everyone else in his house was fast asleep. He picked up a candle and tiptoed to one of the cupboards, close by the little room where Criseyde lay in her linen cocoon. Quiet as a mouse, he opened the door.

'Troilus,' he hissed.

Yes indeed! Pandarus had smuggled Troilus into this very cupboard the previous evening. The lovesick prince had been patiently waiting there ever since.

Pandarus sidled in and closed the door. 'Everything is set up, my friend. Are you ready for bliss?'

'I am desperate for it,' breathed Troilus. 'But I'm also terrified.'

'You wretched mouse-heart! She won't bite you.'

'But someone in your house might hear, and you know how gossip spreads like wildfire.'

'Can't you hear the gale blowing outside, and the rain hammering on the roof? No one will hear anything. Come at once, I order you!'

Pandarus seized his friend's wrist and dragged him along to Criseyde's room, like a fisherman hauling in his catch. Pandarus held up the candle, put a finger to his lips and signalled Troilus to wait. Then he opened Criseyde's door and stepped in.

She sat up with a start and cried out, 'Aargh! Who's there?'

'Hush, niece, it's only me, your favourite uncle. Speak softly, you mustn't wake your maids.'

'But what do you want, at this time of night?'

'Nothing for myself,' said Pandarus. 'It's Troilus...'

'What of him, uncle?'

'He's just arrived here through the downpour, in a terrible state,' said Pandarus. 'He's going insane with misery – because he heard a rumour that you've promised your love to another man. He says if that's true, he'll have to kill himself!'

'Whoever made up that lie? Of course I haven't, uncle, go and tell him so.'

'He won't believe me,' said Pandarus. 'He needs to hear the truth from your own lips.'

'Well, all right then... Tell him I'll put his mind at rest as soon as I rise tomorrow.'

'But tomorrow might be too late,' said Pandarus urgently. 'He could already be dead by then. Everything must be done in its proper time, niece – if a house catches fire at night, you can't wait until morning to extinguish it.'

'I can't possibly see him now, undressed and in bed,' Criseyde insisted. 'Here, give him this ring with a blue

304

gemstone; he's often admired it. Tell him it's to reassure him that I'm not interested in anyone else.'

Pandarus sighed. 'You don't seem to understand the urgency, my dear. The ring can't make him rise from the dead after he's committed the fatal deed. You must let him come to you.'

Criseyde said nothing for a long moment. Then: 'Uncle, you've put me in a terrible dilemma. My honour's at stake.'

'There's no dilemma,' said Pandarus. 'The only right thing is to bring Troilus here to end his anguish.'

'I suppose so... But at least give me time to rise and put on my gown.'

'I assure you, niece, there's absolutely no need. Stay where you are.' He turned to the door and hissed, 'Troilus – you may enter.'

Criseyde sat up wide-eyed as her paramour slipped in. He approached the bed, but not too close, and fell to his knees. 'My lady,' he said courteously.

'You see,' said Pandarus, 'he behaves with the decorum of a true gentleman. There's nothing to worry about.'

Troilus put his hand to his lips and blew her a kiss. In the candlelight, Criseyde blushed. Troilus spoke, but so softly, she could not make him out.

'Let him sit on your bed so you can hear each other properly,' said Pandarus. 'No, closer than that, it's vital to keep your voices right down so no one hears. That's better. I'll draw the curtains round to muffle the sound even more. Perfect. Well, I mustn't eavesdrop on your private conversation, so I'll leave you two alone for a while; but I won't be far away, call me if you need anything.'

Now that Troilus was at last in this intimate and compromising position, he was totally lost for words. So Criseyde took the initiative, saying, 'This ridiculous jealousy of a totally imaginary rival has got to stop. Whatever's come over you?'

Troilus gazed at her silently with moist eyes. At last he managed to groan, 'I believe you, my love. I realise now, it was wicked of me to doubt you. In fact, I curse myself for such false thoughts. I'm not fit to be your lover! You'd best throw me out, go on, forbid me to ever come near you again! Oh! Oh!' He began writhing and thrashing around as if he were having a fit; then suddenly gasped, swooned and fell still.

As Criseyde gazed at him in dismay, Pandarus poked his head around the door. 'Everything all right in there? Oh dear me, I see it's not. You've stabbed his heart with some kind of toxic love thorn. There's only one way to remove it, and that's to assure him that, despite what he said or did to anger you, all is forgiven. Go on.'

With a sigh, Criseyde slid out of bed, knelt beside Troilus and said, 'Listen to me! I'm not angry with you.'

Troilus neither moved nor spoke. His breath came in short, hurried pants.

'For goodness' sake, what's wrong?' she cried. Speak to me!'

Pandarus felt Troilus' pulse. 'He's still alive. Let me lay him on your bed.'

She stood aside, while Pandarus hauled Troilus up onto the sheets. As he lay prone before her, Criseyde could not help but admire his almost perfect features and muscular frame. Her impatience at his foolish doubts melted away; she reached out and, very gently, touched his fingertips with her own. She leaned a little closer, oblivious to her uncle, and stroked his temples and neck. She kissed him chastely on the brow and, as her lips touched him, Troilus opened his eyes and gazed at her adoringly.

'Well,' said Pandarus cheerfully, 'the crisis is over. You don't need me around any longer.' He turned back to the door.

'Wait, uncle!' cried Criseyde.

'Good night,' said Pandarus. 'Sleep tight.' The door closed softly behind him.

Troilus called out weakly, 'My love, how can you forgive my jealousy?'

'How can I persuade you that such jealousy has no cause?' Criseyde retorted.

'Maybe we should put such thoughts behind us?' said Troilus. 'Maybe we should kiss and make up? Come, sit by me on this bed. There's no reason why you shouldn't; it was *your* bed before your uncle carried me here, and I only remain on it to recover from collapse.'

Gingerly, she sat beside him. Trembling like an aspen tree, he put out his arms. She shifted closer, then suddenly coiled herself into him, like honeysuckle round the boughs of a tree. He gasped and began to caress her.

'Teach me to fulfil your wishes!' he whispered. 'My only desire is to obey you.' And at last, he dared to kiss her.

After that...well, suffice to say that, together, they fell into a state of utter bliss. They both wished that the night would last for ever, but not to sleep...

Too soon, however, even through the thick, windowless walls of their secret lair, they heard a cock crow. Their time must soon be over. Hastily, Troilus pinned a delicate keepsake he had brought onto her gown: a golden brooch set with a heart-shaped ruby. They embraced and kissed one last time. Then Troilus rose from the bed, pulled on his crumpled clothes, opened the door, crept out and sped away.

Some time later, Pandarus called through the door, 'Good morning my dear! I hope the rain didn't keep you awake. How are you?'

And Criseyde answered with a smile, 'I've never been better, you old fox – and it's all thanks to you.' In this way, with much laughter, she bid him farewell and hastened home.

No sooner was she gone, than Pandarus hurried round to visit Troilus – who threw himself at his friend's feet, pouring out endless gratitude.

'Oh, it's nothing,' said Pandarus modestly. 'I was very happy to help. But listen, worldly joy hangs by a fine thread that's easily snapped; keeping her may turn out even harder than winning her. So be careful and take things steadily.'

Now Pandarus let the couple enjoy his secret hospitality as often as they wished. This did Troilus the power of good: he was a different man, pleasanter and more cooperative, speaking well of everyone, and a stalwart of jousting tournaments and feasts. Everyone wondered about him; but no one asked any questions.

Then, suddenly, everything changed.

The Trojan War against Greece took a turn for the worse. Many Trojan warriors were killed; many others fled. But at last the Greeks were persuaded to agree a truce – on condition that King Priam of Troy swapped prisoners with them.

This development came to the notice of Criseyde's father, priest Calkas – that traitor who had defected to Greece and left his widowed daughter to fend for herself. He had often regretted leaving her behind, and now he saw his chance to make amends. So he went to the Greek high command saying, 'My lords, I have heard that Troy will soon be burnt to the ground. I don't care that my extensive property there will be destroyed, but I'm very worried about my daughter, Criseyde, who still lives there. Would you be willing to return a captive Trojan to his condemned city, in exchange for her?' He accompanied this request with such a show of tragic weeping, that they readily agreed.

The Greeks sent ambassadors to discuss this with King Priam, who received them in his palace, alongside his sons and assembled councillors. The proposed exchange was discussed soberly, and it was soon agreed to hand over Criseyde in return for a Trojan nobleman called Antenor. Troilus was present, but dared say nothing in defence of Criseyde, in case his secret romance was discovered. His brother Hector did point out that she was not a Greek prisoner, and thus not eligible for the exchange. However, the king's councillors unanimously felt that this consideration should not hinder the return of one of Troy's greatest men. Thus the exchange was formalised.

Criseyde herself had no say in it. Indeed, she knew nothing about it at all.

As soon as Pandarus heard the news, he rushed to Troilus's chamber. He was not surprised to find his young friend totally distraught. Pandarus tried in vain to comfort him, offering to procure other beautiful young women – as many as Troilus wished – to make up for losing Criseyde. Troilus was outraged, accusing the older man of inciting him to betray his beloved.

'Sorry!' said Pandarus. 'Please forgive my outspokenness – just as I excuse your embarrassing self-pity. My friend, let's discuss this calmly. There's a simple solution to this disaster. If you are as great a man as everyone now believes, you won't hesitate to carry it out. Simply go to Criseyde under cover as usual – but instead of spending the night on love games, carry her right away from this city.'

'Obviously, I've already thought of that,' said Troilus. 'But this war's the result of one woman's abduction, and I don't want to cause more trouble by doing likewise. Besides, think of the scandal! I can't inflict that on Criseyde. No, Pandarus, there's nothing to be done. My happiness is about to end for ever.'

'Huh!' said Pandarus. 'How easily you give up, you milksop. Why do you care for opinion? Even if the city elders were angry with you…'

'Not just the elders, but my own father, the king.'

'…Even your father – the fuss will soon pass over. Put Criseyde first. There's nothing dishonourable in taking care of your lover.'

'But *she* might consider it dishonourable. She's probably desperate to see her father. She'll never agree.'

Pandarus shrugged. 'If Criseyde refuses to flee with you, you'll have to wonder whether she loves you as much as you love her. Meet her tonight, and at least discuss it properly. Meanwhile, my boy, get over this latest tantrum, wash those sissy tears off your face, then go and see your father, who must have wondered why you've suddenly vanished. Tell him some yarn to get him off your back, then hurry round to my house.'

Meanwhile, gossipmongers hurried to tell Criseyde about the rumours that were rapidly spreading: 'Have you heard, my lady? The Greeks are going to return lord Antenor to us – and in exchange, King Priam's agreed to let *you* cross the enemy lines and join your father after all these years. Isn't that wonderful news!'

Criseyde was dismayed. 'But my father's a traitor who abandoned me,' she said. 'I have no desire to see him ever again. I shall go to the king at once and plead with him to change his mind.'

'But my lady,' said the gossipers, 'it's too late to change anything. The king's already agreed it with his politicians and military men, in conjunction with the Greek ambassadors, who made the proposal at your father's request. They know what's best. You just have to go along with it. Everyone in the city hopes it might help clear the air and bring a speedier end to the war.'

Criseyde's next visitor was Pandarus, who discussed the calamity only briefly before summoning her to meet Troilus that evening.

As soon as they were privately installed in his secret room, they discussed their predicament urgently.

Troilus merely expressed his despair. But Criseyde had given it much thought and replied, 'Instead of worrying and complaining, we should seek a remedy. Now listen, for I have an idea. Although we must part very soon, I'm told that my father lives only half a day's ride from Troy; so within a fortnight, I'll find an excuse to come back. That's no longer than we're sometimes apart at the moment, when you're away fighting.'

'But how?' said Troilus.

'I'll offer to come back to fetch some of the valuables that my father left behind, pointing out that I'm the only messenger he can trust to do this. That's the perfect excuse, and once I return to Troy I'll simply stay here. No one will ever guess the true reason. And the Greeks won't care where I am; they only agreed to receive me as a favour to my father. When he realises how much I despise him for his treachery, he'll be glad to get rid of me again.'

'It's a good idea in principle,' said Troilus, 'but I can see many problems. As soon as you go to your father, he's bound to forbid you to return, no matter what the excuse. He may already have arranged to marry you off to some Greek knight, and might force you into the wedding at once.

Even worse, you yourself might fall for a Greek man! I've heard they're much more sophisticated than us Trojans; you won't be able to resist them.'

'What nonsense!' cried Criseyde.

'Instead of all that, just run away with me tonight!' Troilus pleaded, following Pandarus' advice. 'Between us we have enough treasure to live on for the rest of our lives.'

'It sounds romantic,' said Criseyde sensibly, 'but we'd both soon regret living as fugitives. After all, you're used to the luxurious life of a warrior-prince; you have too much to lose. And I don't want to give up my home comforts. My idea is definitely the better one: it will enable me to come back here openly and stay permanently. Then we'll be able to continue our relationship just as it is now.'

After much arguing, Criseyde got her way. They spent the rest of the night in passionate lovemaking; and at dawn they parted.

The terrible day came when Criseyde was to be handed over to the Greeks in exchange for lord Antenor. Troilus mingled with the rest of the royal household to watch her go, taking care to hide his distress. It was not eased when he saw the Greek knight assigned to fetch her: the splendid Diomede, who was tall, good-looking and immensely self-assured. As he led her away on horseback, a great cheer rose from the crowd – for Antenor had been released and was running joyfully to greet his countrymen. Troilus joined in half-heartedly; but as soon as he could slip away unnoticed, he dashed to his chamber to grieve.

The next moment, Pandarus burst in and shook him roughly by the shoulder. 'Feeling sorry for yourself again?' he yelled. 'Stop this nonsense! She's promised to return in no time, and it's not as if she's been married off to someone else.'

'Not yet,' Troilus groaned. 'But no doubt that's what her father is planning.'

Pandarus chuckled lecherously. 'Why should that stop her seeing *you*? It will merely add even more spice and frisson to your affair.'

'How can you suggest such disgusting things?' wept Troilus. 'If another man...Ugh! I feel nauseous at the thought of it. I tell you, Pandarus, now she's gone I can feel my life draining away. So here's what I want you to do. After my funeral, you must smuggle my ashes away to Criseyde, and tell her I've died because of her.'

'Oh, shut up and get up,' Pandarus retorted. 'People will think you're a coward, trying to avoid fighting.'

'But there's no fighting going on at the moment. Have you forgotten? They've made a truce – and paid for it with my beloved Criseyde. Oh, oh…!'

'I tell you what,' said Pandarus in exasperation, 'we'll go out together and have some fun. I heard there's an open invitation to a great banquet on the other side of town, with music and dancing girls. Let's go!'

However, Troilus refused to go anywhere, except to Criseyde's house; but that, of course, was now locked, barred and empty.

Almost a fortnight passed. Then, despite much foreboding, Troilus began to hope against hope that Criseyde would shortly keep her promise and find a way to return.

Meanwhile, Criseyde had been escorted to the Greek camp by the handsome Diomede. She hardly gave him a glance. But *he* certainly noticed *her* – such courtliness, such beauty!

Far from putting him off, her indifference fanned the flames of his desire.

He decided to take things slowly, and begin by expressing friendship rather than romantic interest. So he said, 'My lady, the people here are greatly looking forward to meeting you and making you feel at home. You'll find our way of life very similar to yours; after all, we worship the same gods. Look, here's our camp ahead – and there's your father's tent.'

Criseyde glanced up to see Calkas striding towards them. He plucked her from the horse and wrapped her into a warm embrace. 'Welcome, dear daughter!' he cried. 'How are you? Ah, even lovelier than ever! All the eligible Greek princes will be queuing up to woo you! Come in to your new home. Although it's not a permanent house, I've done my best to make it comfortable.' He showed her in to a magnificent tent, adorned with fine furs, linens and ornaments.

Criseyde had little to say to her father, for she was still greatly ashamed of his defection. However, since she had no choice, she resolved to accept the situation and make the best of it. She arranged her belongings in the screened-off section he had assigned to her, befriended the maids that he had appointed to serve her, and gradually settled down.

Around this time, the long period of mourning for her late husband finally came to an end. So Criseyde discarded her black clothes, replacing them with bright colours. She let down her long hair and bound it with a thread of gold.

Handsome Diomede kept his distance but observed all this closely. By the time she had been in the Greek camp for ten days, he could no longer contain himself. So he paid a visit to her father, Calkas, consulting him on some spurious business matter. Criseyde did her filial duty and offered their visitor wine and food, which Diomede accepted enthusiastically. After he had concluded his discussion with the old priest, he turned to Criseyde and asked, 'So, my lady, how do you find life here?'

'Everything is quite satisfactory,' said Criseyde politely.

'No doubt,' said Diomede, fishing for information, 'your father will shortly find you a Greek husband?'

'I hope not,' said Criseyde.

'Why ever not?' said Diomede. 'It's not good for a young woman to be alone, whether she be a maiden or a widow.'

'I think, sir, that's for me to decide.'

'Aha!' said Diomede. 'I know what it is. You have a secret lover back in Troy, eh? Well, let me give you some friendly advice. If that's the case, you're wasting your time. Trojan men are all doomed! For very shortly we will finally break down their defences and raze their city to the ground; and as it burns, every man in it will be slaughtered. Yes!' his voice rose excitedly. 'The whole world will tremble at our cruel revenge for the ravishment of Helen. Then you will be glad you left your inferior lover to his wretched fate!'

Criseyde said nothing. Her father touched her arm and said, 'My dear, did you know? Diomede is one of the Greeks' greatest warriors.'

'Not at all,' smiled Diomede, feigning modesty. 'But I hope I have enough achievements to my name, my lady, for you to accept me as your suitor? May I return tomorrow, so we can get to know each other a little more?'

'If my father wishes you to return,' said Criseyde, 'then of course you may. But I should tell you plainly that I don't plan to take another husband.'

Diomede bowed, saying, 'Even so, I look forward to seeing you again.'

During his next visit to Calkas, Criseyde again dutifully provided hospitality. This time, Diomede spoke to her only of light hearted matters, so charmingly that her coldness thawed a little and she even managed to smile. He did not mention courtship again. However, he greatly admired the brooch she wore. He asked her to unpin it from her gown so he could see it properly; then purposely forgot to give it back. It slipped her mind until he had left with the jewel; and then she was full of remorse and regret, for the brooch was the very one that Troilus had given her. She resolved to ensure Diomede returned it.

However, the next time they met, it was not appropriate to ask for it. For Diomede had been injured in battle, and had specifically requested Criseyde to dress his wound; it would be impolite to refuse this. As she bandaged him, he said, 'Don't mock my injury, Criseyde. At least the man who inflicted it on me was one of Troy's greatest warriors. In fact he's one of the king's sons: they said his name was Troilus.'

Criseyde ran straight home and wept, wracked with shame and guilt, feeling sure that Diomede had somehow discovered her affair with Troilus, and had taken her brooch to torment her.

After that, her resistance was broken. Diomede continued to court her, subtly and confidently. How different he was from the insecure, constantly pleading Troilus!

The date of her planned return to Troy passed unmarked. Time went on, and she stopped thinking about it. In her mind, the city began to fade into a distant, hazy memory.

Troilus had a disturbing dream. In it, he imagined Criseyde embracing a great boar with monstrous tusks. As soon as he awoke, he rushed out to ask Pandarus what it might mean.

'Hmm,' said Pandarus, not believing his own words. 'The boar is probably her old father, to whom she's expressing her relief at being reunited.'

'Why is she so late in keeping her promise to return?' asked Troilus.

'I've no idea, old fellow. Why don't you write and ask her? You haven't exchanged a single letter since she left.'

So Troilus took a quill and, staining the parchment with many tears, wrote:

> My own beloved, my freshest flower
> You assured me of your return within a fortnight, yet eight tedious weeks have now passed with neither sight nor word of you. Have I offended you in some way? Do you no longer care for me? Reply soon, I implore you, and end the misery to which you have subjected me.
> However you respond, I wish you happiness.
> Farewell!
> Your own,
> Troilus.

The letter was smuggled out and delivered speedily. Very soon, Pandarus brought Troilus her very brief reply:

> I greet you, Troilus
> I shall come to you as soon as I can. However, I do not know when that will be.
> Your friend,
> Criseyde

When Troilus read this, he saw only empty phrases. He sent for his sister Cassandra, who claimed mystical powers. He confessed to her his secret entanglement with Criseyde, then asked her to throw light on the dream.

'Alas, poor brother!' she said. 'I already knew of your affair with Criseyde, though you guarded the secret well.

But it is doomed. For the boar you dreamed of is a prince of Greece who has seized your beloved's heart.'

Now, Cassandra had long ago been blessed by the gods with the gift of clairvoyance; but at the same time, they also cursed her to be disbelieved.

Thus Troilus said, 'Since everyone knows that you always tell lies, sister, I'm comforted by your words – for they surely mean that Criseyde is really still true to me.'

Cassandra only shook her head sadly.

Despite his declared belief, Troilus tormented himself more than ever: 'Are Cassandra's words true or false? Is Criseyde a cheat or faithful? Is she beset by trouble or deliberately avoiding me? Should I pity her or hate her?' And on and on. He considered trying to visit her across the enemy lines by disguising himself, but feared being recognised and taken captive. He wrote her dozens more unanswered letters, praising her, pleading with her, accusing her. At last Pandarus pressed a reply into his hand:

> Troilus
>
> I fear this letter may be intercepted so I cannot fully explain why I have not yet returned but it is partly because I am plagued by malicious rumours of your disloyalty.
>
> Also, the war makes it impossible for me to visit Troy for the foreseeable future.
>
> I trust you will always remember me kindly, as I remember you.
>
> From your lifelong friend,
> Criseyde

Some time after that, Troilus saw a group of his fellow knights crowing over a piece of battledress, seized from a noble Greek opponent in a tussle earlier that day. Having nothing better to do, he ambled over to inspect it – and suddenly found himself stifling a cry. For the collar was trimmed with exquisite gold embroidery, and pinned onto this was a brooch – the very brooch that he himself had given Criseyde after their first night together. How could she have given it to another man? He stumbled away to Pandarus's house, raging:

'You rogue! You mocked me for thinking the worst, but you were wrong. For that odious niece of yours – oh, curse the day I first set eyes on her! – has taken another lover.'

Choking with distress, he shared what he had seen. 'What did I do to deserve this dreadful fate? Everything is finished!'

Pandarus had guessed some time ago that Criseyde had broken faith, and was greatly discomfited by his niece. 'Dear friend, you are like a brother to me,' he said softly. 'I did everything possible to help you in this affair. But cruel fortune wrested control from me when Criseyde's father demanded her return, depriving me of any power. From now on I completely disown Criseyde: I no longer regard myself as her uncle, and I will hate her for ever more. If she were taken from this world before her time, I would not grieve. Ach! Let the poets sing of her fickleness and flightiness. May other women despise her for dishonouring their sex.'

Time heals everything, so they say; and as it passed, Troilus's great love was transformed to hatred. He never saw Criseyde again, but his loathing for the Greek who had stolen her inspired him to fight more fiercely than ever before.

The time came when he again found himself opposing Diomede hand to hand. Though Criseyde's name was never spoken, the certainty that they were love rivals hung in the air above them, provoking such fury that both should have been killed; but fortune denied them this satisfaction.

After that, Troilus vanquished more of the enemy than anyone except his brother, mighty Hector, until in the end he was slain by Achilles.

> Listen, all you fresh young men and damsels! Do you not understand now that worldly love is less permanent than the scent of flowers carried on a passing breeze? Heed this sorry tale and entrust your hearts only to God – for He alone will never betray you.

The ancient Greek legend of the Trojan War is as follows: Eris, goddess of strife and discord, presents a golden apple marked 'for the most beautiful' to three other goddesses: Hera, Athena and Aphrodite. The high god Zeus orders Prince Paris of Troy to judge which of them should receive it. Paris awards it to Aphrodite who, in return, promises to make Queen Helen fall in love with him. However, Helen is already married to Menelaus, king of the Greek city-state of Sparta. When she elopes with Paris, Menelaus and his fellow Greeks besiege Troy for ten years in revenge.

According to Chaucer's modern translator, Nevill Coghill, the Siege of Troy was very much part of popular culture in medieval England, due to belief in a strong geographical and historical link. In the 12th century book *Histories of the Kings of Britain*, Geoffrey of Monmouth claimed that Britain (previously known as Albion) was invaded by an ancient Trojan prince called Felix Brutus, who defeated the native giants and renamed the country after himself. Coghill says that, during the 14th century, some people actually wanted London to be renamed as Troynovant (New Troy). Thus setting a love story in Troy was a wise idea for an author hoping to strike a chord with his potential readership; although the behaviour of the characters is more in tune with the conventions of medieval chivalry.

Some scholars describe Chaucer's depiction of the two lovers constantly trembling and sighing, and Troilus's threats of suicide, as representing the epitome of courtly love. However, it could equally be considered parody. The retelling here thus portrays Criseyde as rather embarrassed by Troilus's melodramatic declarations, and accepting her new lover, Diomede, for his more straightforward masculinity. Chaucer himself was not dogmatic about his characterisations, giving carte blanche for future retellings:

> 'Add or diminish, make your own selection
> Of my poor language; let it be your care
> I beg you!...'
> (Book III, verse 202)

The character of Troilus appears in ancient Greek literature as one of the fifty children of King Priam of Troy; his mother is Queen Hecuba. His most famous siblings include Hector, Paris and Cassandra. The earliest surviving reference to him is in Homer's *Iliad* (c.8th century BC), an epic Greek poem about the Siege of Troy. He is mentioned in a number of other ancient Greek works, sometimes described as such a beautiful youth that his real father may have been the god Apollo.

Criseyde is not a mythical character. She first appears, under a different name, in a predecessor of Chaucer's book, the 12th century French *Roman de Troie*, and is first named Criseyde in Boccaccio's *Filostrato*.

Although a man named Pandarus appears in the *Iliad*, his character as a go-between was invented by Boccaccio.

In Greek mythology, Diomede(s) is an outstanding warrior, later king of Argos. Also in ancient myths, Cassandra is the sister of Troilus. She is courted by the god Apollo, who tries to win her with the gift of clairvoyance. When she rejects him, divine laws prevent him from removing the gift, so he modifies it with a curse that no one will ever believe her true prophesies.

The Promise

'The Franklin's Tale' in *The Canterbury Tales*
written 1386–1400

❦

Chaucer began writing *The Canterbury Tales* in 1386, but it was far from finished when he died. He left ten manuscripts containing various parts of the work, which have been arranged by modern scholars into the order it seems he intended.

The book has the following 'frame story': A group of thirty Christian pilgrims embark on a five-day journey from London to Canterbury Cathedral, to visit the shrine of St Thomas Becket. They set out from the Tabard Inn, Southwark. At its landlord's suggestion, they take turns telling stories to help pass the time while they travel. Chaucer intended each pilgrim to tell two stories on the outbound journey and a further two on the return, with the best one winning a free supper at the tavern. However, he only completed twenty-four stories before his death. Most are derived from European and Middle Eastern literature and folklore, but the style of retelling is very much his own.

The book is mostly written in verse, extending to more than seventeen thousand lines. There are colourful descriptions of the narrators, portraying a range of medieval English people. They are: two knights, a miller, a reeve (the official who supervised a landowner's estate), a cook, a lawyer, a sailor, a prioress, a monk, two nuns, a physician, a pardoner (one who sold 'indulgences' – papal grants of remission from spiritual punishment for sins), a several-times-married wife, a friar, a summoner (a minor official who summoned people before the ecclesiastical courts), a clerk, a merchant, a squire, a franklin (a free landowner not of noble birth), a yeoman (small freehold farmer), a manciple (one in charge of buying provisions for a college, Inn of Court, or monastery) and a parson, as well as the innkeeper and Chaucer himself.

The book quickly became a long-term bestseller, with over ninety surviving manuscripts from the 1400s. After William Caxton established England's first printing press in 1476, he produced the first printed edition of *The Canterbury Tales* within two years.

This particular story is narrated by the franklin. Chaucer vividly describes him as white-bearded, sanguine, ruddy and benign. He is an epicure, with a well-stocked larder, his own partridge coop and fish pond, and a table always laid ready for the next meal. He has served as a justice, a 'member for the shire', a sheriff and an auditor. He wears a dagger and a silk purse in his belt.

The introductory passage links this story to the 12th century *Lais of Marie de France* (see p.63), although it is totally different in flavour.

In olden days, the noble Bretons delighted in composing lais about various adventures, either to be read quietly or sung to musical accompaniments. I'll tell you one of these stories as well as I can remember it. But I'm not a cultivated man; so please excuse my uneducated speech and simple narrative style.

There was a knight of ancient Brittany called Arvéragus of Caer-rhud, who persuaded the delightful, high-born lady Dorigen to marry him.

Now, as we all know, the law states that a husband has absolute authority over his wife. However, Arvéragus did not agree with this. He believed that, to ensure a long and happy marriage together, *both* parties should willingly submit to the other. And rightly so; otherwise the god of Love quickly spreads his wings and flies away. No one wants their spouse to treat them like a slave. Besides, we all make mistakes sometimes, but there's no point responding to them with angry words; it's always better to be tolerant and patient.

So Arvéragus said to his new wife, 'My dear, I wish to continue the romance of serving you, as a knight's due to his lady. I promise never to force you into anything against your will. I shall always obey and trust you, and never be jealous.'

'Thank you kindly,' Dorigen replied with a fond smile. 'That's very generous of you. In return, I pray to God that I never cause any arguments or conflict between us. I humbly swear to be a good wife.'

Thus they were both at peace.

Arvéragus took Dorigen to live with him in his castle at Finistère in France. They enjoyed marital bliss for a good twelve months. But eventually, Arvéragus told his wife he really must stop neglecting his chivalric duty. So he crossed the sea to Britain and stayed away there for two years, doing great deeds and achieving much honour in battle.

Poor Dorigen! She loved her husband as much as her own life, and she wept bitterly at his absence. She sighed and pined for him, lay awake every night, fasted and lamented. What could possibly cheer her up? Nothing, except Arvéragus's return. Her friends tried sympathising, then they tried scolding her. Gradually, they persuaded her to pull herself together. Besides, Arvéragus wrote to her regularly, saying that all was going very well for him, and that he intended to be home before long.

Seeing her in a better mood, her friends invited her to join them for a walk by the sea. However, as soon as Dorigen spied a vessel out on the waves, she sank back into her usual misery. 'When, oh when, will I see the ship bringing my darling husband home?' she wailed. 'Oh, oh! But when that ship finally comes, supposing it's dashed against those awful jagged rocks down there? Then I'll never see him again!'

Her friends abandoned the idea of seashore walks, and instead took her out to the countryside. This was much more successful, for they managed to get her dancing and playing backgammon and chess.

One sunny morning – it was the sixth day of May – they took her to a most delightful garden full of trees and scented flowers. Dinner was served there, followed by singing and dancing. Dorigen actually managed to stop thinking about her absent husband long enough to quite enjoy herself.

Amongst the numerous men and ladies gathered there, a young squire stood right out from the crowd. His name was Aurelius. He was extremely good-looking and splendidly dressed, with a lively personality and great talent for singing and dancing. All this made him very popular. Yet he was not a happy man. For he had long been desperately in love with Dorigen, but had never had the courage to do anything about it. She herself was totally oblivious to his desire.

However, on that particular day, Aurelius found himself walking through the garden beside her. He started talking to her, and she did not object, for she already knew him vaguely. This gave him courage to speak up.

'Madam, I-I...have a confession to make,' said he. 'I love you! I realise you probably don't feel the same way, but I beg you to at least have mercy on me: offer some word of pity or I will die of despair!'

Dorigen stared at him in astonishment. 'You don't really mean that, do you?' she replied. 'Well, well, well! I would never have guessed. It's absolutely ridiculous. Don't you know that I'm married? I have vowed always to be totally faithful to my husband, and that's my final answer.'

Aurelius groaned and fixed his gaze on her beseechingly. To try and break the tension, she thought for a moment and came up with a clever idea. 'I tell you what,' she said lightly, 'I'll give you a tiny chance to win my love; but I warn you, it's totally impossible.'

'Tell me!' he cried.

'Well,' said Dorigen, thinking of her fears about her husband's safe return, 'you know those horrible, jagged rocks that cause so many deadly shipwrecks round the local coast? If you can get rid of them all – *every single rock* – then I'll return your love.'

'Is that the *only* way?' he groaned.

'Absolutely,' she laughed. 'And as God knows, that day will never come. So stop these stupid fantasies about me. No man can find happiness by chasing another man's wife.'

Aurelius sighed. 'Madam, as you say, what you suggest is totally impossible. You have just condemned me to die on your account.' With those words, he turned and walked sorrowfully away.

Dorigen stared after him, feeling both embarrassed and discomfited. However, the next moment her friends came up and swept her away for a walk through the garden's leafy alleyways. She decided to say nothing about her awkward encounter with the young squire. The revels resumed, and continued until well after sunset, so that everyone went home in high spirits...

Everyone, that is, except Aurelius. He stumbled home wretchedly, certain that his heart was physically breaking. By the time he arrived, he felt icy cold. He fell to his knees, raised his hands to heaven and uttered an impassioned prayer – not to God, but to an older deity:

'Hail, mighty Apollo, or Phoebus, or whatever people call you these days! When you've got time to spare from turning the seasons and making the plants grow, please, *please* spare a moment for me, lord! My lady-love has just condemned me to death unless I fulfil a totally impossible task. Lord, you know your sister Luna, queen of the Ocean? Please get her to work a miracle for me. Ask her to raise the floods five fathoms high to drown all the rocks on the local coast. Then I can say to my lady-love, "You see, the rocks have vanished, just as you ordered – so you *have* to keep your promise to me." Lord, look how my cheeks are stained with tears. I beg you to have compassion and grant my boon!'

The next moment, he swooned. His brother found him flat out on the floor and carried him into his bed. Which is where we must leave this unhappy fool for a while.

Meanwhile, Arvéragus came home from his travels abroad – the very flower of chivalry. Dorigen was ecstatic, and basked in his love. For his part, he did not worry at all about what she had been up to in his absence, for he had not a single doubt about her in his head. He delighted in making his beloved wife happy.

Two whole years passed, and still Aurelius felt too tormented to do anything useful with himself. His only comfort was his brother, a former scholar, who was sympathetic and most concerned.

One day the brother remembered something from his student days at Orléans in France. Like many young men at that time, he had delighted in dabbling in forbidden matters – particularly the art of sorcery. He recalled finding a curious book a student friend had hidden in his desk. It displayed the phases of the moon, with detailed explanations of its twenty-eight mansions and other such nonsense.

'I wonder if it's possible to convert those theories into action,' he mused. 'There must be someone in Orléans who has such knowledge and power, and who could help Aurelius in this way – someone who could conjure up an illusion of the seashore rocks vanishing, even if only for a few days. Then this lady would have to accept his love; for it would be too shameful to break her promise.'

I won't draw the story out. He went straight to Aurelius, who was lying in bed as usual, and told him of his idea. Aurelius was so excited that he leaped up at once, and the pair started off along the road to Orléans without delay.

And it all worked out splendidly. For as they neared the city, a stranger approached them. He greeted them amicably in Latin, as if he were already acquainted with them, and said mysteriously: 'I know exactly why you're going to Orléans.' He then revealed himself to be a sorcerer! He walked beside them for the rest of the journey, chatting away. It turned out that he and Aurelius's brother had mutual friends amongst the scholarly community in the city.

The sorcerer invited the two brothers to his house. While they waited for dinner, he led them into his book-lined study. 'Take a seat,' said he, 'and I'll show you a bit of fun.'

The next moment, before their eyes, he conjured up a phantasmagoria – a series of extraordinary illusions. It started with a stag-hunting scene; faded into a hawk killing a heron; then changed again to a knights' jousting match. But it was the final, mischievous scene that entranced Aurelius most of all: a vision of his beloved Dorigen dancing that was so realistic, he felt as if he were right there beside her!

After that, the sorcerer clapped his hands to make the marvels disappear, and took them through to dine. They ate an excellent meal, then got down to business.

Aurelius's brother explained the situation and asked the sorcerer if he had enough power to remove every single rock from the entire coast of Brittany.

The sorcerer thought it over, then said, 'I warn you that it won't be an easy task and I'm not exactly eager to try it. But I'll have a go, if you agree to pay me a thousand pounds.'

Aurelius was so excited that he laughed out loud. 'A thousand pounds?' he cried. 'That's nothing – I'd give the

whole wide world to win my lady-love! It's a bargain: I
solemnly swear to pay you the full amount if you succeed.
Can you start work tomorrow?'

'Indeed I can,' said the sorcerer.

The next morning, all three of them set off for Brittany.
When they arrived, Aurelius spared no efforts in making the
sorcerer comfortable, and begged him to waste no time.

The sorcerer set to work on his trick at once, toiling night
and day. Don't ask me how he did it – I don't understand
astrological jargon or occult tricks. But I know that he used
an astrolabe, calculuses, year series, planetary spheres, arcs,
angles, proportionals, phases of the moon, signs of the
zodiac and so on... Until he finally achieved his goal!

Yes, he created an astonishing optical illusion so that, no
matter who looked at the shoreline of Finistère at any point
along the coast, they saw no sign of any rocks at all. He had
somehow made them all vanish into thin air.

When Aurelius saw that the sorcerer had pulled it off, he
fell in rapture at his feet, exclaiming, 'Thank you, oh thank
you! You have saved me from certain death.'

Then he hurried straight into town, in search of Dorigen.
Fortunately for him, she was out and about on that day. He
calmed his trembling heart and ran up to her.

'My truest lady,' he said hoarsely, with a deep bow, 'my
dearest beloved! You have no idea what misery and torture I
have been through on your account since we last spoke.
Normally I would not dare to approach you again; but I
must. For at our previous meeting, you made a solemn
pledge to me. You promised that, if I could remove all the
rocks from the local coast, you would reciprocate my love.
Well, I have done exactly what you asked.'

Dorigen was thunderstruck.

'Let me take you on a tour of the coast to prove that I am telling the truth,' Aurelius babbled on. 'Once you have seen it for yourself, you cannot break your word.'

All the colour drained from Dorigen's face. 'No!' she cried. 'I only gave you that challenge as a tease; I never thought for one moment that you might be able to do it. You've caught me in a trap!'

She turned from him and rushed home, overwhelmed with horror and disgust. There was no one she could confide in, for her beloved Arvéragus was away from town. So she flung herself down on her bed, and wailed, 'Oh, Fortune, you've really snared me. What a choice: to cheat on my husband – that's unthinkable! – or break my pledge to that horrible rogue. Both ways would be utterly disgraceful. How can I escape this dreadful situation?'

Her thoughts swirled around in this mire of misery for two whole days, until Arvéragus came home. He was dismayed to find his beloved crying, and immediately asked why. She told him exactly what had happened.

To her surprise, her husband responded with a kindly smile, 'Is that all, my sweet Dorigen? Well, you'll have to keep your word to this pathetic fellow, won't you? Integrity is the most precious quality in the world; and by God and all the love I bear you, I can't let you break a pledge.'

Despite these brave words, he too lost control and fell to weeping alongside his beloved wife. 'Even so, it pains me dreadfully just to think of what you must do. My dear, please don't ever mention this dreadful business to anyone. Now, now, forget about my own feelings: I'll get over it. Go and wash your face and try to act normally, so that no one has any reason to pry and thus discover our disgrace.'

No doubt, you are shaking your head and thinking, 'What kind of lewd and foolish man would let his wife go ahead with such a horrific thing?' Well, before you pass judgement, hear the rest of the story, for it may not end how you expect.

Meanwhile, Aurelius was burning for his next meeting with Dorigèn. This happened more quickly than he had dared hope. He was thrilled to see her hurrying through the town, in search of him.

'My lady! Wh-where are you off to?' he stammered.

She answered him in a hysterical voice, 'To meet you in the garden, of course. My husband has advised me to go there at once to keep my promise to you.'

'Y-your *husband*?'

Aurelius was stunned. He had never anticipated that she would confess this affair to her husband – let alone that *he* would insist that she kept her pledge.

Embarrassment and shame washed over him like a tumultuous wave. When he finally managed to collect himself, he began to see things in rather a different light. 'What an admirable couple they are,' he thought. 'By comparison, I'm nothing but a complete oaf. By God, how can I even think of forcing myself on such a noble lady? I must abandon my disgraceful passion.'

He took a deep breath said aloud, 'Madam, um...er... Actually, I've...changed my mind. You are so virtuous, and your husband has such a generous spirit! It makes me realise how badly I have wronged you both. I cannot damage such a happy and trusting marriage. So I hereby release you from the covenant between us. Any agreement you feel you made with me is now null and void.'

She fell to her knees and thanked him with all her heart.

Aurelius bowed. 'No wonder I fell in love with you: for you are very best and truest lady in the whole world. May all women be inspired by your gracious example!'

Dorigen hurried home to her husband, her heart bursting with relief. She told him everything that had happened. No words can describe the relief that *he* felt too.

From that time on, Arvéragus and Dorigen continued to live in marital bliss, with no sign of even the slightest discord. She stayed as true to him as she had always been; and he cherished her like a queen.

But what of Aurelius?

Now he had leisure to count up the cost of his foolhardy venture, he thought, 'I've got myself into a really tight corner. I owe the sorcerer a whole thousand pounds – I'm ruined! I'll have to sell my entire inheritance and become a beggar! Hmm…but I wonder if I can persuade the sorcerer to let me pay it off over a period of time? I've got nothing to lose by asking.'

He went off gloomily to search his coffers and gathered up all the gold he had there: around five hundred pounds. He took this to the sorcerer and begged him, as a gentleman, to allow him time to pay the outstanding amount in instalments. 'Sir,' he said, 'if you would grant me a little respite, I guarantee to repay the rest within two or three years. Would you at least consider it? If not, I'll have to sell all the property that my late father left me.'

The sorcerer looked at him askance. At last he said, 'Did I not fulfil your commission?'

'You did indeed, sir,' said Aurelius. 'You did it perfectly.'

'So,' said the sorcerer, 'have you not won your lady?'

'No,' Aurelius admitted, with a deep sigh.

'Why ever not?' said the sorcerer. 'I urge you to explain.'

Reluctantly, Aurelius told him everything that had passed between them. 'Her husband is so noble,' he said, 'that he would rather have died of shame than let his wife break her word. As for my lady, she could not bear to be unfaithful to him and would rather have died than commit adultery with me. I have to admit, she made her pledge to me in all innocence. She'd probably never even heard of magical illusions. I'm sure she never expected in her wildest dreams that I would be able to carry out her impossible challenge. I felt so mortified, that I sent her straight back to her husband, as freely as he had sent her to me. That's the whole story.'

'My dear brother,' said the sorcerer. 'Both you men behaved with impeccable honour. I am so impressed that I hereby release you from the debt you owe me. I will not accept even a penny as my fee. I feel well rewarded for what I did, and that's quite enough for me. Farewell!'

Then he mounted his horse and rode away.

Friends, my tale is done. But let me conclude by asking you a question: which of the three gentleman was the finest and most honourable?

The homeland of the knight in this story, Finistère, is on the northwest coast of France.

The thousand pounds that the sorcerer charges Aurelius for his trick is roughly equivalent to just over £662,000 in today's money. In the 14th century, that amount would have paid the wages of five hundred skilled tradesmen wages for a hundred days' work.

There is a very similar tale in *Decameron* (see p.226: 'The Tenth Day, the Fifth Story'). There, the man who wishes to win a married woman's love is a baron, and the 'impossible' challenge is to make a winter garden bloom with May flowers. This is also achieved by a sorcerer, and the outcome is exactly the same.

AMADIS & ORIANA

Vasco Lobeira: *Amadís de Gaula*
Portugal, late 14th century

Amadís de Gaula is an extensive chivalric epic in four volumes. It is widely believed that its author, Vasco Lobeira, was a Portuguese knight who died in battle in 1403; however, modern scholarship indicates uncertainty about the original author's true identity.

The story was translated into English in 1872 by Robert Southey, from the oldest surviving manuscript. This was a 16th century Spanish translation by Garciordoñez (Garci Rodríguez) de Montalvo who, according to Southey:

> says he has corrected it from the old originals, which were corrupted by different and bad writers, and badly composed in an ancient fashion; that he has abridged it of many superfluous words, and inserted others of a more polished and elegant style.

Southey's translation is almost three-hundred-thousand words long – only half the length of the Spanish version. He explains that he further condensed it by abridging dialogue and detailed descriptions of battle scenes etc, and removing recapitulations, whilst preserving every detail of plot and 'manners'.

Amadís de Gaula is an entertaining saga about several generations of nobles and knights, their quests for fame and their love affairs. It is vividly set against a chivalric background with regular battles and narrow escapes from death. There are parallels to Arthurian legend; but it has a unique flavour of its own.

The short retelling here unravels the love theme from the other story strands. There are a few changes in the order of action for consistency, but it maintains the integrity of the original storyline.

Amadís de Gaula is one of the main books that inspired the famous 17th century Spanish parody of chivalry, *Don Quixote*.

Lisuarte was the youngest son of the king of Great Britain. Since he had no hope of ever inheriting his father's kingdom, he went adventuring abroad. Eventually he settled down in Denmark, and married a local princess called Brisena. They had two daughters, but no son.

One day, when Lisuarte was riding alone in the deepest part of the forest, a horse suddenly sprung out from a thicket before him. Its rider was a damsel with a striking, unearthly grace. She drew up sharply, stared at him, then cried, 'Ah, Lisuarte, I've found you at last! I've come to foretell your future.'

'Who are you?' Lisuarte retorted. 'What can a stranger guess of my future?'

Before his eyes, the damsel suddenly faded away as if she were formed of mist. Lisuarte feared he was having a fit. He blinked in bewilderment…and was startled to see a hideous, wrinkled old hag in her place, quivering in the saddle.

'Who am I?' she said hoarsely. 'Urganda the Unknown. What do I foretell? Ah, what others scarcely even imagine: layer beyond layer hidden from normal sight. So heed what I say, Lisuarte:

You think it will never be yours – but you shall receive it.
You believe that daughters are profitless burdens – yet they will come to equal the world's two greatest men.

The path will not always be easy. You and your kin will be blinded by confusion. Look out for my return!'

She gave a shriek of laughter and spurred her horse. Lisuarte made to follow her and find out more; but fast as a peregrine falcon, the shape-shifter had already vanished into the trees.

Not long after that, a messenger from abroad arrived at Lisuarte's hall, breathless with urgent news: 'Sir, your father, the king of Great Britain, has been slain in battle!'

Lisuarte crossed himself, saying, 'Then my elder brother must be the new king?'

'No, sir, he is not,' said the messenger. 'For all your brothers were also killed, alongside your father. The whole country is in turmoil. The crown of Great Britain is now yours, and our people are desperate for you to return home and take control.'

Lisuarte – *King* Lisuarte as he now was – realised his duty. Echoes of Urganda's eerie prophesy throbbed in his head, but he wasted no time brooding on it. He gathered up his family and hastened with them to the coast, where a fine ship already awaited them. They set sail at once.

As they headed out to sea, a gale blew up, tore the sail asunder and swept them into a fierce storm. Heavy rain battered the open ship mercilessly, drenching everyone aboard. The crew rowed valiantly against the swell; but the heaving ship teetered far off course.

The new king and queen sat it out bravely with their younger daughter, Leonoreta. But their elder girl, Oriana, clung to the side, retching and convulsing. 'Throw me overboard!' the poor child groaned. 'Put me out of my misery!'

At that moment, the captain came over and pointed through the deluge to a thin line, just visible on the horizon.

'Is that land?' cried Brisena. 'Thank God! Have we finally arrived?'

'It's land indeed, my lady,' the captain answered. 'But the storm has blown us far away from Great Britain. Even when it dies down, it will take several more days to reach that land. The coast you can see is the realm of Scotland. Shall we turn aside and go ashore there, to help your daughter?'

Brisena said to her husband, 'If Oriana is sick for much longer, she'll have no strength left to live. Let's seize the chance to break our journey. Perhaps we can find a noble family to care for her until she recovers, while we make haste to claim your kingdom.'

'You speak wisely,' said Lisuarte. 'It so happens that the King of Scotland is an old childhood friend of mine; and our realms have always been allies. We'll go straight to his castle and seek his help.'

So it was done. The king of Scotland, Languines, welcomed Lisuarte heartily. He was delighted to hear of his old friend's ascent to the British throne, and promised to take good care of Oriana. 'She'll be in good company here,' he said, 'for my own daughter, Mabilia, is exactly the same age.'

He gave Lisuarte a fine new ship to replace the storm-battered one, and the new king and queen resumed their journey with their younger daughter. Oriana wept to see them go. But her mother had allowed her favourite young Danish maid to stay with her; and Princess Mabilia, made them both feel at home.

The three girls spent all their days together and became inseparable companions.

One day, Mabilia said to Oriana, 'Have my parents mentioned that I have a foster-brother? He's been away for ages training to be a squire, but he's coming home tomorrow.'

'What's his name?' asked Oriana.

Mabilia smiled. 'Nobody knows – not even he does. You see, he's a foundling, pulled out of the sea by one of my father's old knights, Gandales. He was out fishing and spotted a curious wooden chest floating in the waves. When he hauled it out, he found a tiny baby boy inside it! My mother says he must have been cast adrift because he was born out of wedlock.'

'Wasn't there any way to find out who he is?'

'No,' said Mabilia. 'So everyone just calls him Child of the Sea. He used to lived with Gandales and his wife and grew very close to their own son, Gandalin. But one day, my mother visited them and met Child of the Sea for the first time. He's so handsome, good-natured and self-assured, that she adopted him. He's been part of our family ever since. Gandalin moved here with him; he's coming home too.'

Later that night, the two boys arrived at the castle and at once began to keep company with Mabilia and her new friends. Oriana thought Gandalin very pleasant; but she was dazzled by Child of the Sea. As they talked and laughed together, she could not stop looking at him, though every time he tried to return her gaze, she quickly looked away.

Oriana and her Danish maid stayed for many years with the King of Scotland. As they grew up, they came to regard his castle as their home. All this time, Child of the Sea was constantly coming and going. He grew taller and fairer than ever and his voice deepened; his manners were flawless. Oriana matured too, into a beautiful, honourable damsel.

It happened that Child of the Sea one day came upon Oriana in a secluded corner of the castle. 'May I speak with you?' he asked earnestly.

Blushing, she said, 'Of course.'

Child of the Sea said, 'As you know, I've been training hard for years. At last my foster father, King Languines, says that I'm ready to be made a knight at the next dubbing ceremony.'

'Congratulations!' said Oriana warmly. 'But I've heard that knighthood often brings trouble and danger. Aren't you afraid?'

'No,' he answered, 'I'm not afraid of anything...so long as... if... Oh, Oriana! Will you permit me to be *your* knight? Will you be my own lady? I beg you... Will you let me serve you?'

Oriana was so overwhelmed, she could not speak; but she smiled and nodded eagerly. He took both her hands in his and pledged himself to her. In return, she promised eternal faithfulness to him. As was the custom, they both solemnly agreed to keep their covenant secret until Child of the Sea had proven his gallantry.

At the dubbing ceremony, most of the new young knights were watched by their proud parents, who had been invited to the castle by King Languines. Child of the Sea's own guest was his first foster father, Gandales, the old knight who had pulled him from the waves. He arrived at the castle bearing gifts: a sword, a ring and a small slab of wax.

'My dear boy,' he said to Child of the Sea, 'when I rescued you as a newborn baby, I found these items beside you in the chest. I've kept them safe for you, until you came of age.'

Child of the Sea put the ring on his finger and the sword in his scabbard. After the ceremony, he went to meet Oriana in their usual private corner.

'Now I really am your knight,' he said, 'and you are truly my lady. I must go out into the world, to prove myself.'

'I know,' she said. 'I'll think of you constantly and count the days until you return.'

'I've brought you a small keepsake.' He pressed the wax slab into her hand, explaining how it had been cast out to sea with him. 'Every time you look at it, my lady, remember that all my chivalry is dedicated to you.'

Then they embraced and bid each other farewell.

Oriana missed him terribly. But she received regular news of Child of the Sea. His remarkable feats of bravery and deliverance made her heart swell with pride. He saved virtuous damsels and women from abduction and ravishment. He supported allied knights and kings in fierce wars against roguery and evil. Sometimes he was captured and persecuted; but he always drew on his natural courage and cunning to escape and destroy his tormentors. He gained a reputation for being invincible.

Oriana often held the wax slab he had given her, daydreaming of its mysterious journey alongside him through the waves. No one knew of her love except for Mabilia and the Danish maid – who both swore never to betray her.

Not long after Child of the Sea's departure, Oriana received a letter from her father, King Lisuarte:

> My dear eldest daughter,
> Long years have passed since we left you in
> Scotland. Your mother and younger sister both miss
> you greatly, as I do. Now that I have brought peace

and security to Great Britain, we are anxious for you
to come home. I am sending a ship to fetch you. By
sailing close to the coastline all the way, it will avoid
the rough seas that previously made you so ill.

I have written separately to King Languines inviting
Mabilia to join you here. This will reciprocate the long
years of hospitality you have received in Scotland.
Also, of course, your Danish maid must accompany
you home.

The ship will be with you shortly. Make haste to
prepare and be ready to board it.

Your loving father,
Languines

Oriana was nervous of leaving Scotland after so many
happy years there. Moreover, she knew that Child of the Sea
would be downcast to find her gone when he returned from
his exploits. However, a father must always be obeyed.

When the three damsels were packed and ready, Oriana
went to her chamber for the last time. There she picked up
the wax slab that Child of the Sea had given her, ready to
stow it away. Under her touch, a small fragment of wax
came loose and fell away. It proved impossible to press back
into place. She shook it in irritation – and noticed a soft
rattling, as if something loose were hidden inside it.

She stared at it uncertainly, then rummaged in one of her
packed chests and pulled out a quill. With its sharp end, she
chipped away at the wax to make a hole, then reached into it
and managed to prise out the object within. It was a
fragment of fine-quality parchment, inscribed with the
following words:

This is Amadis
son of a king.

'Amadis!' In the silence of her chamber, Oriana whispered the name aloud. 'So, his father is a king – just like my father. How strange that I now know who he really is, but he has no idea. I must tell him at once!'

Hastily, she found blank parchment and a pot of ink, and wrote a note to her lover. She told of her discovery, and that she was now bound for her father's court in Great Britain. She folded the 'Amadis' inscription inside and sealed it carefully. Then she called her friends, shared the extraordinary news and asked the Danish maid to delay her journey so that she could take the letter to Child of the Sea.

'I'll be glad to do that,' the Danish maid said cheerfully. 'But where can I find him?'

'When he last sent news, he was fighting to help defend the kingdom of Gaul,' said Oriana. 'Is it too dangerous for you to seek him there?'

'Of course not,' said the Danish maid. 'My brother, Durin, is a fearless squire and he'll travel by my side to protect me.'

Oriana and Mabilia sailed to Great Britain without any problems. Oriana was delighted to see her family again, and soon settled in to her father's castle.

It wasn't long before the Danish maid arrived, bursting with good news. Oriana beckoned her and Mabilia into her chamber, locked the door and begged to be told everything.

'Child of the Sea was so excited to get your letter,' said the Danish maid. 'As soon as he'd read it, he told all his comrades-in-arms about the parchment inside the wax showing that he is Amadis, son of a king. He wrote you this reply.'

She handed a sealed letter to Oriana. The other two withdrew to let her read it in private. After a few moments, she called them over, clutching the letter to her heart.

'I must share this with you,' she said. 'Child of the Sea – my Amadis! – writes that his joy at receiving this news is spoiled only by his suffering at being away from me. Listen, I'll read this passage to you:

> 'Several times, I have almost fallen in battle, not for lack of courage or skill, but because I am constantly distracted by thoughts of you, Oriana. I worry that you have forgotten or forsaken me. I fear that because of this I may die. I beg you to save me!

'Dear friends, how can I reassure him of my constant love? Can you advise me?'

Mabilia and the Danish maid smiled knowingly at each other.

'We have often privately discussed your situation,' said Mabilia, 'and I believe that I speak for us both.'

The Danish maid nodded encouragingly.

'Write back to him at once,' said Mabilia. 'Say that, as soon as there's a truce in this war he's fighting, he should hurry to Great Britain and come straight here to the castle. He must send us word when he arrives, then hide by the wall overlooking the garden where we take our daily strolls. At nightfall, he should climb over it and come to your low grated window – where you will be waiting for him, Oriana. Don't request this; be bold and *order* it – for that is a lady's right when a knight has promised to serve her.'

They left Oriana to write the words that best expressed her feelings for Amadis. When the letter was finished, she slipped her favourite ring inside it as a token, sealed it and gave it to the Danish maid – whose brother Durin was waiting for her outside. Together they hurried back across the sea to Gaul and delivered it to Amadis.

After a few weeks, Oriana received a secret message saying that Amadis had now arrived in Great Britain, and would come to her window that very night. Mabilia waited with her. As the summer dusk fell, they heard soft footsteps outside in the walled garden. Mabilia peeped surreptitiously through the grating.

'There's a man coming, Oriana,' she whispered. 'Yes – it's him!'

Oriana began to tremble from head to toe. 'Stay with me,' she murmured, 'in case I swoon.' But Mabilia had already crept out and closed the door behind her. The next moment, a low, familiar voice called: 'Oriana?'

'I am here.'

'Come to the window – with a candle so I can see you.'

With quaking hand, she carried a candle to the grating and balanced it on the sill. By its light, the couple gazed at each other. Amadis reached out a hand through the bars; she took it in her own and clung to it.

'How beautiful you are,' he said. 'More than I even remembered; the source of all my strength and courage. And how soft your touch. I will love and serve you for ever.' His eyes were dark with emotion.

'I too will love you always,' she whispered back.

They talked on in this way through the long watches of the night, with many sighs. As dawn began to break, Amadis said, 'What does your father know of our affection?'

'Nothing,' Oriana answered.

Amadis said, 'It's vital that I impress him before I dare reveal my feelings for you and ask for your hand. To do this I must enter his service. But how?'

'Your reputation as an invincible knight has already reached my father's court from the war in Gaul,' said Oriana. 'Come to him in the next few days, and let it be

344

known that you are the mighty warrior everyone is in awe of. I'm sure he'll welcome you.'

By then the first birds were singing and the sky was streaked with early morning light. They said impassioned and reluctant farewells. Amadis slipped back over the wall to the outside world, and began to prepare his charm offensive on King Lisuarte.

It was far easier than he had feared, for Great Britain was awash with gossip about the invincible young knight who had routed all the King of Gaul's enemies. King Lisuarte was intrigued. He sent envoys to find the knight and invite him to court. Thus, when he finally arrived, Amadis received a rapturous welcome. The king was heartily impressed by Amadis's courtesy, intelligence and quiet courage, and invited him to stay and serve him. Amadis maintained a reserved demeanour and declined to be won over by any inducements of land or treasure. This made King Lisuarte even more eager to employ him. In desperation he asked his wife, Queen Brisena, for advice.

'You're going about it the wrong way,' said the queen. 'A young hero like him doesn't want to be encumbered by possessions; instead, he needs a lady to serve. I'll have a quiet word and persuade him to become *my* knight. Not just mine, but he shall serve our daughter Oriana too. I promise you, husband, he won't turn down the chance.'

So it was arranged. The queen summoned Amadis to her apartment, where she introduced him to Oriana – not realising that they already knew each other very well. Amadis and Oriana played along with it, managing to give nothing away – even though both nearly fainted with delight at spending the evening in the same room. At the end of it, when Oriana went off to bed, Amadis continued the charade by falling on his knees before the queen and begging to serve them. The queen feigned some doubts, forcing Amadis to double his entreaties.

Thus it was settled to everyone's satisfaction. King Lisuarte now had the status of the renowned Amadis in his retinue, the queen had made her husband happy – and Amadis and Oriana could see each other regularly, without arousing suspicion.

Amadis was now based at King Lisuarte's court, from where he rode out to undertake numerous chivalrous deeds. He would return quietly, saying little of what he had achieved. However, his fellow knights were greatly in awe of him and spoke excitedly of his marvellous feats.

Between adventures, he was able to mix freely with Oriana in the presence of the queen and Mabilia. One day, however, they found a chance to be together alone.

'My love,' he said, 'I have some very exciting news to share with you. You know how I often go to Gaul to support King Perion there?'

'Of course,' she said. 'You were in Gaul when I sent you the letter that revealed your name.'

Amadis nodded. 'When I was last there, I happened upon the king's young daughter, Melicia, wandering through the castle garden in tears. Apparently, her father had let her play with one of his rings, and she had carelessly lost it. Do you remember that ring that came from the chest in which I was cast away as a baby? As you know, I always wear it. Well, to comfort little Melicia, I pulled it from my finger and gave it to her. She ran in with it to her father – who had actually just found the original ring on the floor. However, he was far more interested in *my* ring. He called his wife, Queen Elisena, and showed it to her. She became very agitated and demanded to know how the ring had come into my possession. When I explained that it was cast adrift with me as a newborn baby, the queen swooned. After she came round, she called me to her side and cried, "Amadis, you are our lost son!"'

Oriana listened, wide-eyed.

Amadis went on, 'It turned out that, many years ago, when Perion was just a young wandering knight, he and Elisena were secret lovers – like you and me. After a while, Perion left her to continue his adventures, and she found she was carrying his child. That child was me. I was born in secret. My mother named me Amadis, then sent her maid to cast me away to fortune – with the ring, the sword and the letter bearing my name.'

'You must be overjoyed to find your true parents at last, and to learn the story of your birth!' cried Oriana.

'I am indeed. And in addition – King Perion at once declared me heir to his throne.'

Oriana smiled. 'My father can't refuse such a noble suitor.'

'I hope not,' said Amadis. His face grew serious. 'But before I approach him, I need to set out on a personal quest which is very important to me. Don't be angry if I'm away for a long time, you'll understand when I explain. You see, my mother and father revealed that young Melicia – my sister! – is not my only sibling. I also have a brother, whose name is Galaor. But when he was very small, he was stolen from the seashore below my father's castle – by a giant.'

Oriana gasped.

'He's never been heard of since,' said Amadis. 'So my mother, Queen Elisena, has begged me to travel through the world in search of him. Naturally, I'm eager to do so.'

How could Oriana hinder him from such an important expedition? Indeed, she encouraged him to set out at once. She was rewarded by early news that Amadis had found his brother Galaor safe and well. It turned out that the giant who abducted him had raised him diligently, and Galaor was now a knight too.

But instead of coming home, Amadis and his brother went adventuring side by side. Of course, that was natural: they were eager to make up for lost time together, and both were determined to consolidate their growing chivalric reputations. Amadis sent Oriana regular tidings of their achievements, in which they always defeated even the most dangerous foes.

While he was away, Amadis sent one of his servants, a dwarf, to King Lisuarte's castle to fetch a particular sword that he needed for a coming battle. Oriana was sitting with Mabilia and the Danish maid when the dwarf passed on his way to the armoury. Feigning nonchalance, Oriana called out to ask what adventure Amadis was currently engaged in

'Oh, my lady, a fine adventure indeed,' said the dwarf. 'He's fighting to kill the enemies of a very great lady – a queen no less, who rules her own realm. She's an exceptional lady, as brave as he is in her own way. A few days ago, when Amadis himself was in mortal danger, she contrived a clever trick that saved his life. Naturally, he's eager to help her in return. But...' He winked at the three damsels, '...some of us believe he also has another good reason to help her. Rumour has it that he's fallen in love with this queen – and that she is equally in love with him! Well, I'd better be on my way now with that sword.'

The dwarf swept out. As soon as he had gone, Oriana let out a shriek of anguish. 'He's taken another lover!' she groaned. 'How could he? Oh, oh! I shall die of sorrow!'

Mabilia and the Danish maid shook their heads at each other.

'Don't be so hasty,' said the Danish maid. 'They're only malicious rumours.'

'It's most likely some foolish misunderstanding,' said Mabilia. 'Amadis regularly sends you loving messages. You can't let foolish gossip from an ignorant servant make you doubt his devotion.'

'But my rival is a queen in her own right,' groaned Oriana. 'Obviously he'll prefer to marry her – for that way he'll also win her kingdom.'

'Don't forget that *you* are heir to your father's kingdom,' Mabilia reminded her, 'so why should that matter? Besides, Amadis will one day inherit the whole of Gaul from his father, and he's far too noble to covet even more land. He has such a good heart, Oriana; power matters nothing to him compared with true love – and true love is what he has declared to you.'

'But I've never done anything to help him, let alone save his life,' Oriana said. 'That's more than enough to make him prefer her to me. Oh, oh! I'll write to him at once. I'm going to tell him everything is over between us!'

Nothing the other two said would stop her. Oriana locked herself in her chamber where, sighing and shuddering, she sat and wrote the following letter:

> Amadis,
> I have learned the truth and you cannot deny it. For all your promises, you have betrayed me and given your heart to the queen you are fighting for. Go with her! I do not wish to see or hear from you ever again!

She sealed it and ran out past her friends to the Danish maid's brother, Durin. She thrust the letter into his hands saying, 'Seek out Amadis wherever he is, give this to him and bring back his answer. Don't let your sister hinder you.'

Durin, having no idea what this was about, readily agreed.

Within a few days, he returned. 'Amadis seemed extremely distressed to read your letter and told me to be gone at once,' he told Oriana.

'Did he send no reply?' Oriana implored him. 'Are you sure?'

Durin shook his head. 'I left him in a bad way, so after I'd ridden a short distance, I looked back to see what he was up to. I saw him hurling all his weapons about as if he wanted to be rid of them. Then he galloped off in a direction that leads nowhere but the wilderness.'

Oriana was bereft. She locked herself in her chamber, allowing only her two friends to enter. Nothing they said or did could comfort her. Her mother, the queen, fearing that she was seriously ill, sent for doctors, but Oriana refused to see them. She drank little, ate less and wept endlessly.

King Lisuarte's castle stood directly above the seashore. As Oriana grieved inside, watchmen on the battlements suddenly saw an apparition of fire burning on top of the grey waves. As they stared at it, the fire drifted towards them and entered the harbour, where it was revealed to be a huge ship, adorned with countless blazing torches. On the deck stood a very stately woman, holding a lighted candle almost as tall as she was. The woman tossed the candle into the water. In a blinding flash, the blazing torches were transformed into a mass of brightly coloured, heavily perfumed flowers strewn across the decks. The air filled with a sweet serenade, played by invisible musicians.

King Lisuarte strode down to the harbour with his retinue, to greet his strange visitor.

The stately woman stepped ashore and spoke in rich, resonant tones: 'So, Lisuarte! We meet again. Do you not recognise me? We last met long ago, deep in the forest across the sea in your wife's homeland. Much has happened since then.'

King Lisuarte gazed at her for a long moment. 'Urganda the Unknown!' he exclaimed. 'You are most welcome, wise prophetess. Come up to my castle.'

That evening, he organised a feast in her honour. When it was over, the king took Urganda aside, saying, 'You once promised to return when my kin were blinded by confusion. This is such a time – for our elder daughter, Oriana, is struck with a mysterious sickness of the spirit. Perhaps you can help her?'

'I did not arrive here by accident,' Urganda replied. 'If Oriana will allow me to see her, I will try to ease her pain.'

The king summoned Mabilia to take the wise woman to Oriana's chamber. The way was down a dark passage. By the time they reached the door at the far end, Urganda had transformed once more, just as she had long ago in the Danish forest. Thus she entered Oriana's room as a hideous, wrinkled old hag, with eyes like bottomless black pools. Mabilia was startled by this change, but had the sense to say nothing.

Oriana was lying on her bed, pale and drawn. The Danish maid, sitting loyally beside her, persuaded her to receive the guest. Urganda sat down and spoke to the three damsels of mundane matters. At length, she drew a small book from the folds of her robe and beckoned Mabilia and the Danish maid to look at one of the pages. As they peered at it, both yawned, then sank back on their chairs, closed their eyes and fell into deep slumber.

'What have you done to them, old woman?' Oriana cried.

'They will waken soon enough when I have gone,' Urganda replied. 'Now, listen well, Oriana, for truth has

351

many shapes.' Then she repeated the strange words that, years before, she had spoken to Oriana's father:

'You and your sister will come to equal the world's two greatest men.'

'But I want no more dealings with *any* man,' said Oriana. 'I have been betrayed, old woman. I only want my wretched life to end. As for my sister, she is too young to know the ways of the world, but I pray that she never suffers for a man as I have, no matter how great he appears to be.'

'Hush,' said Urganda. 'What is ordained comes from the Almighty and no one can alter the Book of Fate. But look, your friends are stirring; it is time for me to go. Hold on to faith, my dear; then you will lack nothing.' Softly, she opened the door and slipped out.

Within moments, Mabilia and the Danish maid stood up, rubbing their eyes. They remembered little of Urganda the Unknown; but they were relieved to see that Oriana had now stopped weeping and was sitting on the edge of her bed with a look of confusion on her face.

Some days later, the Danish maid told Oriana that her brother Durin had just arrived at the castle, desperate to speak with her. Oriana wearily agreed to see him.

The squire rushed in excitedly and at once started to tell his news: 'My lady, you know that Amadis is universally considered one of the best knights in the world. Now listen to his remarkable achievement on Firm Island.'

Oriana shook her head. 'Firm Island? Where and what is this place?'

'It lies far to the south in the waters of a great blue sea,' said Durin. 'Many generations ago, it was ruled by a Greek prince and his wife who were both so fair, gracious, merciful and wise that all their people adored them.

'On the island they created a wonderful garden of flowers and fruit trees, and in its very centre they built the extraordinary Arch of True Lovers. It is made of pure copper and shaped like a man blowing a trumpet. Its purpose is to test fidelity. It still stands there, and is still in use. If any deceitful lover tries to pass through it, the copper man sounds a fearsome, ear-splitting trumpet blast; then choking smoke and flames billow out to strike the false one down. However, any knight or lady who is faithful to their beloved may pass freely through the Arch, to a cascade of flowers and sweet music.'

Oriana listened in silence.

Durin went on, 'Beyond the Arch stands the Forbidden Chamber – a building that tests visitors' overall virtue. The few who successfully pass through the Arch of True Lovers may attempt to enter it by ascending four sets of jasper steps. Since the prince and his wife died, no one has ever managed to do so. Some climb the first, second and even third sets of steps; but all eventually collapse en route as if struck by lightning, and must be dragged away to revive. It is said that the Forbidden Chamber awaits only one particular knight and his lady, both of perfect virtue. They will be the new rulers of Firm Island, and when they enter the Forbidden Chamber, the whole enchantment will be broken.'

'Speak on, brother,' said the Danish maid impatiently. 'You said that Amadis has been there. What happened?'

'I am told that he arrived with his brother Galaor, his foster-brother Gandalin and many other knightly companions,' said Durin. 'The others all clamoured to take the Arch of True Lovers challenge – but, unfortunately, all were left ashamed. For loud trumpet blasts and choking smoke quickly announced their past contemptible dealings with women.'

'What about Amadis?' said the Danish maid.

Oriana caught her breath.

'Apparently, he strode forward confidently,' said Durin, 'whispering your name, lady Oriana. When he stepped under the Arch, everyone heard music as pure as light. He emerged swathed in pure white flowers scented like angels. A true lover indeed!'

'You see, Oriana!' cried Mabilia. 'That absolutely proves he loves you unwaveringly and truly! Oh, but why are you crying now?'

Tears were flooding from Oriana's eyes. Her two friends ran over and threw their arms around her.

'It's because now I realise that *I* have wronged *him*!' Oriana wept. 'Why did I allow myself to be misled by that dreadful rumour? How can I ever make amends?'

'Write to him again,' cried Mabilia. 'Do it at once! Tell him everything – explain why you doubted him and that you now have proof of your mistake. You must beg, very humbly, for his forgiveness.'

And so she did. When the letter was sealed, the Danish maid promised to help Durin find Amadis, wherever he might be, and deliver it to him – even at risk of their own lives. 'And we won't leave his side,' she declared, 'until he gives us a reply for you.'

When they had gone, Mabilia persuaded Oriana to rise from her bed and assume her normal activities. 'For,' she pointed out, 'now you have every reason to be optimistic.'

Time passed. Oriana's melancholy grew worse.

Some stranger knights arrived at King Lisuarte's' castle. They brought a shield they had found abandoned in the wilderness, and asked if anyone knew whose it was. Its coat of arms was a pair of azure-coloured lions on a background of gold. Mabilia said nothing, but immediately recognised it as belonging to Amadis.

Oriana took this news badly. 'If he's lost his shield, he must be dead,' she wept. 'He died without knowing that I still love him! I can't bear it; I must die too. I'm going to starve myself until I leave this cruel world for ever.'

'I forbid you!' Mabilia cried. 'There could be many harmless reasons why he lost it. Hopefully, our friends will be back soon with some good news.'

'But I can't face my parents' constant concern and questioning,' wept Oriana.

'I have an idea,' said Mabilia. 'Do you remember your mother once took us to their other castle, Miraflores, in the flower meadows? It's a lovely, peaceful place. You'd feel so much better there, than in this gloomy castle full of warriors. Tell your mother I'm taking you there to convalesce from your recent illness.'

Oriana agreed. With her mother's blessing, the two damsels moved to Miraflores, accompanied by just a few sympathetic servants. They lived quietly, eating simple food and taking gentle walks around the garden – until at long last, the Danish maid burst in.

'We've found Amadis!' she cried. 'But in the strangest circumstances. We took a ship for Gaul, thinking maybe he had gone back there. But on the way we ran into a storm…'

'What bad luck,' said Oriana sympathetically, recalling her own storm-bound seasickness.

'No, actually it was the best of luck,' said the Danish maid. 'Because the wind blew us off course to a remote rock, where a hermit had his hut. While the crew waited for the sea to calm, Durin and I went ashore and met the hermit. He was very friendly and told us about his life. He said he'd lived there alone for many years, enjoying God's company. But a few months earlier he had been joined by a young man who arrived in a small boat, refused to give his name, and asked to stay there while he recovered from a broken heart. The good hermit agreed, so long as he built himself a separate hut, and didn't disturb him.'

She glanced at Oriana, who was listening wide-eyed.

'As we were talking,' the Danish maid continued, 'we heard someone outside. "That'll be him," said the hermit, "come to collect the seaweed gruel that I leave out for him each day." We peeped out – and saw a very lean and dishevelled Amadis!'

'Oh!' Oriana could scarcely contain herself. 'Did you speak with him? Did you give him my letter? Is he in good health? What did he say?'

'Everything is mended, and your troubles are over,' smiled the Danish maid. 'He recognised me at once and snatched your letter to read. He reacted much as you have just done. He begged parchment and a quill from the hermit and wrote a reply to you straightaway. Here it is, my dear lady – and also a ring that he asked me to give you.'

The ring was the one Oriana had once sent him with the waxed parchment. With shaking hands, she slipped it onto her finger, then took the letter to a quiet corner. After she had studied it seven times over, she called the others and said, 'He forgives me – totally, utterly, with all willingness! He declares that this quarrel has only made him love me more. And he is not far away! He wrote that he would leave the hermit's island soon after you, dear friend, and return to Great Britain. If everything has gone to plan, he is already lodging near my father's castle, waiting for me to summon him.'

'In that case,' said the Danish maid, 'I'll take him a message to come here at once. We'll let him in, then leave you both alone. Be happy, Oriana! For here at Miraflores no one can intrude on you.'

She soon returned from this errand, saying that Amadis was on his way. The two friends admitted him as promised, locked the gate and made themselves scarce.

Thus, for the very first time, Amadis and Oriana were able to openly display their love for each other. For eight loving days and nights they enjoyed each other without intrusion or hindrance; and by the end of that time, Oriana was no longer a damsel, but a woman.

All too soon, Amadis had to leave her. For a knight was duty-bound to spend his time vanquishing lawbreakers and villains, rescuing the innocent from evil and freeing the oppressed.

'But very soon I shall return openly,' he promised, 'and ask for your hand in marriage.'

Oriana clasped his hand to her breast. 'Now you are named heir to the kingdom of Gaul and are admired far and wide, I have no fear that my father will refuse you.'

However, Amadis had no opportunity to carry out his good intention. For when Oriana returned to the main castle, she found everything in chaos. 'Whatever is the matter?' she asked her mother.

Queen Brisena sighed deeply. 'I'm glad to see *you* looking so much better, my daughter,' she said, 'but unfortunately now your father has fallen into a sickness of the mind. Do you remember that fine young knight, Amadis, who I persuaded to serve us ladies?'

Oriana turned aside to hide her blushes.

'Of course you do,' said the queen. 'By all accounts he has proven himself a great hero, but one of the older knights has turned your father totally against him. This fellow has two sons of similar age to Amadis, both knights as well; and he complains that despite his family's undying loyalty, your father has totally passed them over. So now he is spreading malicious rumours that Amadis is secretly plotting against us! I think you know that Amadis is heir to the king of Gaul? Well, in the old days, Gaul was continually at war with us. This old knight claims that the king of Gaul is planning to revive this ancient enmity, and that he has sent Amadis to infiltrate our court and spy on your father's military advisers.'

'But my father himself invited Amadis to join our court!' cried Oriana. 'How can he turn about like this?'

'Amadis's constant absences have made him suspicious,' said the queen. 'Your father expects all his followers to prove their loyalty with their presence. I myself had been looking forward to Amadis's return, for I miss his courteous company; but I can't persuade your father to change his mind.'

A few days later, Amadis came openly to King Lisuarte's castle, pretending he had only just returned to Great Britain. He sought an audience with the king, eager to present his marriage proposal. At first, the king refused to see him; then he admitted Amadis for a brief, curt conversation before ordering him away.

There was nothing to do but obey him. Amadis managed one last poignant meeting with Oriana, when she explained why Lisuarte had turned against him.

'Ah well,' he said, 'all I can do is continue adventuring across the world. 'Write to me in Gaul; I will collect your letters there. My love, I leave you in the care of your two faithful friends. Hopefully, when I next return, your father's attitude will have changed.'

Queen Brisena had grown very fond of Amadis and could not make sense of her husband's sudden hostility to him.

She took to sitting at her embroidery alone, and brooding. While she was thus engaged, a squire brought her a letter, sealed with an emerald encased in threads of gold. She opened it and read:

A fair boy will arrive. Treat him graciously, for he will bring you unexpected joy.
Urganda

After perusing the letter for a long time, she folded it up carefully and stored it away in a safe place.

Shortly after Amadis went away, Oriana realised that she was carrying his child. She was both ecstatically happy, and devastated. For the laws of Christendom at that time decreed it a grave offence for any unmarried woman, regardless of status, to give birth; and the prescribed punishment was execution. This abhorrent custom was not abolished for many generations until the golden age of King Arthur.

Once more, she took to her bed and wept. But when her friends discovered her latest trouble, they urged her to wipe away her tears and rejoice instead.

'Don't forget that Amadis himself was born out of wedlock,' Mabilia reminded her. '*His* mother wasn't killed – she became queen of Gaul. And Amadis is such a great man, your child is bound to be equally outstanding.'

'We'll take care of you,' the Danish maid promised. 'Let's go back to Miraflores at once, before anyone else guesses your condition. Tell your mother you wish to get away from your father's feuds and bad temper. There's a nunnery near Miraflores with a very kind abbess. When the baby is born,

I'll smuggle it away and leave it at her door, with a note asking her to care for it. There's nothing to worry about.'

Oriana thanked her friends with all her heart.

At Miraflores, in a quiet room overlooking the garden through which Amadis had come to Oriana, she gave birth to a baby boy – a beautiful child with a hearty cry. On his chest was a strange birthmark, shaped like flowing lines of foreign writing. Oriana suckled the baby lovingly until he fell asleep. Then Mabilia wrapped him in swaddling clothes, and the Danish maid and Durin set out through the forest for the nunnery.

They were gone so long, that Oriana and Mabilia began to fear for the safety of the newborn. When at last the Danish maid returned, she could scarcely hide her distress.

'What has happened to my son?' Oriana cried.

'Oh my dearest lady and friend,' said the Danish maid breathlessly. 'Your son is safe now, thank God, but what an adventure we had on the way! For as I carried him through the forest, with Durin watching out for danger, we suddenly heard a fearsome roar. My brother shouted, "Run! A lioness is coming!" I spun round and saw an enormous beast. Her swollen teats showed that she had young of her own, which made her doubly dangerous. Durin brandished his sword at her, while I fled, desperately clutching your baby. But I kept tripping over tree roots and almost dropping him. So I laid him carefully under a bush and ran on, hoping to lure the lioness away. At last Durin caught me up and said the lioness had vanished, so we went back together to fetch your little boy. But as we got near the bush where I'd left him – we saw that the lioness was carrying your baby away in her mouth!'

Oriana screamed.

'Dear friend, don't worry, he's safe now,' said the Danish maid. 'We followed the lioness. Durin waited for a chance to strike her without harming the child, more than willing to give up his own life in the process. But that chance never came. For the lioness carried your baby all the way back to her lair – where she began to suckle him alongside her own cubs!'

Before Oriana could say anything, Mabilia exclaimed: 'Suckled by a lioness! What a lucky little boy. Oh, Oriana my dear, how strong and courageous your son will grow to be!'

'Did you leave him there?' whispered Oriana.

'No,' the Danish maid reassured her. 'For near the lioness's lair stands the hut of the old hermit, Nasciano.

'I've heard of him,' said Mabilia. 'He's famous for his kindness and wisdom.'

The Danish maid nodded. 'As we watched from behind the trees, we saw this hermit approaching the lair. He stood watching the curious scene for some time, then stepped forward and spoke in a soothing tone. The lioness at once went to greet Nasciano as if they were old friends. He had brought her some hunks of meat. While the lioness was eating these, the hermit darted into her lair, gently picked up your baby and carried him away. As soon as we were sure he was in safe hands, I hurried back to tell you.'

Four years passed quietly. Oriana had written to tell Amadis about their son, and he had responded with pride and joy. His own letters lovingly and modestly told her of ever more marvellous deeds that he had accomplished far and wide.

Meanwhile, after King Lisuarte banished Amadis, he put aside his rage and ruled Great Britain peacefully.

One day, when Oriana was sitting with her mother, the king brought in an elderly holy man with a kindly face, dressed in rough sackcloth and wearing a plain iron cross on a chain around his neck. As the queen stood up to welcome him, a small boy trotted through the door behind him. The lad was fair of face with a ready smile and sturdy limbs. Oriana could not take her eyes off him.

'My dears,' said Lisuarte, 'this is Nasciano the hermit. And this is his young foster son, who was abandoned as a newborn baby in the forest.'

Oriana held her breath.

The king went on, 'When I was out hunting the other day, I happened to pass the hermitage. This bright little lad came running up and engaged me in conversation. I was most impressed by him; he has both knowledge and wisdom far beyond his years. So I offered to raise him here in the castle and train him as a squire when he is old enough. The idea pleased him greatly, so long as his foster father agreed.'

The hermit said, 'I give permission freely, for it will be a great honour. But with one proviso: the boy must receive affection and moral instruction as well as military training.'

The queen recalled the strange, prophetic letter she had received from Urganda the Unknown. She rose to her feet, holding out her hands to the child. 'I assure you,' she said, 'he will receive both in good measure. My elder daughter, Oriana here, will help me care for him. What is your name, young man?'

The boy piped up, 'Esplandian.'

'That means "splendid",' said the queen. What a perfect name. Did you choose it for him, good hermit?'

'No, my lady,' said Nasciano. 'When I found him and unwrapped his swaddling clothes, I saw a strange birthmark on his chest. I consulted my books of learning, and discovered they are ancient Greek letters spelling out that word.'

'You have a charming background, young man,' said the queen. 'Come, let me find you a bed, some toys and some good food.' She led Esplandian away.

The king thanked the old hermit courteously, then made his excuses as he had court business to attend to. But Oriana lingered behind.

'Holy sir,' she said hesitantly, 'before you leave, I wonder if you might hear my confession? It's a very long time since I last had a chance to do this.'

Nasciano looked at her with shrewd eyes, taking in her pale face and quivering hands. 'Willingly,' he said, 'if there is a room in this castle where you will not be overheard.'

She led him to her chamber and closed the door. In this seclusion she opened her heart to the good hermit and told him everything: how she was married to the renowned knight Amadis in every way except by ceremony and law; and that she believed young Esplandian was their secret lovechild. The hermit listened to her calmly, swore confidentiality, absolved her and blessed her.

As he went on his way, Oriana felt a lightness of being. She ran to her mother and asked if she and her two friends could be responsible for Esplandian until he was mature enough to learn how to be a man.

At that time, the Roman Empire was still the mightiest power in Europe. The emperor himself was very old, and his eldest son, El Patin, was preparing to inherit his father's domain. El Patin had a lover, Queen Sardamira of Sardinia, who was not only a ruler in her own right, but also a widely acclaimed beauty. However, the arrogant El Patin refused to marry her until he was certain that she was *the* most beautiful lady in all the world. So he travelled around all the royal courts, viewing potential rivals to ensure that none could surpass her. On this mission, he eventually reached King Lisuarte's castle, where he demanded to view Oriana.

Oriana naturally resisted this imperious request; but the king and queen insisted. She came to meet El Patin with a brusque, frosty manner. Even so, he was instantly smitten by her.

He said to the king, 'Lisuarte, your daughter out-dazzles my friend Queen Sardamira, just as the sun outshines the moon. I intend to marry her. When I come into my inheritance, she will look perfect sitting on the throne beside me as the new empress of Rome.'

'No!' Oriana cried.

Lisuarte took her aside. 'My dear,' he said. 'No lady could hope for a better offer than this. You have previously declined countless suitors, claiming that none was your equal; but El Patin will shortly become the world's pre-eminent ruler, with unlimited treasure. You cannot refuse him.'

'Never,' she replied. 'Father, long ago you promised that neither my sister nor I should be forced to marry against our will.'

Lisuarte patted her arm patiently and went back to El Patin. 'Good sir,' he said, 'my daughter is of nervous disposition, and...um...takes time to adapt to new situations. But as far as I am concerned, your offer is accepted.'

El Patin departed looking very satisfied.

Oriana immediately shared this terrible turn of events with her friends.

'Don't worry,' Mabilia reassured her, 'he probably makes marriage proposals at every court he visits. Besides, the queen of Sardinia won't let go of him so easily. You'll probably never hear from him again.'

But she was wrong. Shortly afterwards, Roman envoys arrived and announced to King Lisuarte that the old emperor of Rome had died and El Patin had taken control.

'We have come to fetch his bride, the princess Oriana,' they said.

'Wonderful news!' King Lisuarte declared. 'My dear, fetch Oriana at once.'

The queen hurried off but returned alone. 'She refuses to come,' the queen said. 'She's had plenty of difficult moods in the past, but I've never seen her so distressed. She's screaming, wringing her hands and tearing her hair. She says that even if they put her in chains and drag her to Rome, she will never submit to El Patin.'

The king turned to the envoys. 'Pray, give us a little time,' he said. 'This will soon be resolved.'

The envoys went back to Rome. After they left, Oriana pulled herself together and went around the court, putting her case to all her father's counsellors. None guessed her commitment to the long-banished Amadis; but many took her side and spoke to the king.

'Sir,' said one, 'this proposal will lower your status and bring you much dishonour. At the moment you are a free and independent monarch; but if you marry off your daughter to the emperor, you will become subject to Rome and forced to obey his will.'

'Nonsense!' said Lisuarte. 'It's the greatest honour for me as well as for Oriana.'

'Sir,' said another, 'if your daughter is taken to Rome, she will be deprived of her rightful inheritance. For as your eldest child, she is your heir to the kingdom of Great Britain. Who then will rule this country after you die?'

'My younger daughter will do just as well,' said Lisuarte.

Nothing and no one could persuade him to change his mind, not even the queen. The envoys returned to say that El Patin himself would come to fetch Oriana within a month. Oriana threatened to kill herself. Her father ordered her to be kept under constant guard to ensure she did not. His only concession was to agree that Mabilia and the Danish maid could accompany her to Rome.

All too soon, the Roman ship arrived to fetch Oriana. It was a magnificent vessel, captained by El Patin himself, who spared no expense in abducting her. However, Oriana had little chance to admire it, for as soon as they hauled her on board, she and her friends were locked into a cabin with multiple keys and bolts.

It was an interminable voyage over tempestuous seas. The three ladies were shut up in the windowless, airless cabin with only smoking candles to light the gloom; once again, Oriana was badly seasick. Mabilia and the Danish maid tried their utmost to comfort her, but to no avail.

At long last they entered calmer waters. But just as Oriana was starting to recover from her nausea, the ship began to lurch about in an even more alarming way. They heard heavy footsteps stomping across the decks above them, with raucous shouting and the clang of striking swords.

'We must have been taken by pirates!' cried the Danish maid.

'Let's pray they overcome El Patin and his cronies,' said Oriana bleakly.

'No, that would be even worse,' said Mabilia, 'because then all three of us will be defiled by them. It's better to pray for the whole ship to sink so we can drown quickly before they find us.'

The tumult above went on and on... Then suddenly everything fell still. In the ominous silence, they heard someone rapidly descending a nearby ladder, and approaching their locked cabin door.

'There's no escape,' whispered Oriana, 'but I'll fight to the death rather than let any man touch me.'

'Kick them,' hissed the Danish maid, 'bite them!'

'Knee them in the groin!' said Mabilia.

Keys turned in the locks. Bolts were drawn. Quaking from head to toe, the three ladies blew out the lights and seized the heavy bronze candlesticks as makeshift weapons. They stood side by side, refusing to cower, ready to spring on their assailants like cornered animals. The heavy door swung open. In the flickering candlelight, they saw a tall, imposing figure...

'Amadis!' cried Oriana.

She stared at him in disbelief; then her legs gave way and she swooned. At once, Amadis darted forward to catch her, and laid her tenderly on the bed. He knelt at her side, stroking her hair with soothing whispers until she came to.

'Dear foster brother,' said Mabilia, 'whatever has happened?'

Amadis said, 'I've been staying with comrades not far from here in the southern sea, near the shipping route to Rome – on Firm Island.'

'Firm Island?' said Mabilia. 'Where the Arch of True Lovers and Forbidden Chamber both stand?'

Amadis nodded. 'Yes indeed. So you have heard of that marvellous place, eh?' He put his arm around Oriana, and gently helped her to sit up. 'My love, as soon as I heard that El Patin had abducted you, I called up a fleet of ships, supported by my father's troops in Gaul, and mustered to attack the Romans as they passed. The battle is now over – and El Patin is dead.'

The three ladies clapped their hands and exclaimed their thanks to God. Then the Danish maid stood up and beckoned to Mabilia. 'These two have a lot to catch up on since they were last together,' she said. 'Come on, they need to be alone for a while.'

Mabilia smiled indulgently and made to follow her. At the door she asked, 'When can we announce to the world that you two will formally be married?'

'When my father is reconciled with Amadis,' said Oriana.

Amadis escorted Oriana and her friends to safety on Firm Island. From there Oriana wrote a letter to her mother, Queen Brisena, telling how Amadis had rescued her from the Romans. She concluded:

> I trust you will not be angry at this news, since
> Amadis long served as your knight. You have never
> expressed any doubts about him, despite my father's
> hostility. Besides, you several times expressed your
> opposition to my forced marriage to El Patin. So now,
> dearest mother, I beg you to persuade my father to
> come to terms with what has happened, and end his
> enmity towards Amadis.

However, instead of the hoped for conciliatory reply from the queen, she received a letter from her father, King Lisuarte:

> I am outraged at this news, which has also reached me
> from Rome. It confirms that Amadis of Gaul will
> forever be my foe. The new Roman emperor, Arquisil,
> is sending troops to attack Firm Island in revenge. I
> have assured him that I shall send a huge army from
> Great Britain in support.

Within weeks, the war broke out. Oriana, Mabilia and the Danish maid took refuge in a strong fortress, alongside all the other ladies of Firm Island. The battle raged for days. Oriana fell into fresh despair, knowing that, whichever side won, either Amadis or her father would be killed. Thus she must spend the rest of her life burdened with sorrow and guilt for having caused this war.

As she sat lamenting this tragedy with her two friends, someone knocked on the door of their chamber. The Danish maid opened it – and ushered in the bent and kindly figure of Nasciano the hermit.

Oriana greeted him desolately: 'It's good to see you, holy father. But what madness brings you to this battlefield?'

'Not madness, my dear, but hope,' Nasciano replied. 'May I speak openly before your companions?'

'Of course,' said Oriana. 'They've both supported me through thick and thin, and know everything.'

The hermit nodded. 'I come with advice – the only advice that may stop this pointless slaughter. Some time ago, Oriana, you made confession to me. You admitted that you and Amadis are married in all but name, and that your shared love brought that admirable child Esplandian into the world. Now, listen carefully. If you revealed all this to your father, he would have to accept that you already have a husband and thus could never have legally married the emperor of Rome.'

Oriana said, 'No! In my father's view, I'll have shamed him by giving birth to a child out of wedlock. He'll have me killed.'

Mabilia said, 'Despite your father's recent folly, he would never kill his own daughter. Besides, your mother would stop him.'

'And he dotes on your son, Esplandian,' said the Danish maid.

Eventually, they persuaded her.

Out on the battlefield, the opposing armies were fighting and slaughtering each other fiercely, both on horseback and on foot. Old Nasciano hobbled out into their midst, holding up his crucifix and a white flag. At the sight of him, warriors on both sides dropped their weapons and fell back.

'What do you want, holy man?' someone called.

'I have pressing need to speak with the king of Great Britain,' he said quietly.

Someone took his arm and led him through the Roman and British ranks to King Lisuarte, who stared at him in astonishment.

Nasciano said, 'Sir, your daughter, Oriana, has found refuge here on Firm Island. She wishes to tell you something that I believe will end these hostilities. Will you hear her?'

The king stood on the wrecked ground, chewing over his answer. At last he said, 'After all the trouble she's caused, it's astonishing that she has the gall to ask me anything. But very well, bring her to me.'

Nasciano beckoned towards the fortress where Oriana stood at the door. She stepped out nervously. As she came, Nasciano called in his quavering voice, 'Where is Amadis the Gaul?'

'If I see that brute!' spluttered Lisuarte, 'I'll behead him on the spot!'

But Amadis had already come forward from his own army. He offered his hand to Lisuarte – who spat at it.

Oriana and Amadis stood on either side of the hermit, facing King Lisuarte.

'Sir,' said Nasciano, 'you remember when I brought young Esplandian to your castle, and you eagerly adopted the little boy?'

'Of course I remember. I have no regrets,' growled Lisuarte.

Nasciano continued, 'As I was leaving the castle, Oriana beseeched me to hear her confession. One of the matters that she previously told me in confidence, she now wishes to share with you.'

Lisuarte turned to her, his face dark with displeasure. 'Well?'

'Father,' she said. 'Amadis and I are already married in everything but name. We have declared our love and lain together – and Esplandian is our son.'

The king's mouth dropped open. He turned to Amadis. 'Is this true?'

Amadis fell on his knees before the king. 'It is, sir.'

King Lisuarte caught his breath and reeled in shock. 'Then...then...' he spluttered, 'Esplandian is my grandson! Why did you not tell me before?'

'I would gladly have done so, father,' said Oriana, 'if you had not defamed Amadis as your enemy and expelled him from your kingdom.'

'I have been a fool,' groaned the king. He put his hands over his face, rocking backwards and forwards. 'I fell too easily under malicious influences. Thus I have lost both the best knight in the world, and my beloved elder daughter.'

He turned to Oriana. 'But what a turn of events! What an undeserved blessing to be grandfather to such an outstanding boy! Oriana, if only I had listened to your protests! I beg you to forgive me. And may God forgive me too.'

She fell into his arms, sobbing. He clasped her earnestly and turned to Amadis. 'My...my son-in-law, I humbly entreat you to make peace and renew our severed bonds.'

'Gladly, sir,' smiled Amadis. 'But I cannot return to your court. For now my home is here on Firm Island, with Oriana – my wife.'

'Indeed,' said Lisuarte. 'But I hereby announce that when I die, Great Britain shall join your realm. For I name Oriana and yourself, Amadis, to be my joint heirs.'

The two men embraced.

King Lisuarte said, 'I cannot formally declare peace without consulting my commander in this conflict. Where is Emperor Arquisil, who led his army before mine to avenge the death of his brother?'

The new Roman emperor pushed through his troops and came forward at once.

'Sir,' said Lisuarte, 'I request your agreement to end this war.'

Arquisil was the exact opposite of his late brother. Whereas El Patin had been arrogant and heavy-handed, Arquisil was courteous and magnanimous. 'I have heard and considered this extraordinary new development,' he said. 'I agree: let there be peace.'

All the warriors let out a hearty cheer. At this, the other ladies hiding inside the fortress now ventured out. They were relieved and thrilled to learn that the war was over, and readily joined in the celebration.

When everything eventually quietened down, Emperor Arquisil held up his hand to speak again.

'King Lisuarte,' he said. 'May I ask you a simple favour?'

'Of course, sir, ask away,' the king replied.

'A short time ago,' said Arquisil, 'I was one of the ambassadors who my brother, El Patin, sent to your court, to take away Oriana. For my role in that, I apologise. However, while I was there, I had the good fortune to meet and talk with your younger daughter, Leonoreta. I developed feelings of great affection for her, and she admitted openly that she felt the same. May I ask for her hand in marriage?'

'This is extraordinary!' cried King Lisuarte. 'Many years ago, when I was only a young knight, the great seeress, Urganda the Unknown, honoured me with a prophesy. She foretold that my daughters would one day equal the two greatest men on earth. And now that has come true! I do not deserve such double good fortune.'

'I am glad to be here, the seeress replied. 'For this is pethemns of the best in all the world, in honour of true love.

The good tidings were sent to Queen Brisena and Leonoreta, urging them to sail to Firm Island without delay, and bring young Esplandian. The queen was beside herself with joy when she learned that the boy was her grandson, not to mention her delight at hearing of her two daughters' happy romances.

By the time they arrived, the battlefield had been transformed into a celebration ground, dotted with brightly decorated festive pavilions. The good Emperor Arquisil got down on his knees to Leonoreta, imploring her to marry him and become empress of Rome, promising always to honour her. She did not hesitate to accept him.

As Amadis watched the preparations for the two couples' joint wedding, he remembered that many of his knightly comrades also had long-standing sweethearts. So he invited them to hold their own weddings at the same time. Never had there been such a happy occasion! There was boundless feasting and dancing, jousting, music and storytelling.

However, just as the festivities were reaching their peak, some of the ladies suddenly began to scream and point in terror towards the sea. An ominous cloud of thick black smoke had gathered over the waves. A monstrous, dark winged dragon emerged from it and soared over the pavilions, its wings flapping like thunderclaps.

It landed in the shallows beside the shore and slowly transformed into a small boat, which came drifting onto the sand. Out of it stepped a magnificent lady clad in silk and velvet. She walked up to the wedding party.

The guests were all mesmerised. But King Lisuarte held out his hand and exclaimed, 'Welcome, Urganda the Unknown! Yes indeed, a hearty welcome! Everything that you foretold has come to pass.'

'I am glad to be here,' the sorceress replied. 'For this is a gathering of the best in all the world, in honour of true love.'

Queen Brisena led Urganda through the guests, telling everyone about her prophesies and how they had all now been fulfilled; for Urganda was the very embodiment of knowledge and wisdom.

By now, the festivities were almost at an end. But there was to be one final ceremony: those who wished, could try their luck at passing through the Arch of True Lovers.

First, various young knights, squires and damsels amongst the guests were invited to attempt it. One by one they trooped through with much laughter. Most caused ugly trumpet blasts and fell flat on their faces due to their fickleness; though a few achieved brief snatches of tune and small handfuls of petals. Then the newlyweds took their turns. All won abundant music and flowers, to the delight of the watching crowd. Amongst them, Emperor Arquisil and Leonoreta did particularly well, for both were youthful and innocent.

Last of all, Oriana and Amadis took their turn. He went first through the Arch, causing such a triumphant serenade that everyone burst into applause. He reached out his hand for Oriana, who followed him blushing nervously. At once, the music became gentler and sweeter, and a fragrant shower of roses cascaded down. Everyone cheered.

The other couples that had passed successfully through the Arch were waiting on the far side. Beyond, lay the four flights of steps leading up to the Forbidden Chamber.

'Shall we all try to enter it?' someone called. Voices shouted out encouragement. Hand-in-hand, the couples stepped forward in turn.

The first couple managed to mount two sets of steps. Then suddenly they screamed and fell back, as if pushed by cruel, invisible hands. The next couple was cast away even more quickly. Others followed, making varied progress before suffering the same painful and ignominious banishment.

Now only Amadis and Oriana were left to try.

Amadis took his beloved wife's hand. As they drew near, she sensed the force of the enchantment and crossed herself, motioning Amadis to do the same. They took the first set of steps slowly. Nothing happened. Carefully they walked onto the second set, still hand in hand. Both had begun to sway a little; but they kept their balance and managed to ascend to the next level. Here they staggered as the invisible hands resisted them; but, clinging to each other, they withstood the spell and went on, one slow step at a time.

Every eye was fixed on them. They progressed right up to the chamber door. It was tightly closed. They were both exceedingly weary. The obstructive forces made them teeter first one way, then the other.

'We come with pure hearts and endless perseverance,' Amadis roared. 'Let us in!'

Hand in hand, they pushed with all their shared strength against the door. It sprung open. They tumbled over the threshold together – and entered the Forbidden Chamber.

'Welcome!' sang a thousand invisible voices. 'Welcome to the noblest lady and greatest knight in the world! Your joint virtue and purity has broken the long enchantment of this island. May you and your descendants rule it in peace for ever!'

Hidden harps, lutes and fiddles took up the joyful tune.

Thus the ancient spell was finally ended. The Forbidden Chamber was now open to all. Amadis and Oriana beckoned to all their kin and friends from both sides of the Arch to follow them in. As they arrived, tables appeared out of thin air, miraculously laden with a feast that excelled even the joint weddings.

At the end of the feast, there were many fond farewells and sincere promises of everlasting peace as all the guests departed.

Oriana and Amadis remained alone in the Forbidden Chamber, which they had won for the succour of all. They made their marriage bed within it; and from there spread their joy throughout Firm Island and beyond, to their family homes in Great Britain and Gaul, and thence to the furthest edges of the world.

In the original text, Amadis has five different aliases as he moves through the story. He has two full siblings, a half-brother born when his real father was seduced by an unnamed woman, and three foster siblings by two different foster fathers, including Mabilia. Through numerous twists and turns of fate, he is portrayed consistently as an admirably noble and honourable man, who stalwartly refuses any temptation to be unfaithful to his beloved. Likewise, Oriana is a perfect woman, whose only fault is her regular bouts of despair when events threaten her relationship with Amadis.

By contrast, other characters – both female and male – are more interesting and colourful.

The enthusiastic friendship shown by the go-betweens, Mabilia and the Danish maid (the source book does not mention her name) is a particular feature of the book. Perhaps the most intriguing woman is Urganda the Unknown, whose regular appearances engage the reader with revelations, enigmatic predictions and other dramatic supernatural interventions.

Another strong female character is Queen Briolania (not to be confused with Oriana's mother, Brisena), on whose behalf Amadis fights a battle, restoring to her the kingdom she has inherited in her own right. She considers proposing marriage to him herself but she refrains, correctly guessing that he loves someone else. She later meets and befriends Oriana, though there is constant unease on Oriana's part due to the love rivalry.

Alongside the many chaste and faithful love affairs enjoyed by lesser characters, there are also several scenes of blatant lust, some initiated by women.

One memorable male character not mentioned in this retelling is the evil Arcalaus the Enchanter, who fails to force Oriana to marry him, and holds Amadis and his half-brother captive in a castle with a floor that can move up and down by a lever. Towards the end of the story, he is offered a pardon if he will renounce his past crimes; but he declines, saying he is addicted to evil.

The hermit Nasciano – wise, pious and fearless – plays a pivotal role in the second half of the story, with his peaceful wisdom counterbalancing the constant violence engaged in by the kings and knights.

There are several 'giants' and 'dwarfs' in the original story, though it is not clear whether these are supernatural beings or just normal men of unusual size; they are often associated with malevolence, though sometimes reveal themselves to be virtuous.

Artist unknown: *A Bridal Couple*
Germany, c.1470

15th CENTURY

Amidst widespread political and military upheaval, western Europe began to move towards the modern age and the high culture of the Renaissance. An important development for literature of all kinds was the invention of moveable type printing, which made books available to much wider readerships.

The century began with Christine de Pizan's groundbreaking work which considered the complexities of real-life romantic relationships solely from a woman's point of view. Meanwhile, the old chivalric fantasy legends remained as popular as ever, inspiring Thomas Malory to consolidate them into his definitive collection, *Le Morte d'Arthur*.

THE CITY OF LADIES

Christine de Pizan: *The Book of the City of Ladies*
France, 1405

Christine de Pizan (or Pisan) is celebrated as the first medieval woman to earn her living by writing, and the first to criticise the misogyny of male writers.

She was born in Italy in 1364, but was brought up in Paris, where her father worked as a physician and astrologer to the French king. It was her father who encouraged her to become literate in both French and Latin, against her mother's wishes. At the age of fifteen, she married a royal secretary, and they had three children; but after ten happy years together she was widowed. To support her family, including her recently widowed mother, she began working as a copyist in a manuscript workshop, but later began a successful career as a professional writer. Towards the end of her life, when France was threatened by civil war, she withdrew from court and took refuge at a covent where her daughter was a nun. She died in 1430.

She published at least forty-one books of poetry and prose, often working to commission for various patrons. She became renowned throughout Europe. Her work included love ballads, lyric poetry and etiquette books, alongside more serious texts such as royal biographies, religious books and political treatises.

One day I, Christine, was sitting at my desk, surrounded by piles of learned books. I had been studying them for so long that I felt quite exhausted. So I decided to relax a little by reading something lighter, and picked up a volume by the poet Matheolus. It had been recommended to me as an amusing read, but I soon realised that it was not in the slightest bit funny. For it mainly comprised slanders against women, expressed in the most immoral language.

I put it down and sighed deeply. 'Why,' I said out loud, 'do so many men write books that disparage and criticise women? Why do they condemn my whole sex as useless and full of vice? Can it be true what they say? Did God really create us solely to be vessels for all the world's sins?'

I thought of other women I knew; not just educated ones like myself, but even servants. I could not think of any who fitted these malign descriptions. Yet surely not all eminent male scholars were liars? Should I believe them, and thus despise my whole sex?

Sick at heart, I slumped wretchedly in my chair.

Suddenly, I noticed a curious beam of light shining into my lap. Then I heard a soft movement and looked up. To my astonishment, three unknown ladies had somehow entered my room through the locked door. Each was splendidly dressed and wore a crown. Were they ghosts? In terror, I jumped to my feet and hastily made the sign of the cross.

But the closest one quickly assuaged my fears. 'Christine, my friend,' she said. 'Don't be afraid. We saw from afar that you were in great distress. We have come to comfort you, by answering men's disgraceful insults once and for all.'

'But who are you?' I cried.

'We are daughters of God,' said she, 'sent to earth to restore order and justice. We have come to teach both men and women to acknowledge their strengths and weaknesses.

But our greater task is to ensure the safety of all virtuous ladies for ever more.'

'Why have you come to *me*?'

'Because, Christine, your quest for knowledge makes you the ideal person to construct the City of Ladies.'

'The City of Ladies?' said I. 'Whatever is that?'

'It is to be a magnificent walled city, more splendid even than Amazonia of ancient legend,' she told me. 'It will provide a home solely for praiseworthy women of good reputation. To shield them from the wiles of men, it will be made impregnable.' She smiled. 'My name is Lady Reason. I will help you dig and lay the foundations of this city.'

The second lady stepped out of the shadows. 'Hello, Christine,' she said. 'My name is Righteousness. I am here to help you construct the city's buildings.'

The third lady came forward and greeted me: 'My name is Justice. After the city is built, I shall help you fill it with suitable ladies, and bring the queen who is to rule over it.'

What a unique and marvellous opportunity! I was quite overwhelmed. To express my heartfelt gratitude, I prostrated before them and kissed the ground.

But Reason exclaimed impatiently, 'Oh, do stand up, daughter! You have work to do. Come at once to the Field of Letters, where you must use your intelligence as a spade.'

I jumped up and followed the three ladies out. My body felt much stronger and lighter than before. Soon we reached the Field, which was a stretch of flat, fertile ground surrounded by streams and abundant fruit trees. She had already traced an outline on the earth there, showing where the city was to stand. She set me to dig a deep trench around it, while she herself removed the excavated earth and loaded it into great hods.

As I worked, my head buzzed with questions, for I could not stop thinking about men's abuse of power, hypocrisy and lack of remorse for their own sins. I put these questions to Reason. Before answering each one, she first carried away a full hod of earth on her strong shoulders, as if to dispose of the nonsense. Then she proceeded to use brilliant arguments to demolish all my concerns.

'Don't forget,' she reminded me, 'alongside the slanderers, there are also many decent, wise and admirable men.'

'Sometimes,' I said, 'it's difficult to distinguish between what is slander and what is actually true. For example, I recently read a disturbing book that claimed the female body is inherently flawed and defective in its functions.'

'Huh!' she retorted. 'Consider your own body and you will quickly realise the falsehood of that!'

'Thank you, my lady. Perhaps you can answer this concern for me too: if a man defers to a woman, does he bring shame on himself?'

'Everyone should defer to their superiors,' she said. 'But superiority is not a matter of sex; it is determined by noble behaviour.'

Our discussion turned to the male writers of antiquity who denigrated women, yet are still universally revered for their so-called wisdom. To refute their slurs, Reason used pithy, often amusing arguments, backed up with examples from the Bible. She had me enthralled by her endless tales of women from history whose achievements clearly equalled or exceeded those of many men.

'My dear daughter and beloved friend,' she said, 'just look at your own remarkable achievement here and now: you have prepared a splendid trench for the City of Ladies! Now it is time to take up your pen, and use it as a trowel to lay the foundations.'

She demonstrated how to lay the first stone, then stepped back to let me continue. It scarcely seemed like work, for I was so entertained by her endless stories of female courage, strength and independence; of extraordinary queens, valiant maidens, devout virgins and fearsome women warriors.

'But why are women never renowned as scholars?' I asked.

'The simplest reason,' she said, 'is that respectable girls are usually kept locked away from the outside world, and thus denied the schooling that boys receive as their right. Yet those women who *do* manage to get an education, often become more accomplished and erudite than men.' She named many women from antiquity who had excelled as scholars, poets, musicians, seers and magicians. Some had even initiated totally new skills in both science and the arts; for it was women who invented agriculture, numbers and even the alphabet itself. 'Men enjoy the benefits of women's innovations,' she declared, 'yet they still refuse to acknowledge female achievements.

'But look, my dear Christine, you have finished the foundations. And I have completed my task too: I have conclusively proved that there's no God-given reason to criticise women more than men. Now it's time to hand you over to my two sisters. With their help and advice, the city will soon be ready.'

At these words, the lady Righteousness stepped up to me. 'My dear Christine,' she said, 'prepare your tools! It's time to put up the buildings. All the materials are ready; for while you were toiling away with Reason, I quarried and cut these.' She pointed to a huge pile of beautiful, gleaming stones. 'Take some mortar and mix it well in your inkpot; then use strokes of your pen to arrange these stones in order, following the lines I have already traced.'

'Most excellent lady,' I replied, 'I am ready to do your bidding.'

As I set to work again, Righteousness continued the lessons that Reason had begun. She instructed me first on the top ranks of famous ladies: sybils and other prophetesses, explaining how they always follow the highest moral standards. Next, she discussed whether parents should prefer sons or daughters. 'Daughters are more likely to care for their fathers and mothers in adversity,' she pointed out, 'so that proves that the birth of a girl is definitely the greater blessing.'

In no time at all, it seemed, I had built the entire city, complete with houses and mansions of every type, including palaces and even defence towers.

'Now, Christine,' said Righteousness, 'it is time to fill this excellent place with valiant and virtuous women – the only ones permitted to dwell here. The city is strongly fortified, thus protecting them from fear of either invasion or expulsion. They will all continue to live here until the end of time, so they won't need daughters to inherit it; thus they won't ever have to associate with men. Come, let us go and summon them to move in.'

As we walked out to do this, I took the opportunity to ask Righteousness about a problem that had long been troubling me.

'My lady,' I said, 'do men speak the truth when they say that marriage is utter hell for them, because of women's sharp tongues, malice and nagging? And what about their claim that few women are ever faithful to their husbands? Many books advise men to avoid marriage for those very reasons.'

'My dear Christine,' Righteousness laughed, 'were any of the books that make such claims written by a woman? Do you think they are based on careful gathering of true facts? Of course not! Any man can win his case when there's no one to argue against him. I'm sure you know of many

385

marriages where the exact opposite is true, of wives shackled like slaves to brutish husbands who curse, abuse and viciously beat them. Not to mention all those poor women working their fingers to the bone for their countless children, while their husbands go out drinking and visiting brothels.'

'I have seen many wretched marriages like that,' I agreed.

'But don't forget, there are plenty of happily married couples,' said Righteousness hastily, 'where both spouses are faithful, sensible, gentle and kind. You yourself once had the best of husbands, who I'm sure you will never stop grieving for. And of course, it's equally wrong to claim that all wives are paragons of virtue.'

She then proceeded to tell me of women so devoted to their beloved husbands that they willingly suffered all kinds of trials in order to look after them. I added some examples from amongst my own acquaintances. But still I was not appeased, because I recalled a passage from that ever-popular book, *The Romance of the Rose*, which assures men that women are totally incapable of keeping secrets.

Righteousness sighed, 'My dear Christine,' she said, 'surely you don't take such arrogance seriously? Reason has shown you how ridiculous it is to generalise about either sex. Many men have trustworthy wives whom they totally rely upon.' As proof she recited another list of fascinating stories, concluding, 'How can men forget that it is thanks to a *woman*, the Virgin Mary, that God took human form and thus opened the gates of Paradise?'

Next she turned to the malicious male lie that very few women are chaste, using examples from both the Bible and pagan history to disprove it. Indeed, she cited women who had played with fire in order to save themselves from violation.

'What about that heinous claim of licentious men that all women secretly wish to be raped?' I asked.

'Every women agrees that rape is the most despicable crime of all,' Righteousness said firmly. 'The laws that sentence rapists to death are totally fitting and just.'

After considering the various faults of both men and women, we concluded that the number of dishonourable men is similar to the number of highly principled women.

'But why,' I asked, 'has no woman ever written a book to refute men's false accusations against us?'

'Those most capable of producing such a book are no doubt occupied with more pressing work,' said Righteousness. 'In connection with that, you must finish constructing the City of Ladies – for this will display to the whole world all the feminine virtues.'

'Before I get back to work, Lady Righteousness,' I said hesitantly, 'may I ask you something rather delicate?'

'Of course,' she replied. 'It's a pupil's right to question her teacher on any subject.'

'Then perhaps you could throw some light on men's view of carnal desire,' I said. 'Numerous writers accuse women of being unable to control their passions. We are all supposed to be intrinsically unfaithful, flitting callously from one lover to another. They deny that this is slander, and argue that they are simply issuing a warning for the common good. Are they right?'

'My dear!' said Righteousness, 'how can it be for the *common* good if only *half* the population benefits from it? Why don't they also tell women to beware of *men's* cunning snares, eh?'

'It seems to me that passionate love is like a dangerous sea,' I said, 'and best avoided by anyone with any sense. But even that isn't straightforward, because we are assured that ladies who dress in finery, only do so to attract men.'

'Most women get pleasure out of looking pretty,' said Righteousness, 'without it even occurring to them that men regard this as temptation. Anyway, decent, reliable men – the only ones worth attracting – aren't impressed by glamour.'

'What are your thoughts about men who accuse all women of greed and parsimony?' I asked.

'Fools are always quick to spot the faults of others whilst being blind to their own failings,' said Righteousness scathingly. 'All sensible women hoard household necessities, and those who live in poverty must be thrifty out of necessity. Even rich husbands often keep their wives short of money, forcing them to carefully guard what little they have. But women with funds to spare are often more generous in almsgiving than men are.'

'That's true,' I said. 'My female friends enjoy helping the poor – far more than any miser enjoys hiding cash in his coffers.'

Righteousness spoke of other ladies who proved this, including an exceptionally generous Frenchwoman who is still alive today.

'Are any French ladies, or immigrants to our country, coming to live in the new city?' I asked.

'Of course,' she replied. 'The noble queen herself, Isabeau of Bavaria is completely free of evil, so she is certainly invited; as are several duchesses and countesses.' I was delighted to learn their names, for some were friends of mine. 'But remember,' she said, 'many admirable women belong to the lower classes too; ignore anyone who tries to tell you otherwise.'

'I'm very glad to hear that,' I said. 'You've certainly answered all my questions thoroughly, my lady, and completely disproved all the slurs against our sex.'

'Thus my role in the construction of the City of Ladies is finished,' said Righteousness. 'All the splendid houses, mansions and palaces are now ready. And here come the excellent ladies of every rank to move into them. Wait here for my sister, Justice, who will secure the gates. Meanwhile, you must make a speech to welcome the new arrivals.'

So I stepped forward and cried, 'Worthy ladies, maidens and matrons, women of all classes who love good morals, raise your heads and rejoice! Thanks to God's help, the formidable job of building this city is now complete. May you all live here in safety and happiness for ever more!'

Lady Justice now came to me. 'Well done, Christine,' she said. 'With my sisters' help, you've made a fine job of building the City of Ladies.'

She turned to the crowd of assembled women.

'I am delighted to see the streets bedecked with flowers, for I am about to introduce your queen, who will live amongst you and govern your city. She is the most blessed of all women, more virtuous even than the angels, as humble as she is glorious. She is the supreme authority over all earthly powers, second only to her son, whom she conceived by the Holy Spirit – the Son of God the Father. Yes, it is the Virgin Mary herself.'

Every lady in the city cried out their excited greeting: 'Ave Maria!'

The next moment, the holy Virgin Mary herself appeared before us in all her splendour!

'Oh, Queen of Heaven,' said Justice, 'your perfect light obliterates all wickedness. I implore you to grace the honourable ladies gathered here, by living amongst them. May they drink deeply from your fountain of goodness and absorb the light of your perfection, thus raising womankind to the highest esteem.'

The Virgin Mary answered, 'Lady Justice, my son's beloved, I gladly accept your invitation. I shall live amongst these ladies as my sisters and friends, and lead them to eternity, as God Himself has ordained.'

Everyone fell to their knees and bowed their heads.

Now the Virgin Mary's exalted company came to join her: first Mary Magdalen, followed by numerous female saints and martyrs. As each one arrived, Justice announced her inspiring story, so that no one noticed the passing of time.

Finally, Justice turned back to me and said, 'My dear Christine, the last stories I just told form the gate and portcullis of the City of Ladies. It is now safely locked against intruders. Every worthy woman living, dead or yet to come, has her place in it. May God's peace be on it always. I commend it to your care and bid you farewell.' Thus she departed.

I stepped forward in her place and made the following speech:

'My dearest ladies, see how you are all reflected from the brightly shining walls of our city. That is because it is built from your combined virtue. I beg you not to abuse it by becoming arrogant. Follow the example of our queen, the noble Virgin, who accepted her supreme honour with humility.

'Remember that patience is the key to Paradise. Discard foolish ideas, petty jealousies, stubbornness, malicious gossip and scandal. Such things are both unhealthy and unseemly; even worse, they twist the mind. If you follow this advice and take good care of the city, it will always shelter you and protect you from attackers.

'I would like to give some advice to all the married ladies here. If your husband is loving, what more could you ask for? Cherish him and praise the Lord. If your husband is neither good nor bad – try to live with him amicably, and be grateful that he's no worse. If your husband is abusive, wayward or cruel, try to tolerate him and show him a better path. Everyone will praise and support your efforts, and it will enhance your soul.

'As for all you single young women: I urge you to be pure, modest and steadfast. Be strong and cautious in everything; beware the snares of evildoers and seducers.

'Widows, maintain your respectability. Be devout, prudent, patient, strong, resilient and unassuming. Practise charity.

'More than anything, whatever your situation – guard against those who seek to demean you. Prove them all wrong! Repel the treacherous liars and tricksters who try to steal your chastity and destroy your good name. Fly from their temptations, my ladies, fly from them all!

'Let our hearts rejoice in doing good, for this will increase the inhabitants of our city. May God's grace help us all to devote our lives to His service; may He pardon all our faults; may He grant us all everlasting joy when we die.'

All the ladies cried as one: 'Amen!'

Thus ends *The Book of the City of Ladies*.

Christine was an active participant in literary debates about how women are portrayed by male writers. In 1399 she wrote a long poem called *Epistre au dieu d'Amours* (Letter of the God of Love), and followed this up three years later with a book called *Le Dit de la Rose*; in both, she directly criticised the 13th century *Romance of the Rose* (the later section, written by Jean de Meun, see pp. 170

and 181) for characterising women as fickle, foolish seducers; adding scathingly that the whole gist of that book comprised:

> So many efforts made and ruses found
> To trick a virgin – that and nothing more!

The slanderous book about women, which so upsets Christine at the beginning of this story, is *The Lamentations of Matheolus*, written in Latin by Mathieu of Boulogne c. 1295. Presumably intended to be hilarious for its male readership, its series of disparaging statements can be summed up by this one:

> Whoever sets out to expose the evils of the female sex, finds her poisonous acts too numerous to relate. Nature shows and teaches us that every woman is a real monster and that she is quite happy to put up with her own faults.

Many of the misogynist claims that Christine refutes are a direct response to Mathieu's claims.

The 'dream sequence' used in *The Book of the City of Ladies*, and the use of allegorical characters, are both common devices in medieval literature. So too are the discussions about characters from antiquity, the Bible and mythology, which form the bulk of Christine's original text. Like the male authors who preceded her, Christine is selective in her examples. However, her own choices are perhaps unique, in exclusively showing women in their most positive light. Though Christine complains profusely about all the men who defame women, she also concedes that some do the opposite – notably Boccaccio (see p.226) whom she quotes several times, for example as saying, 'What a great honour it is for a woman to put aside all feminine things and to devote her mind to studying the words of the greatest scholars.' She cites a number of stories that he told in his book *Concerning Famous Women*, alongside others from *Decameron*.

Nevertheless, some of the opinions Christine expresses in this book would make modern feminists cringe. She says, for example, that female nature is typically timid, meek and pure; and declares, 'It's not necessary for the public good for women to go around doing what men are supposed to do...It's quite adequate that they perform the tasks for which they are fitted.'

FORTUNE'S WHEEL

King James I of Scotland: *The Kingis Quair*
Scotland, c.1424

In 1406, James, the eleven-year old crown prince of Scotland, was sent to France to escape the political enemies of his father, King Robert III. En route along the Yorkshire coast, his ship was captured by pirates who delivered him to King Henry IV of England. He was held hostage by Henry for eighteen years, split between living within the English royal household, and imprisonment. He was finally released in 1424, shortly after his marriage to the English noblewoman Joan Beaufort, granddaughter of John of Gaunt (see p. 288). He was assassinated in 1437.

The Kingis Quair ('The King's Book') is a narrative poem probably written around the time of his marriage and return to Scotland. It is believed to be inspired by the day he first saw and fell in love with Joan. It survives in a single manuscript copied in the late 15th or early 16th century.

One May morning during my imprisonment, I looked out from the tower window, to raise my spirits with the sight of its beautiful garden. A nightingale was loudly singing as if in celebration of love, and walking past the leafy arbours was the fairest, sweetest young woman that I had ever seen.

Her hair was golden, her neck as white as fired enamel. She wore a headdress of pearls, rubies, emeralds and sapphires with a feathered coronet; and a white cloak embroidered with golden thread, left half untied in her haste to go out and enjoy the day. She looked up for a brief moment. In her face I saw wisdom, generosity and dignity: she was perfect. Then, oblivious to me, she turned and continued on her way.

Ah, how I sighed and lamented for her! At last, exhausted, I swooned onto my bed. And there I had the following marvellous dream.

A dazzling light seemed to enter through the window. A voice cried: 'Have no fear! I bring you comfort and healing.'

The next moment, two invisible arms lifted me up into a crystal cloud, which carried me through air, water and fire into the heavenly spheres. I found myself standing before a palace of crystal gems. The door burst open and I walked into a great chamber, crowded with countless people.

As I gazed around, the voice spoke again:

'Look! Do you see that orderly line of elders standing over there, chatting contentedly to the one who's called Good Will? Those are the highest rank of lovers, the ones who have always been true and never failed in their efforts. As a reward, they have won their hearts' desires.

'That group below them, being entertained with songs by the one called Courage, they are people who died in the service of love – from broken hearts, foolish desires, excess or jealousy.

'Those on the lower level, in long capes with deep hoods covering their eyes, are speaking to Repentance. They are all former clerics who secretly snatched forbidden love – bringing great shame upon themselves.'

The room was divided by a white curtain. Behind it stood a mass of people with despairing faces, each clutching a legal petition. 'Those people are waiting to appeal to the judge,' the voice explained. 'Some were sent away to the cloister before they even had a chance to sample love's delights. Others are protesting against being forced to give their bodies to someone against their will. Some were unjustly separated from their true loves and married off to ones they could not bear. The last group is made up of people who were once happily married – but their beloved partners were cruelly snatched away from this world.'

At the head of the room, on a great throne, sat Cupid, holding his bow. In his quiver was a golden arrow to land softly, a silver one to inflict a severe wound, and a steel arrow to strike so hard that there was no hope of recovery.

I hastened past him to a door. It was opened by the lady Fair Welcome, who beckoned me into a small room, decorated with sighs. The chambermaid, Privacy, led me across to a bed. There, clad only in a cloak and a coronet of red roses, Venus herself, goddess of love, was reclining.

My heart began to quake. I approached her with outstretched hands and fell to my knees. 'Oh bright, blissful queen of love,' I cried. 'You have conquered this callow man completely. But I am too ignorant to follow your laws. I implore you to have compassion and guide me to salvation!'

She turned her bright eyes to me and said gently, 'Young man, I already know of your distress. Submit to your fate; serve it in humility. It is true that I wield the sceptre of Love's law, and I would like to help you. However, I cannot do so alone; for I must work according to God's eternal plan, and within the boundaries set by other people. Your case is a particularly difficult one, since others have deprived you of liberty. Moreover, you have neither the wisdom nor the power to match your loved one's high status and beauty;

you are like sackcloth to her fine crimson silk, like cold January to bright May. In these circumstances, other goddesses are more capable of shortening your suffering. Thus I am going to pass you on to Minerva. Good Hope will guide you to her house. When you meet her, follow her commands exactly, put in the necessary effort and be patient. Then you will win the golden flower of your heart.

'By the way, when you eventually return to earth, please ask your fellow men to stop holding me in contempt, and urge them to obey my laws! I weep such tears, like rain drumming on the ground, because they have abandoned the merriment of former times. Tell them that if they repent and return their hearts to me, I shall forgive them at once, and send all the comfort that they long for.'

I thanked her, then followed Good Hope to Minerva's house. There I humbly explained the reason for my visit.

'My son,' Minerva said, 'Listen carefully. You have a choice to set your heart in one of two ways.

'The first is the path most men follow: ruthless lust, hiding sinful thoughts under silken words of fickleness and deceit – like a fowler hiding in a bush, whistling to lure poor birds into his net. If you choose that way, all your efforts will be in vain, leading only to pain and remorse.

'On the other hand, if you pursue love with virtue and a firm heart, if you follow God's path and pray for guidance, you will build a strong foundation. I will help you, and eventually you will find success. That is the way of truth and meekness, steadfast thought, patience and diligence.'

'Madam,' I cried, 'I love my golden flower truly and faithfully, more than anything! No amount of treasure would ever persuade me to use her for my own gratification, or to blemish her reputation in any way. I only wish to worship her. I promise to spare no labour or expense, in the hope of eventually standing in her grace.'

'That is good,' said Minerva. 'Since your love is fixed in virtue, I am happy to help you – so long as Fortune does not oppose it. For you must understand that all you creatures down on earth are born with your fates already decided, and only Fortune has the power to interfere with them. Approach her humbly and beseech her for help. You may find that she brings about surprising changes when you least expect them.'

I thanked her profusely and took my leave, following a beam of light down through the firmament. It led to a delightful plain covered in flowers, where I walked along the bank of a burbling river full of brightly coloured fish; then on down a road lined by fruit trees, amongst a host of wild animals ambling around in peace.

At last I came to a circular wall – and spied Fortune hovering above it. She wore a long surcoat of many colours and a mantle edged with ermine; her hair was all in ringlets. At first, her face was wreathed in smiles; but while I watched, it changed to glowering, then gradually softened back to smiling again.

Beside her, a great wheel was spinning round. Swarms of people were clambering all over it, struggling to keep hold of its slippery surface. As each group reached the top, the wheel spun down in the twinkling of an eye, so that they lost their footing and tumbled off it. Some rolled onto the ground, but others fell straight down into an ugly pit below, as deep and dark as hell. There was a long queue of new arrivals who quickly took their places. Those who survived the fall nursed their injuries ruefully, reluctant to climb back onto the wheel; but Fortune plucked them up and set them on it anyway.

As I stared at them, I heard Fortune call out my name. Embarrassed, I fell to my knees before her.

'What are you doing here?' she said in an amused voice. 'Who sent you? What is your heart's desire? I can see from your face that things aren't going well for you, eh?'

'Madam,' I said, 'I suffer constantly from the pain of love. I implore you to use your power to extinguish the fire before it burns me, and guide my game before I reach checkmate.'

'It is clear from your deathly pallor that you are too feeble to mount my wheel unaided,' she replied. 'You've been worn out by endless bad luck, haven't you? And from keeping everything trapped in your heart. God's plan gave you a bad start in life. But be cheered, for my wheel will soon move you around.'

She led me over to it and showed me how to clamber on. 'Don't lose your grip,' she warned. 'Almost half your life is already over, so be sure not to waste the rest of it. Learn from the example of those you have seen rolling off; I have the power to make everyone go up and down just as I please. Farewell!'

With those words, she seized my ear…

…With such force that I suddenly awoke from my dream.

If I had been troubled before, now it was twenty times worse! Was this dream merely a product of my own distressing thoughts? Or could it be a heavenly vision? I uttered a humble prayer to the goddesses I had met, then rose from my bed and went across to the open window.

At that moment, a chalk-white turtle dove suddenly flew in, alighted upon my hand, dropped a pretty sprig of gillyflowers before me, then spread its wings and flew away.

I picked up the sprig and saw, inscribed on its green stalk in golden letters, the following message:

Rejoice, lover.

You are close to a happy fate
For your cure is decreed in heaven.

And afterwards? Ah, it would take too long to describe everything that happened to end my suffering. But in the fulness of time, good Fortune brought me to live in bliss with my sovereign lady. She accepted me, unworthy though I was, fully into her grace.

Some readers might wonder why I wrote this. It is because, having crept from Hell to Heaven, I wish to give thanks every day for my joy. I thank the merciful goddesses who gave me everything I asked for, and the nightingale who sang sweet notes of love before my lady, and the gillyflower, and the castle wall where I looked out, and the green boughs under which I first found my heart's comfort. My happiness is complete.

May Venus above help all my friends in similar situations, servants of love who receive no reward, and bring each one to grace. And I pray for those not yet entered into the dance of love, and for those who have overcome love's tribulations, and for those with no courage to pluck the rose: may good fortune come to them all!

In ancient Roman mythology, Venus was the goddess of love, Minerva was the goddess of handicrafts and Fortuna was the goddess of luck.

The education that James received while living in the English royal household is demonstrated by his use of these classical characters; and also in his apparent knowledge of earlier romantic works such as *The Romance of the Rose* (see p. 170) and *The City of Ladies* (p. 380), from which he seems to have borrowed the allegorical characters, and the concept of the dream.

ARTHUR, GUENEVER & LAUNCELOT

Sir Thomas Malory: *Le Morte d'Arthur*
England, completed c.1470, first published 1485

Sir Thomas Malory (c.1415–71) is a shadowy figure, known for certain only as a 'knyght presoner'. Although there are several possible authors of his name, many scholars believe that he was a knight in the service of the Earl of Warwick; that he was convicted of attempted murder, rape and/or armed robbery; and that he spent most of his last years in prison, where he wrote his masterpiece.

In *Le Morte d'Arthur*, Malory brought together countless strands of older Arthurian legend, drawing on manuscripts and legends from England, France, Germany and beyond. It comprises twenty-one books with five-hundred-and-seven chapters in total, evocatively written with plentiful dialogue.

It is the only source used in the present book to have been first published by a printer rather than in handwritten manuscript form. The publisher was William Caxton, who is believed to have opened England's first printing press in 1476. A slightly older, and slightly different handwritten version, known as 'The Winchester Manuscript', also exists.

Caxton published the book in 1485. He is believed to have lightly edited the text and possibly changed Malory's original title. Caxton's own preface explains what led him to publish it:

After that I had accomplished and finished divers histories,
as well of contemplation as of other historical and worldly
acts of great conquerors and princes, and also certain
books of samples and doctrine, many noble and divers
gentlemen of this realm of England came and demanded
me, many and ofttimes, wherefore that I have not do made
and imprint the noble history of...the most renowned
Christian king...King Arthur... Wherefore...I have...
enprised to imprint a book of the noble histories of the
said King Arthur and of certain of his knights, after a copy
unto me delivered, which copy Sir Thomas Malory did take
out of certain books of French, and reduced it into
English... And for to understand briefly the content of this
volume, I have divided it into twenty-one books.

In the early days of King Arthur's reign at Camelot, the
barons of the realm began pressing him to take a wife. He
sought advice from his counsellor, the wise diviner Merlin,
confiding that he long had loved the fair and valiant
Guenever, daughter of the lord Leodegrance.

'That is a bad choice,' said Merlin. 'For I have dreamed
that Guenever will one day bring about your downfall. But
if there is no other lady that you desire, you must surely
have her.'

He accompanied Arthur when he went to ask Leodegrance
for his daughter's hand. The lord was more than delighted.
He sent the Round Table to Arthur as a wedding gift, and
soon all the best knights in the land had taken up their seats
at it. The wedding was celebrated by a great feast in the
castle at Camelot.

Of all the knights in King Arthur's realm, there was one who
the king admired and trusted most, for he had the greatest
reputation of any knight in the world. His name was Sir

Launcelot. Whenever a joust or tournament was fought, Launcelot was always the victor; whenever evil needed to be vanquished, Launcelot could be relied upon to achieve it. He was the flower of chivalry in every way.

As time went by, Guenever too noticed Launcelot's virtue and held him in great favour above all the other knights. In his turn, he came to love the queen more than any other lady; and because of this, he vowed never to take a wife.

Guenever and Launcelot established a custom of meeting together often – and in private. This brought both of them much joy. The affair did not always run smoothly. Sometimes, Guenever would fly into a rage of jealousy over other ladies who benefitted from Launcelot's deeds, or they would quarrel over some trivial matter. However, afterwards their love was always renewed even more deeply than before. So the years passed very happily and they caused no harm to anyone.

However, their secret trysts did not go entirely unnoticed at court. They were observed by two knights, Sir Mordred and Sir Agravain, who had long nursed secret grudges against Launcelot and the queen.

It happened that one day, these two were seated in a company that included one of Agravain's brothers, worthy Sir Gawain. Agravain spoke up, saying, 'I marvel that no one else has remarked on how Launcelot takes every opportunity to lie with the queen. It's a disgrace! We cannot just stand by and permit such treachery. We should tell the king of their affair.'

'By God, brother,' Gawain cried, 'I strongly urge you not to, for you'll only bring trouble on everyone; it could even lead to civil war. Besides, over the years Launcelot has never failed to dutifully serve King Arthur just as much as the queen. For my part, I am constantly mindful of the time that he saved me from great danger – just as he has several times saved you two as well. Such great deeds deserve honour, not a stabbing in the back.'

At that moment, King Arthur himself came in and saw their wrathful faces. 'What's going on here?' he demanded. 'Have you brothers quarrelled?'

'I'll tell you straight,' said Agravain at once. 'Though my brothers and I are all your nephews, I am the only one who does not keep dangerous secrets from you. So I must speak to you of Sir Launcelot. You personally knighted him, sir, and granted him special favours. Yet you seem oblivious to his long, duplicitous romantic entanglement – with your lawful wedded wife, the queen.'

The king considered Agravain's odious words for a long moment. Then he said, 'Launcelot is both my greatest knight and my closest comrade. This is a very serious allegation. It can only be proved or otherwise by challenging him to a duel. I'm confident he will easily trounce you, and thus reveal your words as merely mischievous slander.'

Agravain retorted, 'A far better way to prove it is to catch him red-handed. I suggest that tomorrow, sir, you announce that you will go hunting and stay away overnight. When the queen and Launcelot hear this, they are both sure to stay behind to sport together. That very night I shall surprise Launcelot while he's compromising the queen. He will be unable to deny his guilt.'

Arthur was appalled, but he could not refuse this reasonable test. So the next day he rode out with his hunting band, leaving Agravain, Mordred and twelve of their fellows to conceal themselves in a quiet corner of the castle.

As soon as all was quiet, Guenever summoned Launcelot to come urgently to her chamber. He went to her at once, seeing no need to take his armour but, as always, carrying his sword. They were soon enjoying themselves; but whether it was in bed or in some other way, I cannot tell; for love in those times was so very different from today.

While they were thus engaged, there suddenly came a great commotion outside the door. Agravain, Mordred and their twelve co-conspirators rapped upon it and roared as one: 'Open up, Launcelot! We know you are inside there, with the queen in your arms!'

Guenevere began to scream in terror. Launcelot kissed her, then drew his sword, whispering, 'Most noble queen, my special lady, pray for my soul if I am slain.'

'If they slay you,' she replied, 'I have no wish to live either. I beg you: let them kill *me* instead, and you escape.'

'God defend me from such shame!' cried Launcelot.

Since he had no armour, he wrapped his mantle around him for protection. Then he called out, 'Stop all this noise! I'm going to open the door. Then you may do whatever you wish with me.'

He unbarred the door with his left hand and held it slightly ajar, giving just enough room for a single man to pass through at a time.

The first one entered. At once, Launcelot raised his sword and struck him dead. The victim fell just inside the chamber door. Launcelot slammed it shut, dragged the dead knight aside, pulled off his armour and used it to clothe himself. Thus protected, he opened the door again and strode out. Like a whirlwind, he hacked at Agravain; then spun round and tore into the other treacherous knights gathered there, one by one.

In no time, all were dead except Sir Mordred. That false coward turned on his heels, blood dripping from his wounds, and fled.

Launcelot went back inside to the queen. 'By God,' he cried, 'when the king hears of this, he will declare me his mortal enemy. We will be forced apart for ever – unless I can persuade you to abscond with me.'

Guenever, weeping and trembling, replied, 'No, it is far better for you to leave alone at once, for I would only hinder your escape.'

'Very well,' said Launcelot, 'but you must put your faith in me. Know that, for as long as I live, I will always come to save you from any danger.'

They exchanged rings and hastily kissed one last time. Then Launcelot crept out softly and returned to his lodgings.

As soon as King Arthur was back from the hunt, Mordred, sore wounded, went and told him everything that had happened. The king could not help but be impressed by Launcelot killing thirteen fully armed opponents single-handed, and wounding the fourteenth. However, his admiration was quickly overwhelmed by despair.

'Launcelot must now be my enemy,' he said. 'This is the worst thing that could possibly have happened. The fellowship of the Round Table is broken and we will have to go to war – in which many of my finest knights are bound to fall. But, worst of all, my beloved wife is guilty of treason; and the law clearly states that the punishment for that, regardless of status, is death by burning.'

Then Gawain spoke up, saying 'My lord Arthur, do not be overhasty in your judgement. Sir Launcelot may have been in the queen's chamber for a totally innocent reason. We all know that he has saved her life on many occasions; perhaps she simply wanted to give him a reward, and their secrecy was because of the malicious rumours already circulating against them. I fervently believe that the queen is faithful to you. As for Sir Launcelot, it is a natural reaction to take revenge on any knight who slanders him.'

'Be that as it may,' said the king grimly, 'but the queen must submit to the law. And if ever we manage to catch Launcelot, the same will apply to him.'

'I pray to God that I never see it happen,' said Gawain.

Meanwhile, Launcelot called his most loyal and trusted nephew, Sir Bors, and explained the situation.

'Have no fear, uncle,' said Bors. 'For many years, I have benefitted from your help, as have many other knights here. It is time to repay your kindness, by helping you in return.'

He went around telling everyone what had happened. Soon he had gathered a good number of knights to their side. When they were all assembled, Launcelot said, 'I am greatly afraid that Arthur will sentence my lady to be burned. Who can advise me what to do?'

With one voice, they all answered, 'Sir, it is on your account that she will be sent to the fire. If you are caught, you will be condemned to a similar death or even worse. In the past, you have often saved the queen from other men's sins; now it is time to save her from the consequences of your own. If she is allowed to die in shame, that shame will also be yours.'

'I heed your counsel,' said Launcelot. 'Let me ask you something more: if I am successful in rescuing the queen, where should I take her?'

'To your own castle, Joyous Gard,' said Bors. 'Keep her there until the heat of Arthur's anger burns out; then bring her back to the king and submit to him. Hopefully, in spite of everything, he will thank you for returning her, and show mercy. If he does, all will be well, for Arthur never reneges on a promise.'

To make this tale short, all the knights gathered there with Launcelot agreed, for better or worse, to help him rescue the queen. To this purpose, they all hid in a wood as close to the castle as was safe, waiting to see how events would unfold.

The queen was imprisoned. The next day, the king had her led out beyond the castle walls. There she was stripped of her robes, clad in a simple smock and allowed to make confession.

Countless lords and ladies had gathered there to watch, with much weeping, wailing and wringing of hands. Amongst them was a spy sent by Launcelot. As soon as he saw the queen being prepared for execution, he hurried to tell his master.

The queen was led out to the stake and bound to it.

At that moment, just as the fire was being lit, Launcelot and his supporters suddenly burst from their hiding place. Spurring their horses, they galloped to the fire, blindly cutting down any man who tried to stand in their way.

Alas! Amongst the dead were two more of Gawain's brothers.

Launcelot reached Guenever, threw a kirtle and gown over her, snatched her from the rising flames and set her up on the horse behind him. Guenever exclaimed her thanks to God with all her heart as Launcelot swept her away.

Over endless miles they rode, on and on, all the way to Joyous Gard.

There Launcelot kept the queen, chastely, and in the manner she was accustomed to, attended by many who had joined his side.

After that, the realm was torn in asunder. Half the Round Table remained loyal to King Arthur. The rest defected to

Joyous Gard, pledging to support Sir Launcelot against the king. Both sides, with heavy hearts, prepared for war.

The two leaders met to fight face to face; but neither could bring himself to harm his one-time dearest friend.

News of this deadlock quickly spread throughout Christendom, until at last it reached the ears of the Pope. He pondered long on the great virtue of both men, then sent a messenger with a decree to King Arthur, charging him to take Queen Guenever back and reach a settlement with Launcelot.

King Arthur was greatly relieved, and eager to obey. However, Gawain would not sanction the king making peace with Launcelot, because he had lost so many close kin to that knight's sword.

Eventually, Gawain was persuaded to submit to the Pope's order that the king should accept the return of the queen. He sent a message to Launcelot, guaranteeing him safe passage to escort Guenever – on condition that he would then depart at once.

Launcelot was greatly relieved. In truth, he had only abducted the queen to save her life, and had longed for a safe opportunity to deliver her back to her rightful place beside King Arthur.

Sir Launcelot led Queen Guenever to Carlisle, where King Arthur was holding court. They were followed by a throng of knights and gentlewomen bearing olive branches as tokens of peace.

Launcelot and the queen both alighted from their horses, walked to where King Arthur awaited them and humbly knelt before him. The sight was so pitiful, that all those gathered to watch began to weep.

Launcelot's eyes met Arthur's, then he rose to his feet, pulling Guenever up beside him. 'Most honoured king,' he said, 'in obedience to the Pope's command, I bring you my lady, the queen. Evil lies have caused this conflict between us. If any knight here dares accuse the queen of unfaithfulness to you, I will fight him to the death to defend her. In the past, you have often praised me for protecting the queen's honour. It is because her accusers greatly wronged her that I followed my duty to rescue her from the fire. As you know, I recently vanquished fourteen armed knights, when I myself was neither armed nor prepared for battle; does that not prove that God is on my side? I believe I have always served you better than any other knight, rescuing you from many dangers, and bringing acclaim to your court in countless jousts, tournaments and wars.'

'Indeed,' said Arthur wretchedly. 'And I have always honoured you far more than any of my other knights.'

At that moment, he was moved to forgive Launcelot. However, Gawain was standing in attendance, and he was in much anguish on account of Launcelot slaughtering his three brothers. Launcelot now expressed remorse for this, almost equal to Gawain's grief.

Yet Gawain would not back down. Voicing what the king could not bring himself to say, he declared coldly, 'Launcelot you must hand over the queen, then leave the country within fifteen days. Once you are abroad, you will be beyond the papal edict of reconciliation. Thus we will be free to go to war.'

'Let me just say this,' said Launcelot. 'If I had really been having an affair with the queen, I would not have brought her back here.'

He turned to Guenever. 'Madam, I must leave you and this noble fellowship for ever. I beseech you to pray for me and always speak well of me. If ever you are troubled by further

409

slander, send me word: I promise to despatch knights to defend you.'

He kissed her, handed her over to the king, then departed from the court and returned to his own castle. He changed its name from 'Joyous' to Dolorous Gard, on account of his great sorrow.

He did not stay long, but sailed from there to France.

Urged by Gawain, King Arthur then formally declared war against Launcelot, to the deep regret of both sides.

Arthur was away at war for so long, that Mordred spread rumours he would never return. That malevolent knight not only seized the throne, but also tried to take Guenever for his wife. She outwitted him by taking refuge in the Tower of London.

King Arthur returned to Britain and fought his last campaign. He killed Mordred – but was himself mortally wounded. Some say that his corpse was found on the battlefield. However, others claim that he survived and was carried away across the water to be healed, in the mysterious realm of Avalon.

After the war was over and the whole kingdom lost, Guenever, in much distress, stole away with five ladies to Almesbury. There she became a nun. With fasting, praying and almsgiving, she made greater penance than any other lady had ever done before.

As for Launcelot, he returned from France and travelled far and wide in search of her. At last he too reached Almesbury. Guenever saw him approach the nunnery and swooned three times. When she recovered, she told her ladies to bring him in.

'You well know, Launcelot,' said she, 'that Arthur was the greatest king the world has ever known, and it was our wrongful love that caused him to be slain, alongside all his noblest knights. Because of that, I am determined to purge my soul. I cling to the hope that, after I die, I may yet sit on Christ's right side at Doomsday. You must never try to see me again. Forget me, return to your own realm, take a wife and strive to find some joy. As for me, I only ask that you pray for my sins to be absolved.'

Launcelot answered, 'Sweet madam, you well know that I will never marry, for my heart belongs only to you. God knows, we've had more than our share of earthly joy together. Now I will follow your example, and go into penance for the rest of my life. But before I do, I beg you for one final kiss.'

'No,' said the queen, 'Everything is over now between us.'

After that, Launcelot too turned his back on the world and became a monk.

Some time later, he dreamed three times of Guenever's death: He hastened back to her nunnery with all speed; but she had died half an hour before he arrived.

Guenever had left instructions for Launcelot to take charge of her funeral, and bury her beside King Arthur.

Launcelot fulfilled her wishes. Afterwards, so deep was his sorrow, that he fell on their tomb and refused both food and drink. In this way, he starved himself to death beside the two people that he had always loved most dearly.

Thus ends this noble story.

Nowadays, love blows hot and cold without any stability: men expect to have all their desires fulfilled, and after that their love quickly cools. But love in King Arthur's day was different. It was a genuine expression of truth and faithfulness, so that men and women could desire each other for seven years without ever once succumbing to lust. So, all you modern lovers, remember Queen Guenever; for as long as she lived, she was always the truest lover.

The main episodes retold here are taken from Books Eighteen to Twenty-one of *Le Morte d'Arthur*, but the love triangle is the central theme that weaves in and out of the lengthy plot to the climax. Malory makes it clear that the story is not his own invention, frequently justifying the plot with the words, 'as the French book says'. Its heart-wrenching tragedy provides an interesting contrast to the lighthearted 13th century story about the same love affair, retold in the present volume as *Guinevere and Lancelot* (p. 141).

Malory narrates the story as a medieval chivalric fantasy, set in England. However, the oldest Arthurian legends hark back to a much earlier era, around the 6th century AD. At this time there was a warrior culture rather than a chivalric one, and it was long before 'England' existed as a separate kingdom within Britain.

Le Morte d'Arthur's descriptions of the affair between Guenever and Launcelot are inconsistent; despite Launcelot's protestations of chastity after they have been discovered, there are several episodes that clearly imply they have been physically making love.

King Arthur's headquarters seem to move between Caerleon, Camelot (often identified as Winchester), and Carlisle. Malory states that Launcelot's castle of Dolorous Gard (also see p. 146 and p.155) was located at either Alnwick or Bamburgh in Northumberland, both of which still have notable castles today. Almesbury has been identified with Amesbury in Wiltshire.

Le Morte d'Arthur also features a number of other love stories drawn from earlier legends and manuscripts, including 'Tristram and Isolde', 'Merlin and Nimue' and 'Lancelot and Elaine of Astolat'. These have been retold in another of the present author's books, *Arthurian Legends* (Batsford 2018), with notes explaining the provenance of the tales.

SOURCES

Abelard, Peter and Heloise: *The Letters of Abelard and Heloise*, written in the 12th century, translated with an introduction and notes by Betty Radice, revised by M.T. Clanchy (London: Penguin Books, 1974, 2003)

Andreas Capellanus (André le Chapelain): *De Amore ('About Love')*, also known as *De arte honeste amandi (The Art of Courtly Love')*, originally published in the 12th century, translated into English by John Jay Parry (New York: Columbia University Press, 1941)

Boccaccio, Giovanni: *Decameron*, originally published in the 14th century, a new English version by Cormac Ó Cuilleanáin, based on John Payne's 1886 translation (Ware, Hertfordshire: Wordsworth Editions, 2004)

Chaucer, Geoffrey: *The Canterbury Tales*, originally published in the 14th century, translated into modern English by Nevill Coghill (London: Penguin Books, 1951, 1977)

Chaucer, Geoffrey: *Troilus and Criseyde*, originally published in the 14th century, translated into modern English by Nevill Coghill (London: Penguin Books, 1971)

Chrétien de Troyes: *Arthurian Romances*, originally published in the 12th century, translated with an introduction by W.W. Comfort (Letchworth: J. M. Dent & Sons, 1914)

Christine de Pizan: *The Book of the City of Ladies*, originally published in the 15th Century, translated with an introduction and notes by Rosalind Brown-Grant (London: Penguin Books, 1999)

Dante Alighieri: *The New Life (La Vita Nuova)*, originally published in the 13th century, translated by Dante Gabriel Rossetti (London: Ellis and Elvey, 1899)

Dante Alighieri: *The Divine Comedy*, originally published in the 14th century, translated, with notes, by Henry Francis Cary, with an introduction by Claire E. Honess, and additional notes to the Inferno by Stefano Albertini (Ware, Hertfordshire: Wordsworth Editions, 2009)

Guillaume le Clerc: *Fergus of Galloway*, originally published in the 13th century, translated from the Old French by D. D. R. Owen (London: J.M. Dent & Sons, 1991)

Guillaume de Lorris & Jean de Meun: *The Romance of the Rose*, originally published in the 13th century, translated by Frances Horgan (Oxford University Press, 1994)

Hartmann von Auë: *Henry the Leper (Der arme Heinrich)*, originally published in the 12th century, translated by Dante Gabriel Rossetti, reproduced in 'The Collected Works of Dante Gabriel Rossetti, Volume II (Boston: Roberts Brothers, 1887)

Jacob ben El'azar: *The Story of Maskil and Peninah*, originally written in Hebrew and published in Spain in the 13th century, translated by Tova Rosen in *Love and Race in a Thirteenth Century Romance in Hebrew, with a Translation of the Story of Maskil and Peninah* (Florilegium, vol. 23.1, University of Toronto Press, 2006)

James I of Scotland: *The Kingis Quair*, translated by Jenni Nuttall (Stylisticienne Publishing, 2017)

Marie de France: *The Lais of Marie de France*, originally published in the 12th century, translated with an introduction by Glyn S. Burgess and Keith Busby (London: Penguin Books, 1986, 1999)

Sir Thomas Malory: *Le Morte D'Arthur*, originally published by William Caxton in 1485, edited by Janet Cowen and published in two volumes (London: Penguin Books, 1969)

Vasco Lobeira: *Amadis de Gaul*, originally published in Portuguese in the 14th century, translated into Spanish by Garciordoñez de Montalvo in 1508, translated from Spanish into English by Robert Southey in four volumes (London: T. N. Longman and O. Rees, 1872)

Wace: *Roman de Brut*, originally written in the 12th century, translated by Eugene Mason (www.gutenberg.org, 2003)

Wolfram von Eschenbach: *Parzifal* and *Titurel*, originally published in the 13th century, translated by Cyril Edwards (Oxford University Press, 2006)

Works by Anonymous authors:

Aucassin and Nicolete, originally written in the 12th or 13th century, translated from the Old French by Andrew Lang (London: David Nutt, 1910)

Beatrijs, originally written in the 14th century, translated from the Middle Dutch poem by P. Geyl in 1927, reproduced on the website of The National Library of the Netherlands, dbnl.org

Fleur & Blanchefleur, originally published in the 12th century, translated from the Old French by Mrs Leighton (London: D. O'Connor, 1922)

Floris and Blauncheflour, originally published in the 13th century, translated and retold in modern English prose by Richard Scott-Robinson (privately published online, 2010, 2016)

Lancelot of the Lake, originally written in the 13th century, translated by Corin Corley (Oxford University Press, 1989)

The Mabinogion, based on stories originally written down in the 14th – early 15th centuries, translated by Gwyn Jones and Thomas Jones (London: J. M. Dent & Sons Ltd, 1974)

The Mabinogion, based on stories originally written down in the 14th – early 15th centuries, translated by Sioned Davies (Oxford University Press 2007)

OTHER BOOKS BY ROSALIND KERVEN

Native American Myths

Viking Myths & Sagas

Faeries, Elves & Goblins: The Old Stories

Arthurian Legends

English Fairy Tales and Legends

'The stories are short and lively...
There is a strong focus on character and dialogue.'
– TLS

'Rosalind Kerven's selection and retelling is very good...
Her copious notes draw the reader into a world of other stories,
and whets the appetite to read and listen further.'
– Folklore

'Fascinating collection...I recommend it without reservation;
the scholarship is excellent.'
– Grammarye

workingwithmythsandfairytales.blogspot.co.uk